Solid Edge V20
for Designers

CADCIM Technologies

525 St. Andrews Drive
Schererville, IN 46375
USA
(www.cadcim.com)

Contributing Authors

Sham Tickoo

Professor
Department of Mechanical Engineering Technology
Purdue University Calumet
Hammond, Indiana
U.S.A.

Surinder Mohan Raina

Sr. CADD Engineer
CADCIM Technologies

CADCIM Technologies

Solid Edge V20 for Designers
Sham Tickoo

Published by CADCIM Technologies, 525 St Andrews Drive, Schererville, IN 46375 USA. ©
Copyright 2008, CADCIM Technologies. All rights reserved. No part of this publication
may be reproduced or distributed in any form or by any means, or stored in the database
or retrieval system without the prior permission of CADCIM Technologies.

ISBN 978-1-932709-48-3

CADCIM Technologies Staff:

Business Managers	**Technical Editor**	**Senior Copy Editor**
Meenu Bhat	D. Saravanan	Anju Jethwani

Art/Cover Designers	**Marketing Managers**	**Copy Editors**
Nirupama Gupta	Santosh Tickoo	Sudam C. Mishra
Vikas Saini	Shafali Pandita	Renu Bala

www.cadcim.com

DEDICATION

*To teachers, who make it possible to disseminate knowledge
to enlighten the young and curious minds
of our future generations*

*To students, who are dedicated to learning new technologies
and making the world a better place to live*

SPECIAL RECOGNITION

*A special thanks to Mr. Hulas King and Ms. Tavia Carson
of UGS Corporation for their valuable support and professional guidance
to procure the software for writing this textbook*

THANKS

*To the faculty and students of the MET department of
Purdue University Calumet for their cooperation*

To engineers of CADCIM Technologies for their valuable help

Online Training Program Offered by CADCIM Technologies

CADCIM Technologies provides effective and affordable online training on various software packages including Computer Aided Design and Manufacturing (CAD/CAM), computer programming languages, animation, civil, and GIS. The training is delivered at any time, any place, and at any pace to individuals, students of colleges, universities, and CAD/CAM training centers. The main features of this program are:

Training for Students and Companies in a Class Room Setting

Highly experienced instructors and qualified Engineers at CADCIM Technologies, under the guidance of Prof. Sham Tickoo of Purdue University Calumet, USA, conduct the classes. This team has authored several textbooks that are rated "one of the best" in their categories and are used in various colleges, universities, and training centers in North America, Europe, and in other parts of the world.

Training for Individuals

The cost effective and time saving initiative of CADCIM Technologies strives to deliver the training in the comfort of your home or work place, thereby relieving you from the hassles of traveling to training centers.

Software Packages Offered

We provide basic and advanced training on the following software packages:

CAD/CAM/CAE: CATIA, Pro/ENGINEER Wildfire, SolidWorks, Autodesk Inventor, Solid Edge, NX, AutoCAD, AutoCAD LT, AutoCAD Electrical, Customizing AutoCAD, EdgeCAM, ANSYS, and Mastercam

Computer Programming Languages: C++, VB.NET, Java, Oracle, Dreamweaver, Microsoft Word, and Microsoft Excel

Animation and Styling: Autodesk 3ds Max, Autodesk AliasStudio, Adobe Flash, and Autodesk Maya

Architecture and GIS: Autodesk Revit Architecture, AutoCAD Civil 3D, and AutoCAD Map 3D

For more information, please visit the following link:

http://www.cadcim.com

Note
The free teaching and learning resources, mentioned in the cover page of this textbook, are available only for the students who buy the textbook from our website www.cadcim.com or the university/college bookstores. We need proof of purchase when you request the technical support from us.

Table of Contents

Chapter 3: Adding Relationships and Dimensions to Sketches

Chapter 6: Advanced Modeling Tools-I

Chapter 10: Assembly Modeling-I

Chapter 11: Assembly Modeling-II

Chapter 12: Generating, Editing, and Dimensioning Drawing Views

Chapter 13: Surface Modeling

Preface

SOLID EDGE VERSION 20

Solid Edge, developed by UGS Corporation, is one of the world's fastest growing solid modeling software. It is a parametric feature-based solid modeling tool, which not only unites the three-dimensional (3D) parametric features with 2D tools but also addresses every design-through-manufacturing process. This solid modeling package allows the manufacturing companies to get an insight into the design intent, thereby promoting collaboration and letting the companies have an edge over their competitors. This package is remarkably user-friendly and helps the user to be productive from day one.

After creating solid models and assemblies, the 2D drawing views can be easily generated in the drafting environment. The drawing views that can be generated include orthographic views, isometric views, auxiliary views, section views, detail views, and so on. You can use any predefined drawing standard file for generating the drawing views. You can display the model dimensions in the drawing views or add reference dimensions whenever you want. The bidirectional associative nature of this software ensures that any modification made in the model is automatically reflected in the drawing views. Also, any modification made in the dimensions of the drawing views automatically updates the model.

Solid Edge V20 for Designers is a textbook written with the intention of helping the readers effectively use Solid Edge V20. This book is written with the tutorial point-of-view and learn-by-doing as the theme. A number of mechanical engineering industry examples are the used as tutorials in this book, so that the users can relate the knowledge gained with the actual mechanical industry designs. The salient features of this textbook are as follows:

- **Tutorial Approach**

    The author has adopted the tutorial point-of-view and learn-by-doing as the theme throughout the textbook. This approach guides the users through the process of creating the models in the tutorials.

- **Real-World Projects as Tutorials**

    The author has used about 50 real-world mechanical engineering projects as tutorials in this book. This enables the reader to relate the tutorials to the real-world models in the mechanical engineering industry. In addition, there are about 30 exercises that are also based on the real-world mechanical engineering projects.

- **Tips and Notes**

   Additional information related to the topics is provided to the users in the form of tips and notes.

- **Learning Objectives**

   The first page of every chapter summarizes the topics that are covered in the chapter.

- **Tools Section**

   Each new topic begins with the tools section that provides a brief information of the Solid Edge tools.

- **Self-Evaluation Test, Review Questions, and Exercises**

   Every chapter ends with a Self-Evaluation test so that the users can assess their knowledge of the chapter. The answers to the Self-Evaluation Test are given at the end of the chapter. Also, the Review Questions and Exercises are given at the end of each chapter and they can be used by the Instructors as test questions and exercises.

- **Heavily Illustrated Text**

   The text in this book is heavily illustrated with about 1100 line diagrams and screen capture images.

Features of the Text

Note

The author has provided additional topic-related information in the form of notes.

Tip

The author has provided a lot of useful information to the users about the topic under discussion in the form of tips.

New

This indicates the new commands or tools introduced in Solid Edge V20

Enhanced

This indicates the existing commands and tools that have been enhanced in Solid Edge V20

Chapter 1

Introduction to Solid Edge

Learning Objectives

After completing this chapter, you will be able to:

- *Understand the advantage of using Solid Edge.*
- *Know the system requirements of Solid Edge.*
- *Know various environments of Solid Edge.*
- *Learn various important terms and definitions in Solid Edge.*
- *Know about the user interface of Solid Edge.*
- *Modify the color scheme in Solid Edge.*
- *Automatically save Solid Edge designs after regular intervals.*

INTRODUCTION TO SOLID EDGE

Welcome to the world of Solid Edge, a Solid Modeling tool developed by the UGS Corporation. As a new user of this software, you will join hands with thousands of users of this high-end CAD tool worldwide. If you have used the previous releases of this software, you will significantly improve your design skills with this latest release.

Solid Edge is a powerful program that is used to create complex designs with great ease. The design intent of any three-dimensional (3D) model or an assembly is defined by its specification and use. You can use the powerful tools of Solid Edge to capture the design intent of any complex model by incorporating intelligence into the design.

To make the design process simple and quick, this software package divides the steps of designing into different environments. This means that each step of designing is completed in a different environment. For example, generally a design process consists of the following steps:

*   Sketching by using the basic sketch entities and converting them into features or parts. These parts can be sheet metal parts, surface parts, or solid parts.
*   Assembling different parts and analyzing them.
*   Generating drawing views of the parts and the assembly.

All these steps are performed in different environments of Solid Edge, namely, **Part, Sheet Metal**, **Weldment**, **Assembly**, and **Draft**.

Solid Edge provides a Students Development Kit (SDK) that helps you use the Microsoft's Visual Basic Environment by which you can customize Solid Edge.

Solid Edge supports data migration from IDEAS. In Solid Edge, the users can convert all files and documents created in IDEAS to Solid Edge. Data exchange from other CAD packages like Catia V4, Catia V5, and Pro/E using other file formats is also supported in Solid Edge.

Solid Edge is a parametric and feature-based solid modeling tool. The bidirectional associativity of this solid modeling tool makes the design process very simple and less time-consuming. The parametric, feature-based, and bidirectional properties of this solid modeling tool are explained next.

Parametric Nature

Parametric nature of a solid modeling package means that the sketch is driven by dimensions, or in other words, the geometry of a model is controlled by its dimensions. For example, to model a rectangular plate of 100X80 units, you can draw a rectangle of any dimension and then modify its dimensions to the required dimensions of the plate. You will notice that the dimensions drive the geometry of the sketch.

Therefore, using this parametric property, any modification in the design of a product can be accomplished at any stage of the product development. This makes the design flexible.

Feature-based Modeling

A feature is defined as the smallest building block of a model. Any solid model created in Solid Edge is an integration of a number of features. Each feature can be edited individually to make any change in the solid model. As a result, the feature-based property provides greater flexibility to the created parts.

The advantage of dividing a model into a number of features is that it becomes easy to modify the model by modifying the features individually. For example, Figure 1-1 shows a model with four simple holes near the corners of the plate.

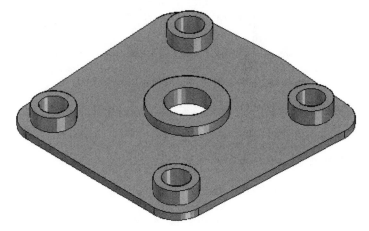

Figure 1-1 Model with simple holes

Now, consider a case where you need to change all outer holes to counterbore holes. In a nonfeature-based modeling package, you need to delete all the holes and then create the counterbore holes. However, in Solid Edge, you can modify some parameters of the holes in the same part and convert the simple holes to counterbore holes, see Figure 1-2.

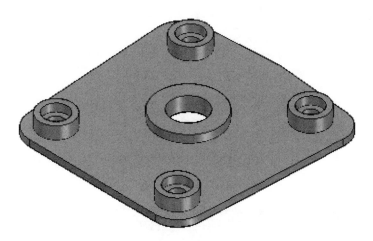

Figure 1-2 Model with counterbore holes

Bidirectional Associativity

The bidirectional associativity of a software package is defined as its ability to ensure that any modification made in a particular model in one environment is also reflected in the same model in the other environments. For example, if you make any changes in a model in the **Part** environment, the changes will be reflected in the same model in the **Assembly** environment and vice-versa.

Figure 1-3 shows the top view and the sectioned front view of the part shown in Figure 1-1.

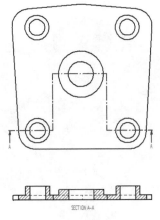

Figure 1-3 *Drawing views of the model before modification*

These drawing views are generated in the **Draft** environment. The views show that the part consists of a simple hole at the center and four near the corners. Now, when the model is modified in the **Part** environment, the modifications are automatically reflected in the **Draft** environment, as shown in Figure 1-4. This figure shows that the four simple holes are converted into counterbore holes. This implies that the **Part** environment and the **Draft** environment of Solid Edge are bidirectionally associative.

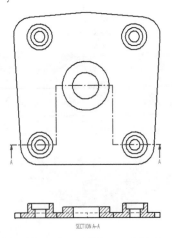

Figure 1-4 *Drawing views of the model after modification*

Consider the assembly shown in Figure 1-5. The piston is connected to the connecting rod through a pin. It is clear from the assembly that the diameter of the hole is more than what is required. In an ideal case, the diameter of the hole on the piston should be equal to the diameter of the pin.

Figure 1-5 Piston, connecting rod, and pin assembly

Now, when you open the piston in the **Part** environment and modify the diameter of the hole on it, the same modification is also reflected in the **Assembly** environment, as shown in Figure 1-6. This is due to the bidirectional associativity of Solid Edge.

Figure 1-6 Assembly after modifying the diameter of the hole on the piston

Similarly, if the modification is made in the **Assembly** environment, the piston, when opened in the **Part** environment, is also modified automatically. This shows that all environments of Solid Edge are associative by nature.

SOLID EDGE ENVIRONMENTS

To reduce the complicacies of a design, this software package provides you with various design environments. You can capture the design intent easily by individually incorporating the intelligence of each design environment into the design. The design environments available in Solid Edge are discussed next.

Part Environment

This environment of Solid Edge is used to create parametric and feature-based solid and surface models. You can enter this environment by choosing **Start > All Programs > Solid Edge V20 > Solid Edge** from the taskbar menu. After Solid Edge is started, the welcome screen will be displayed. From this screen, choose the **Solid Part** option from the **Create** area. The sketches of the models or features are also drawn in this environment. Once the sketch is drawn, you can convert it into a solid model using simple, but highly effective modeling tools. One of the major advantages of using Solid Edge is the availability of **SmartStep**. The **SmartStep** is a ribbon bar that is displayed above the drawing window when you invoke a feature creation tool. It helps you to create a feature step by step. Using the **SmartStep**, you can also easily go one or more steps backward to modify a parameter. The models created in the **Part** environment can also be used in the other environments of Solid Edge to complete the model's life cycle, also known as the Product Life Cycle.

Assembly Environment

This environment of Solid Edge is used to create an assembly by assembling the components that were created in the **Part** environment. This environment supports animation, rendering, piping, and wiring. Other visualization and presentation tools are also available in this environment.

Draft Environment

This environment is used for the documentation of the parts or the assemblies in the form of drawing views. The drawing views can be generated or created. All the dimensions added to the component in the **Part** environment during its creation can be displayed in the drawing views in this environment.

Sheet Metal Environment

This environment is used to create sheet metal components. If you are conversant with the **Part** environment, then modeling in this environment becomes easy. This is because in addition to the sheet metal modeling tools, this environment works in a way similar to the **Part** environment.

Weldment Environment

This environment enables you to insert components from the **Part** or the **Assembly** environment and apply weld beads to the parts or the assembly. This environment is associative with the **Part** and **Assembly** environments.

SYSTEM REQUIREMENTS FOR SOLID EDGE V20

The system requirements for Solid Edge V20 are as follows:

1. An Intel Pentium, AMD Athlon, or AMD Opteron processor-based PC.
2. Windows 2000 Professional running Service Pack 3/4 or Windows XP Professional running Service Pack 2.
3. Microsoft Internet Explorer 6.0 or later.
4. 256 MB RAM (512 MB recommended), 640MB hard disk space, OpenGL Accelerator with 65K colors, and CD-ROM for installation.

IMPORTANT TERMS AND DEFINITIONS

Some important terms that are used in this textbook are discussed next.

Relationships

Relationships are the logical operations that are performed on a selected geometry to make it more accurate for defining its position and size with respect to the other geometry. There are two types of relationships available in Solid Edge and these are discussed next.

Geometry Relationships

These logical operations are performed on the basic sketched entities to relate them to the standard properties such as collinearity, concentricity, perpendicularity, and so on. Although Solid Edge automatically applies these relationships to the sketched entities at the time of drawing, you can also apply them manually. You can apply eleven types of geometry relationships, which are discussed next.

Connect

This relationship connects a point to another point or entity.

Concentric

This relationship forces two selected curves to share the same center point. The curves that can be made concentric are circles, arcs, and ellipsis.

Horizontal/Vertical

This relationship forces the selected line segment or two points to become horizontal or vertical.

Collinear

This relationship forces two line segments to lie on the same line.

Parallel Relationship

This relationship is used to make two line segments parallel.

Perpendicular

This relationship makes a line segment perpendicular to another line segment or series of line segments.

Lock

This relationship is used to fix an element or a dimension so that it cannot be modified.

Tangent

This relationship is used to make the selected line segment or the curve tangent to the selected line or curve.

Equal

This relationship forces the selected line segments to be of equal length. It also forces two curves to be of equal radius.

Symmetric Relationship

This relationship is used to force the selected sketched entities to become symmetrical about a sketched line segment, which may or may not be a center line.

Rigid Set

This relationship is used to group the selected sketched entities into a rigid set so that they behave as a single unit.

Assembly Relationships

The assembly relationships are the logical operations that are performed on the components to assemble them at their respective working positions in an assembly. These relationships are applied to reduce the degrees of freedom of the components.

Mate

This relationship is used to make the selected faces of different components coplanar. You can also specify some offset distance between the selected faces.

Planar Align

This relationship enables you to align a planar face with the other planar face.

Axial Align

This relationship enables you to make a cylindrical surface coaxial with the other cylindrical surface.

Insert

This relationship is used to mate the faces of two components that are axially symmetric and also to make their axes coaxial.

Connect

This relationship enables you to connect two keypoints, line, or a face on two different parts.

Angle

This relationship is used to place the selected faces of different components at some angle with respect to each other.

Tangent

This relationship is used to make the selected face of a component tangent to the cylindrical, circular or conical faces of the other component.

Cam

This relationship applies the cam-follower relationship between a closed loop of tangent face and the follower face.

Parallel

The **Parallel** relationship is used to force two edges, axes, or an edge and an axis parallel to each other.

Gear

The **Gear** relationship allows you to apply rotation- rotation, rotation-linear, or a linear-linear relationship between two components.

Entity

An element of a geometry is called an entity. An entity can be an arc, line, circle, point, and so on.

Concept of a Profile and a Sketch

In Solid Edge, there are two methods of drawing a sketch. The first method is to draw a sketch using the **Sketch** tool available in the **Features** toolbar. The second method is to invoke a feature creation tool such as **Protrusion**, **Swept Protrusion**, and so on and then draw the sketch for the feature. The sketch drawn using the first method is called a Sketch and the sketch drawn using the second method is called a Profile. You will learn more about this in later chapters of this book.

Intent Zone

This zone enables you to draw or modify various elements of a geometry within the same tool. For example, while drawing a line tangent to an arc, you can draw a tangent arc or a perpendicular arc by moving the cursor in the intent zone. The movement of the cursor in the intent zone determines the creation of a tangent or a perpendicular arc. In the geometry, this zone is represented by two perpendicular lines inside a circle, or by a circle, as shown in Figures 1-7 and 1-8.

Prompt Line

If you invoke a tool, the prompt line is displayed below the ribbon bar. This is helpful while creating a model because it provides you with the prompt sequences to use a tool.

GETTING STARTED WITH SOLID EDGE V20

Once you have installed Solid Edge on your computer, choose **Start > All Programs (or Programs) > Solid Edge V20 > Solid Edge**, as shown in Figure 1-9. On doing so, the welcome screen is displayed and you can select any environment of Solid Edge to start using the links in the **Create** area. As discussed earlier, Solid Edge divides the steps of designing a

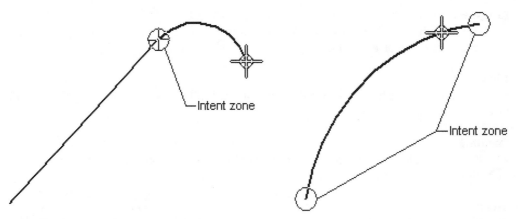

Figure 1-7 *Intent zone displayed while drawing a tangent arc*   ***Figure 1-8*** *Intent zone displayed while drawing a three point arc*

feature into various environments. The welcome screen will also display the **Tip of the day** area that shows a useful tip. You can click on the **Next** link at the lower right corner of this area to display the next tip.

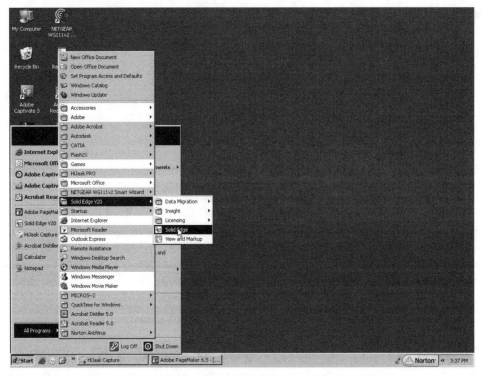

Figure 1-9 *Windows screen with taskbar and application icons*

USER INTERFACE OF SOLID EDGE

Solid Edge provides you with various toolbars and menus while working with various environments. This means that the toolbars available while working in the **Part**, **Assembly**, **Draft**, **Sheet Metal**, and **Weldment** environments are different. Also, every environment has the **EdgeBar** that assists you in creating the design. The **EdgeBar** is discussed next.

EdgeBar

The **EdgeBar**, as shown in Figure 1-10, is present on the left of the main window. It lists all occurrences of features and sketches of a model in a chronicle sequence. When you choose **Tools > EdgeBar** from the menu bar, by default, a check mark is displayed on its left. As a result, the **EdgeBar** is displayed. If you choose this option again, the display of **EdgeBar** will be turned off. The **EdgeBar** has a toolbar at the top that you can use to activate the feature library, family of parts, and so on. The options available in the **EdgeBar** are discussed later in this book.

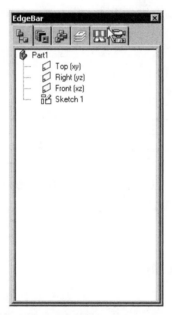

Figure 1-10 The EdgeBar

 Note
*Remember that though the profiles of the features are not displayed in the **EdgeBar**, the sketches are displayed. You will learn the difference between the sketches and the profiles later in the textbook.*

Some of the toolbars available in various environments of Solid Edge are discussed next.

Part Environment Toolbars

There are several toolbars that can be invoked in the **Part** environment. The toolbars that are extensively used during the designing process in this environment are discussed next.

Main Toolbar

This toolbar is common to all environments of Solid Edge. However, all options will not be available in all environments. The **Main** toolbar is shown in Figure 1-11. Some of the important buttons in this toolbar are discussed next.

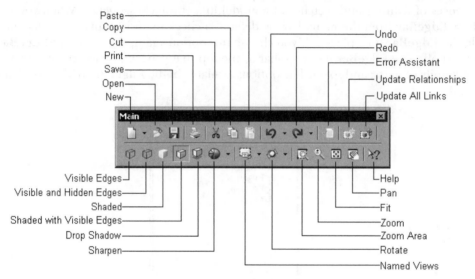

Figure 1-11   *The* **Main** *toolbar*

Update Relationships

This button is chosen to update both the dimensions in the **Part** environment and the relationships in the **Assembly** environment.

Print

When you choose this button, the **Print** dialog box will be displayed, as shown in Figure 1-12. You can use your printer to print a drawing sheet or a model.

Features Toolbar

This toolbar consists of the modeling tools that are used to convert a sketch into a solid model. The **Features** toolbar, along with all the buttons available in it, is shown in Figure 1-13.

Surfacing Toolbar

This toolbar consists of the modeling tools that are used to create surface models. This toolbar is available only when you are in the **Part** environment. The **Surfacing** toolbar, along with all buttons, is shown in Figure 1-14.

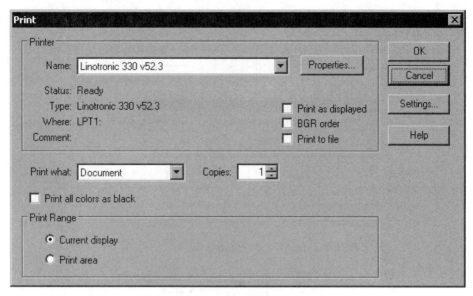

*Figure 1-12 The **Print** dialog box*

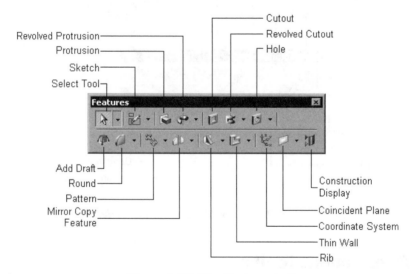

*Figure 1-13 The **Features** toolbar*

Assembly Environment Toolbars

There are several toolbars that can be invoked in the **Assembly** environment of Solid Edge.

Assembly Commands Toolbar

The **Assembly Commands** toolbar is shown in Figure 1-15. The buttons in this toolbar are used to create and manage assemblies.

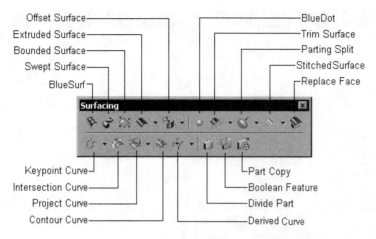

*Figure 1-14 The **Surfacing** toolbar*

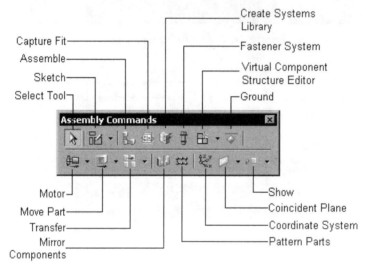

*Figure 1-15 The **Assembly Commands** toolbar*

Draft Environment Toolbar

The **Main** toolbar, the **EdgeBar**, and other toolbars are also available in this toolbar. In addition to these toolbars, the **Draft** environment provides you with the following toolbars:

Drawing Toolbar

This toolbar is extensively used in the **Draft** environment for generating and creating drawing views. The **Drawing Views** toolbar is shown in Figure 1-16.

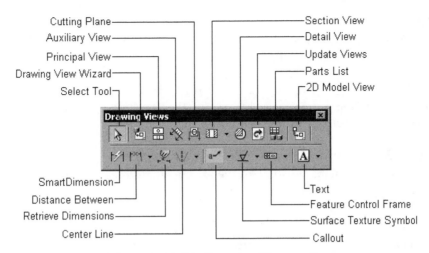

Figure 1-16 *The **Drawing Views** toolbar*

ADDITIONAL DESIGN TOOLS

Designing in Solid Edge has been made easier by introducing the ribbon bar and the **EdgeBar**. The tools available in the ribbon bar and the **EdgeBar** are different for different tools and environments of Solid Edge. The **EdgeBar** was discussed earlier and the ribbon bar is discussed next.

Ribbon Bar

The ribbon bar enables you to switch back and forth while creating a model, an assembly, or a drawing. It is available in all environments of Solid Edge and contains different buttons. The ribbon bar that is available by default in the **Part** environment is shown in Figure 1-17.

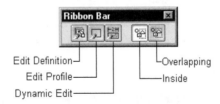

Figure 1-17 *The **Ribbon Bar***

Plane or Sketch Step

 You can choose this button from the ribbon bar and redefine the sketch plane. When you choose this button, the **Create-From Options** drop-down list is displayed in the ribbon bar.

Draw Profile Step

 Using the **Draw Profile Step** button, you can select a profile from the drawing window or sketch a new one.

Side Step

The **Side Step** button is used to specify the side of the sketch to or from which the material will be added or removed.

Extent Step

The **Extent Step** button is used to specify the depth of the material addition. This button is used with the other buttons for depth specification.

Treatment Step

This step is available in some of the sketched-based features and is used to add a draft or a crown feature to the model.

QuickPick

This tool enables you to select elements from the drawing window. This tool is used when the elements or the components are overlapping and you need to make a selection. The following steps explain the procedure of using this tool:

1. Bring the cursor near the element or the component that you need to select. Pause the cursor and when three dots appear close to it, right-click on the screen.

2. The **QuickPick** list box appears with an entry of each possible selection, as shown in Figure 1-18. Each entry represents an element. As you move your cursor on elements in this list, the corresponding components get highlighted in the drawing window

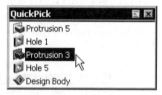

*Figure 1-18 The **QuickPick** list box*

Tip: *You can use the **Options** button available on the left of the **Close** button in the **QuickPick** list box to invoke the **QuickPick Options** dialog box. You can use the options in this dialog box to modify the **QuickPick** options.*

3. To remove the **QuickPick** toolbar, click on the screen.

COLOR SCHEME IN THIS TEXTBOOK

In Solid Edge, you can use various color schemes as the background color of the drawing window and for displaying the entities in it. Note that this book uses white as the background color. To change the background color, choose **Tools > Options** from the menu bar; the **Options** dialog box is displayed. Choose the **Colors** tab in the dialog box to display various colors, as shown in Figure 1-19.

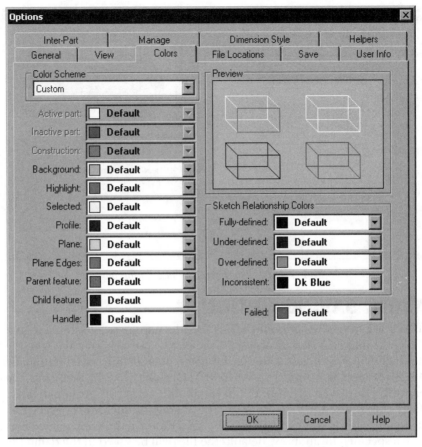

*Figure 1-19 The **Colors** tab of the **Options** dialog box*

From the **Background** drop-down list, select the **White** color. Choose **OK** from the **Options** dialog box.

Next, choose **Format > View** from the menu bar; the **Format View** dialog box will be displayed. Choose the **Background** tab and select **Solid Edge default** from the **Type** drop-down list, as shown in Figure 1-20. Choose **OK** to exit the dialog box. Note that the current file and all the files that you open henceforth will use this color scheme.

UNITS FOR DIMENSIONS

When you install Solid Edge V20, you need to specify the units of dimensions that will be used in all the environments of Solid Edge. The units can be in inches or millimeters. If you select inches as the unit for measurement, the English standard will be followed. Similarly, if you select millimeter as the unit for measurement, the Metric standard will be followed. This book follows the Metric standard. Therefore, it is recommended that you install Solid Edge for Metric standards by selecting the unit in millimeters.

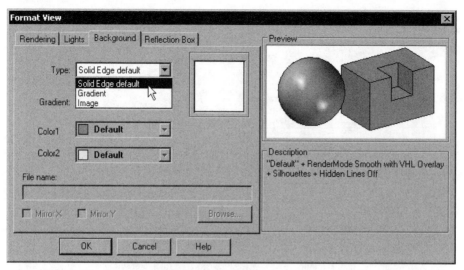

Figure 1-20 *The **Format View** dialog box*

AUTOMATIC SAVING OPTION

In Solid Edge, you can set the option for saving the files automatically after a regular interval of time. While working on a design project, if the system crashes, you may lose the unsaved design data. If the option of automatic saving is on, your data is saved automatically after regular intervals. To set this option, choose **Tools > Options** from the menu bar; the **Options** dialog box will be displayed. Choose the **Save** tab and select the **Automatically preserve documents by** check box. You can also select the **Saving all documents every** radio button and set the minutes in the spinner. You can also select to save uniquely named copies of the documents at a specified location. By default, the files will be saved in the default folder. You can change the default backup folder location by selecting the **File Locations** tab from the dialog box.

Self-Evaluation Test

Answer the following questions and then compare them to those given at the end of this chapter:

1. The **Part** environment of Solid Edge is a feature-based parametric environment in which you can create solid models. (T/F)

2. Any solid model created in Solid Edge is an integration of a number of features. (T/F)

3. The welcome screen displays the **Tip of the day** area that shows a useful tip. (T/F)

4. In Solid Edge, the solid models that are not created by integrating a number of building blocks are called features. (T/F)

5. The _____ property ensures that any modification made in the model in any one of the environments of Solid Edge is automatically reflected in the other modes immediately.

6. The _____ relation forces two selected arcs, circles, a point and an arc, a point and a circle, or an arc and a circle to share the same center point.

7. The _____ relation is used to make two points, a point and a line, or a point and an arc coincident.

8. The _____ relation forces two selected lines to become equal in length.

9. The _____ lists all occurrences of features and sketches of a model in a chronicle sequence.

10. The _____ **Step** is available in some of the sketched-based features and is used to add a draft or a crown feature to the model.

Answers to Self-Evaluation Test
1. T, 2. T, 3. T, 4. F, 5. bidirectional associativity, 6. Concentric, 7. Coincident, 8. Equal, 9. EdgeBar, 10. Treatment

Chapter 2

Drawing Sketches for Solid Models

Learning Objectives

After completing this chapter, you will be able to:

- *Understand the need for the sketching environment.*
- *Understand the base reference planes that can be selected to create sketches.*
- *Understand various drawing display tools.*
- *Understand various sketching tools.*
- *Use various selection methods.*
- *Delete sketched entities.*

THE SKETCHING ENVIRONMENT

Most designs created in a solid modeling tool consist of profile-based features, placed features, and reference features. A profile is a combination of a number of two-dimensional (2D) entities such as lines, arcs, circles, and so on. The profile-based features are created using these entities. A profile-based feature is the base feature or the first feature in most designs. For example, refer to the solid model shown in Figure 2-1.

Figure 2-1 Solid model

This model is created using the profile shown in Figure 2-2.

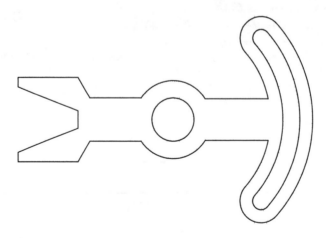

Figure 2-2 Profile of the solid model shown in Figure 2-1

In most designs, you first need to invoke the sketching environment and then create the profile of the model in it. After creating the profile, exit the sketching environment and then use the solid modeling tools to complete the design. You can invoke the sketching environment in the **Part** environment of Solid Edge.

There are two methods of starting a new document in the **Part** environment. The first one is to start Solid Edge and then use the welcome screen to start a new file in the **Part** environment. The second one is to start a new part document using the **New** dialog box. These methods are discussed next.

Starting the Part Environment in Solid Edge

To start the **Part** environment, you first need to start Solid Edge. This can be done using the taskbar menu. Choose the **Start** button on the lower left corner of the screen to invoke the menu and then choose **Programs > Solid Edge V20 > Solid Edge**. Alternatively, you can choose the shortcut of Solid Edge V20 from the desktop of your computer.

The system will prepare to start Solid Edge. Once all the files are loaded, the Solid Edge window will be displayed along with the welcome screen, as shown in Figure 2-3.

To start the **Part** environment, choose **Solid Part** from the **Create** area of the welcome screen.

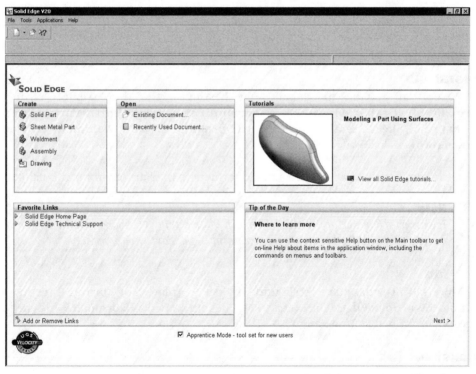

Figure 2-3 Welcome screen of Solid Edge

Starting a New Part Document Using the New Dialog Box

You can also start a new part document using the **New** dialog box. To do so, choose the **New** button from the **Main** toolbar of the welcome screen; the **New** dialog box will be displayed, as shown in Figure 2-4. The options in this dialog box are discussed next.

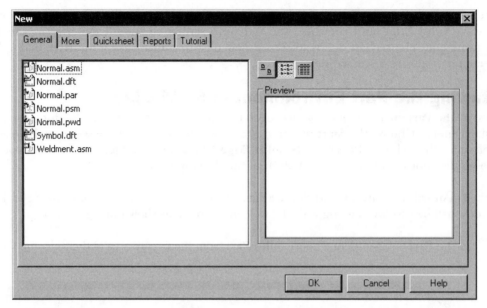

*Figure 2-4 The **New** dialog box*

General Tab

The **General** tab provides the default templates for starting the **Assembly** environment (**Normal.asm**), **Draft** environment (**Normal.dft** and **Symbol.dft**), **Part** environment (**Normal.par**), **Sheet Metal** environment (**Normal.psm**), and **Weldment** environment (**Normal.pwd**).

Double-click on **Normal.par** to open a new document in the **Part** environment of Solid Edge.

Note
*It is assumed that you installed Solid Edge in **Metric** units. Therefore, you can use **Normal.par** from the **General** tab to open a new document in the **Part** environment.*

More Tab .

The **More** tab provides the Metric and English templates for starting files in various environments of Solid Edge. The Metric templates are named as **Normmet.*** and the English templates are named as **Normeng.***.

Quicksheet Tab

The **Quicksheet** tab provides the drawing template with empty (blank) drawing views of a part or an assembly. You can simply drag and drop any part or assembly document from the EdgeBar to populate the drawing views.

Tip. *There is a difference between the Metric and English templates. In the Metric templates, the length is measured in millimeter (mm) and the mass is measured in Kilogram (Kg). Whereas in the English templates, the length is measured in inches (in) and the mass is measured in pounds (lbm).*

Reports Tab
The **Reports** tab provides the template for generating reports of the Solid Edge assemblies. You will learn more about these reports in the later chapters.

Tutorial Tab
The **Tutorial** tab provides the Metric template for starting various environments of Solid Edge.

Large Icon Button
The **Large Icon** button is used to display the templates in various tabs of the **New** dialog box in the form of large icons.

List Button
The **List** button is used to display the templates in various tabs of the **New** dialog box in the form of a list.

Detail Button
The **Detail** button is used to list the details of the templates in various tabs of the **New** dialog box. When you choose this button, the area on the left will be divided into four columns. The first column lists the names of the templates, the second column lists the sizes, the third column lists the types of the template files, and the last column lists the dates when the templates were last modified.

Preview Area
The **Preview** area shows the preview of the selected template.

A new Solid Edge document in the **Part** environment is shown in Figure 2-5. This figure also shows various components of the part document of Solid Edge.

Note
*Solid Edge also gives you an option to start this program directly in a particular environment. To do so, choose **Tools > Options** from the menu bar; the **Options** dialog box will be invoked. Choose the **Helpers** tab and select the required environment from the drop-down list available on the right of the **Start with this environment** radio button.*

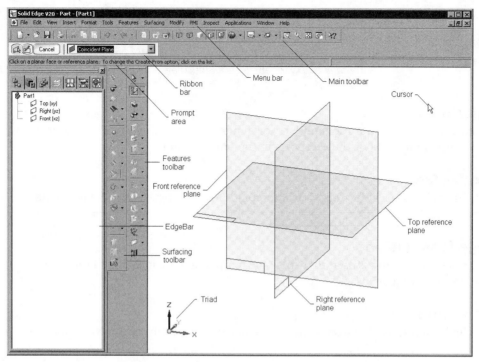

Figure 2-5 *New document in the **Part** environment*

INVOKING THE SKETCHING ENVIRONMENT

As mentioned earlier, whenever you start a new document in the **Part** environment of Solid Edge, three reference planes will be displayed, as shown in Figure 2-5. You can invoke the sketching environment using any one of these reference planes. The sketching environment can be invoked using the **Sketch** tool. The sketches drawn using this tool are independent and are not used by any feature. These sketches can be used multiple times to create features.

To invoke the sketching environment, choose the **Sketch** button from the **Features** toolbar; you will be prompted to select a planar face or a reference plane. As soon as you select a reference plane, it will be oriented parallel to the screen and the sketching environment will be invoked. Figure 2-6 shows the default screen in the sketching environment of Solid Edge.

Tip. *If the toolbar icons appear large in size, you can make them small. To do so, choose **Tools > Options** from the menu bar; the **Options** dialog box will be invoked. Choose the **Helpers** tab and clear the **Large buttons** and **Text on buttons** check boxes from the **Toolbar Buttons** area.*

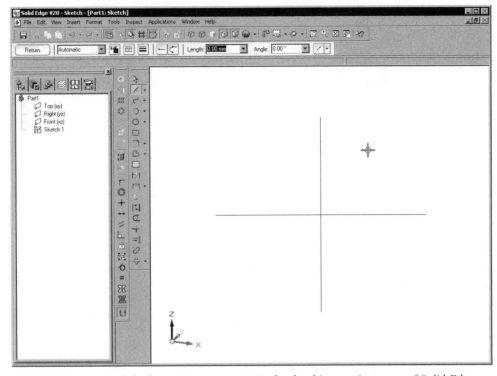

Figure 2-6 *The default screen appearance in the sketching environment of Solid Edge*

THE DRAWING DISPLAY TOOLS

The drawing display tools are an integral part of any solid modeling tool. They enable you to zoom and pan the drawing so that you can view it clearly. The drawing display tools available in Solid Edge are discussed next.

Zooming to an Area

Menu:	View > Zoom Area
Toolbar:	Main > Zoom Area

The **Zoom Area** tool allows you to zoom on to a particular area by defining a box around it. When you choose this button, a plus sign(+) of unknown length will be attached to the tip of the cursor and you will be prompted to click for defining the first corner or drag for specifying the box. Specify a point on the screen to define the first corner of the zoom area. Next, move the cursor and specify another point to define the opposite corner of the zoom area. The drawing window defined inside the box will be zoomed and displayed on the screen.

Note

*If triad is not available in the sketching environment of Solid Edge, choose **Tools > Option > View** from the menu bar and select the **Show orientation triad** check box in the **Options** dialog box.*

Dynamic Zooming

Menu:	View > Zoom
Toolbar:	Main > Zoom

 The **Zoom** tool enables you to dynamically zoom in or out of the drawing. You can also use this tool to increase the display area to double the current size. To zoom in, press and hold the left mouse button in the center of the screen and then drag the cursor down. Similarly, to zoom out, press and hold the left mouse button in the center of the screen and drag the cursor up.

For increasing the drawing display area to double the current size, invoke this tool and click anywhere in the drawing window. Note that the drawing display area will be increased such that the point at which you clicked will be brought to the center of the screen.

Fitting All Entities in the Current Display

Menu:	View > Fit
Toolbar:	Main > Fit

 The **Fit** tool enables you to modify the drawing display area such that all entities in the drawing fit in the current display.

Panning Drawings

Menu:	View > Pan
Toolbar:	Main > Pan

The **Pan** tool allows you to dynamically pan the drawings in the drawing window. When you invoke this tool, the arrow cursor will be replaced by a hand cursor and you will be prompted to click to select the origin or drag the cursor for the dynamic pan. Press and hold the left mouse button in the drawing window, and then drag the cursor to pan the drawing. You can also pan the drawing by specifying two points in the drawing window. First, specify a point anywhere in the drawing window and then move the cursor. You will notice that a rubber-band line is displayed. One end of this line will be fixed at the point you specified and the other end will be attached to the hand cursor. Move the cursor and specify another point in the drawing window to pan the drawing.

 Tip. *You can also use the keyboard to modify the drawing display area. To do so, the following combinations of keys can be used:*

CTRL+ Top/Left arrow key = Zoom In
CTRL+ Bottom/Right arrow key = Zoom Out
SHIFT+ Left/Bottom arrow key = Rotate Left
SHIFT+ Right/Top arrow key = Rotate Right
CTRL + SHIFT+ Top arrow key = Pan Upward
CTRL + SHIFT+ Left arrow key = Pan Toward Left
CTRL + SHIFT+ Bottom arrow key = Pan Downward
CTRL + SHIFT+ Right arrow key = Pan Toward Right

Restoring the Original Orientation of the Sketching Plane

Toolbar: Main > Sketch View

Sometimes while using the drawing display tools, you may change the orientation of the sketching plane. The **Sketch View** tool enables you to restore the original orientation that was active when you invoked the sketching environment. Note that this tool is available only in the sketching environment.

SKETCHING TOOLS

All the tools required to create a profile or a sketch in Solid Edge are available in the **Draw** toolbar and are discussed next.

Drawing Lines

Toolbar: Draw > Line

Lines are the most widely used sketched entities in any design. In Solid Edge, the **Line** tool enables you to draw straight lines as well as tangent or normal arcs originating from the endpoint of a selected line. On invoking the **Line** tool, the **Line** ribbon bar will be displayed, as shown in Figure 2-7, and you will be prompted to specify the first point of the line. The methods of creating lines and arcs using this tool are discussed next.

Figure 2-7 *The **Line** ribbon bar*

Drawing Straight Lines

To draw a straight line, specify a point in the drawing window by pressing the left mouse button; a rubber-band line will be displayed with the start point fixed at the point you specified and the second point will be attached to the cursor. Now, you will be prompted to select the second point of the line. Note that on moving the cursor in the drawing window, the length and angle of the line also get modified accordingly in the **Line** ribbon bar. Next, you need to specify the endpoint of the line in the drawing window by pressing the left mouse button. Alternatively, you can draw a line by specifying its length and angle in the **Line** ribbon bar.

While drawing a line, you will notice that some symbols are displayed on the right of the cursor. For example, after specifying the start point of the line, if you move the cursor in the horizontal direction, a symbol similar to a horizontal line will be displayed. This symbol is called the relationship handle and it indicates the relationship that is applied to the entity being drawn. In the above-mentioned case, the horizontal relationship handle is displayed on the right of the cursor. This relationship will ensure that the line you draw is horizontal. These relationships are automatically applied to the profile while drawing a line.

Note

Relationships are also applied between the sketched entities and the reference planes. You will learn more about relationships in the later chapters.

The process of drawing lines does not end after defining the first line. You will notice that as soon as you define the endpoint of the first line, another rubber-band line starts. The start point of this line is the endpoint of the first line and the endpoint of the new line is attached to the cursor.

This process of drawing consecutive lines continues until you right-click to terminate it. However, note that even after right-clicking, the **Line** tool will not be terminated and you will still be prompted to specify the first point of the line. You can terminate the **Line** tool by choosing the **Select Tool** button from the **Draw** toolbar or by pressing the ESC key. Figures 2-8 and 2-9 show continuous lines being drawn.

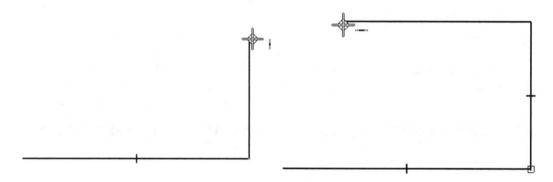

Figure 2-8 Vertical relationship handle displayed while drawing the vertical line

Figure 2-9 Horizontal relationship handle displayed while drawing the horizontal line

While drawing lines, you will notice that if the cursor is horizontally or vertically aligned with the endpoint or midpoint of a line or reference plane, some dashed lines will be displayed. These dashed lines are called alignment indicators and are used to indicate the horizontal or vertical alignment of the current location of the cursor with a point. Figure 2-10 shows the alignment indicators originating from the endpoints of the existing lines.

Tip. *If the alignment indicator is not displayed, move the cursor over the entity from which you want the alignment indicator to originate; the entity will turn red in color and the alignment indicator will be displayed.*

Drawing Tangent and Normal Arcs

As mentioned earlier, you can also use the **Line** tool to draw a tangent or a normal arc. To switch to the arc mode when the **Line** tool is active, press the A key or choose the **Arc** button from the ribbon bar. You will notice that the **Length** and **Angle** edit boxes in the ribbon bar will be replaced by the **Radius** and **Sweep** edit boxes. These edit boxes can be used to define the radius and the included angle of the resulting arc.

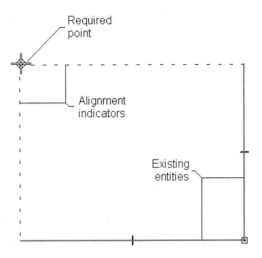

Figure 2-10 *The alignment indicators originating from the endpoints of the existing lines*

Also, a small circle will be displayed at the start point of the arc. This circle is divided into four regions. These regions are called intent zones and are used to define the type of arc that will be created. To create an arc tangent to the line, move the cursor through a small distance in the zone that is tangent to the line; the tangent arc will be drawn. Similarly, if you move the cursor in the zone that is normal to the line, the normal arc will be drawn. After drawing the required arcs, you can switch back to the line mode by pressing the L key or by choosing the **Line** button from the ribbon bar. Figure 2-11 shows a tangent arc being drawn from within the **Line** tool.

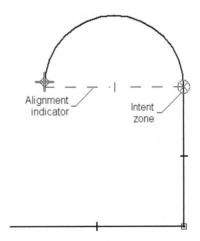

Figure 2-11 *A tangent arc drawn from the **Line** tool*

Tip. *If you have selected an incorrect point as the start point of a line, right-click to cancel it; you will be again prompted to specify the first point of the line.*

The buttons in the **Line** ribbon bar can be used to specify the color, type, and width of lines. You can also draw a projection line of infinite length using the **Projection Line** button available on the right side of the **Line** ribbon bar. The projection lines are generally used in the drafting environment.

Drawing Circles

In Solid Edge, you can draw circles using three methods, which are discussed next.

Drawing a Circle by Specifying the Center Point and Radius

Toolbar:	Draw > Circle by Center

This is the most widely used method of drawing circles. In this method, you need to specify the center point of a circle and a point on it. The point on the circle defines the radius of the circle. To draw a circle using this method, choose the **Circle by Center** button from the **Draw** toolbar; the **Circle** ribbon bar will be displayed and you will be prompted to specify the center point of the circle. Specify the center point of the circle in the drawing window. Next, you will be prompted to specify a point on the circle. Specify a point on the circle to define the radius. Alternatively, you can enter the value of the diameter or radius in the ribbon bar. Figure 2-12 shows a circle drawn using this method.

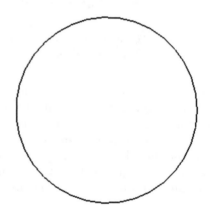

Figure 2-12 *Circle drawn using the* *Circle by* *Center* *method*

Drawing a Circle by Specifying Three Points

Toolbar:	Draw > Circle by Center > Circle by 3 Points

This method is used to draw a circle using the three points that you need to define on it. To use this method, click on the down arrow available on the right side of the **Circle by Center** button in the **Draw** toolbar; a flyout will be displayed. From the flyout, choose the **Circle by 3 Points** button; you will be prompted to specify the first and then the second point on the circle. On specifying these two points, small reference circles will be displayed on these two points, as shown in Figure 2-13. Now you will be prompted to specify the third point. Specify the third point on the circle. This completes the circle.

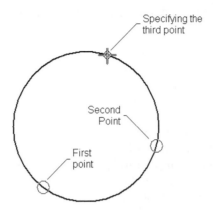

*Figure 2-13 Circle drawn using the **Circle by 3 Points** method*

Drawing a Tangent Circle

Toolbar: Draw > Circle by Center > Tangent Circle

This method is used to draw a circle that is tangent to one or two existing entities. To draw a circle using this method, choose the **Tangent Circle** button from the **Circle by Center** flyout in the **Draw** toolbar; you will be prompted to specify the first point on the circle. The circle will be drawn using two or three points, depending on how you specify the first point of the circle. If you specify the first point on an existing entity, then you will be prompted to specify the second point and the circle will be drawn using these two points. However, if you do not specify the first point on any existing entity, then you need to define the circle using three points.

When you move the cursor close to an existing entity to specify the second or third point, the tangent relationship handle will be displayed. Now, if you specify the point, the resulting circle will be tangent to the selected entities. Also, small reference circles will be displayed at the points where the circle is tangent to the selected entities. Figure 2-14 shows a circle tangent to two lines.

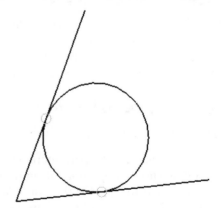

Figure 2-14 A circle drawn tangent to two lines

Drawing Ellipses

In Solid Edge, you can draw ellipses using the following two methods:

Drawing an Ellipse by Specifying Three Points

Toolbar: Draw > Circle by Center > Ellipse by 3 Points

This method is used to draw an ellipse by specifying three points. The first two points are the first and second endpoints of the primary axis of the ellipse and the third point is a point on the ellipse. To draw an ellipse using this method, choose the **Ellipse by 3 Points** button from the **Circle by Center** flyout in the **Draw** toolbar. You will be prompted to specify the first and second endpoints of the primary axis of the ellipse. After you specify these two points, a reference ellipse will be displayed on the screen and you will be prompted to specify a point on the ellipse. The primary axis will act as the major or the minor axis, depending on where you specify the point. Figure 2-15 shows a profile in

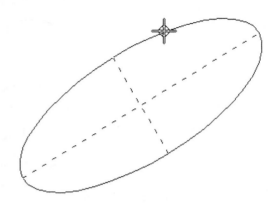

Figure 2-15 *An ellipse drawn by specifying three points*

which the cursor is moved to define the point on the ellipse after defining the primary axis. Note that to draw an ellipse you can also enter values in the **Ellipse** ribbon bar, which is displayed on invoking this tool.

Drawing the Center Point Ellipse

Toolbar: Draw > Circle by Center > Ellipse by Center

In this method, you need to define the center point of the ellipse first. After you define the center point, you will be prompted to specify the endpoint of the primary axis. Next, you will be prompted to specify the endpoint of the secondary axis. Alternatively, you can enter the values in the ribbon bar.

Placing Sketched Points

Toolbar: Draw > Line > Point

Points generally help as references in drawing the other sketched entities. To place a point, choose the **Point** button from the **Line** flyout in the **Draw** toolbar; you will be prompted to click for the point. You can place the point by defining its location in the drawing window or by entering its coordinates in the **Point** ribbon bar.

Drawing Arcs

In Solid Edge, you can draw arcs using the following three methods:

Drawing a Tangent or a Normal Arc

Toolbar: Draw > Tangent Arc

This method of drawing arcs is similar to drawing tangent and normal arcs using the **Line** tool. On invoking this tool, you will be prompted to specify the start point of the arc. Move the cursor close to the endpoint of the entity where you want the tangent arc to start. You will notice that the endpoint relationship handle is displayed on the right of the cursor. This handle has a small inclined line with a point at the upper end, which suggests that if you select the point now, the endpoint of the entity will be snapped. Select the endpoint and then move the cursor; the intent zones will be displayed. Move the cursor through a small distance in the required intent zone and then specify the endpoint of the arc. Alternatively, you can enter the radius and included angle of the arc in the **Arc** ribbon bar, which is displayed when you invoke this tool.

Drawing a Three-Points Arc

Toolbar: Draw > Tangent Arc > Arc by 3 Points

This method is used to draw an arc by specifying its start point, endpoint, and the third point on it. You can specify the radius of this arc in the ribbon bar. However in this case, you will be allowed to specify only the start point and the endpoint of the arc. The third point specifies the direction in which the arc will be drawn. Figure 2-16 shows a three-points arc drawn.

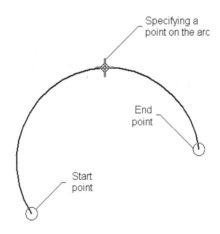

*Figure 2-16 An arc drawn using the **Arc by 3 Points** method*

Drawing a Center Point Arc

Toolbar: Draw > Tangent Arc > Arc by Center

This method is used to draw an arc by specifying its center point, start point, and endpoint. On invoking this tool, you will be prompted to specify the center point of the arc. Next, you will be prompted to specify its start point and endpoint. Note that when you specify the start point of the arc after specifying the center point, the radius will be automatically defined. Therefore, the endpoint is used only to define the arc length. Figure 2-17 shows an arc being drawn using this method.

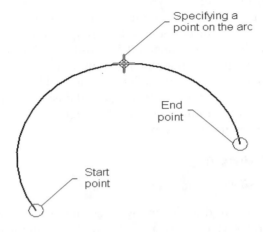

Figure 2-17 *An arc drawn using the **Arc by Center** method*

Drawing Rectangles

Toolbar: Draw > Rectangle

In Solid Edge, the rectangles are drawn by specifying three points. The first two points define the width of the rectangle and the third point defines the height. When you invoke this tool, you will be prompted to specify the first corner. Specify a point in the drawing window to define the start point of the rectangle. Next, you will be prompted to specify the second point. This point will define the width of the rectangle. You can also define this point at an angle. As a result, the rectangle will be drawn at an angle. Finally, you will be prompted to specify a point to create the rectangle, which will define the height of the rectangle. Alternatively, you can specify the width, height, and angle of the rectangle in the **Rectangle** ribbon bar. Figure 2-18 shows a rectangle drawn at an angle.

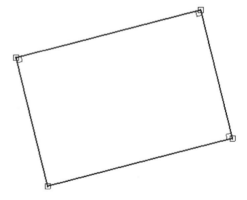

Figure 2-18 *Rectangle drawn at an angle*

Tip. *You can also draw a rectangle by pressing and holding the left mouse button at a point and dragging the cursor across to define the opposite corner of the rectangle. When you release the left mouse button, the rectangle will be drawn.*

This tool also enables you to draw a square. To draw a square, specify the first two points to define the width of the square. Next, press and hold the SHIFT key and then move the mouse to a small distance; the square will be drawn.

Drawing Curves

Toolbar: Draw > Curve

 The **Curve** tool allows you to draw curves using two methods: specifying points in the drawing window and dragging the cursor in the drawing window. These methods are discussed next.

Drawing a Curve by Dragging the Cursor

In this method, you need to press and hold the left mouse button and drag the cursor to create the curve. A reference curve will be displayed in the drawing window as you drag the cursor. Once you release the left mouse button, a curve will be drawn that has exactly the same shape as the reference curve. Figure 2-19 shows a curve drawn using this method.

Drawing a Curve by Specifying Points in the Drawing Window

In this method, you need to continuously specify points on the curve to draw it. After specifying the first point, you do not need to drag the cursor. You can simply move the cursor and specify the second point. Continue this process until you have specified all the points required to draw the curve. Figure 2-20 shows a curve drawn using this method.

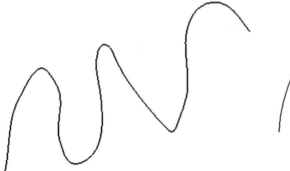 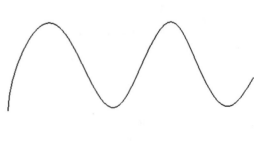

Figure 2-19 Curve drawn by dragging the cursor in the drawing window   *Figure 2-20* Curve drawn by specifying the points in the drawing window

Converting Sketched Entities into Curves

Toolbar: Draw > Curve > Convert to Curve

In Solid Edge, you can convert the sketched entities such as lines, arcs, circles, and ellipses into bezier spline curves using the **Convert to Curve** tool. On invoking this tool, you will be prompted to select an element to be converted into a curve. As soon as you select the element, it will be converted into a bezier spline curve. Note that you may not be able to view the changes in the sketched entity unless you select it. When you select the sketched entity, you will notice that the number of handles in it has increased and the control polygon is displayed on that entity. If you drag the converted entity using any of its handles, it will become a curve.

Filleting Sketched Entities

Toolbar:	Draw > Fillet

Filleting is defined as the process of rounding the sharp corners of a profile to reduce the stress concentration. You can create a fillet by removing the sharp corner and replacing it with round corners. In Solid Edge, you can create a fillet between any two sketched entities. On invoking the **Fillet** tool, the **Fillet** ribbon bar will be displayed. Enter the radius of the fillet in the **Radius** edit box of the ribbon bar, and press ENTER. Now, select the two entities that you want to fillet; the fillet will be created. You can also directly select the sharp corner to be filleted. The two entities comprising the corners will be highlighted in red when you move the cursor over the corner. Select the corners at this stage to create the fillet. Figure 2-21 shows a profile before and after filleting.

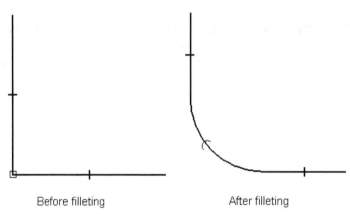

Before filleting   After filleting

Figure 2-21 Sketch before and after creating the fillet

You are given an option of retaining the sharp corner even after creating the fillet. If you want to retain the sharp corner after filleting, choose the **No Trim** button from the **Fillet** ribbon bar and then select the corner to be filleted. The fillet will be created and the sharp corner will also be retained. Figure 2-22 shows a profile in which the fillet is created and the sharp corner is also retained.

 Note
Ideally, the profiles that have the fillet created with the sharp corners retained may not give the desired result when used to create features. Therefore, they should be avoided.

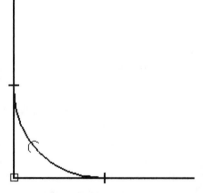

Figure 2-22 Sharp corner retained after creating the fillet

Chamfering Sketched Entities

Toolbar: Draw > Fillet > Chamfer

Chamfering is defined as the process of beveling the sharp corners of a profile to reduce the stress concentration. You can create the chamfer only between two linear entities. The chamfer can be created by defining the distance of the corner being chamfered from the two edges of the profile, or by defining the angle of the chamfer and the distance along one of the edges. To create a chamfer, invoke the **Chamfer** tool; the **Chamfer** ribbon bar will be displayed. You can specify the angle, setback A, and setback B values using this ribbon bar. The setback A and the setback B values define the chamfer distance along the first and the second edge, respectively. Note that you can specify any two of the three values. The third value is automatically updated on the basis of the two values that you define.

After setting any two values in the **Chamfer** ribbon bar, select the first and the second line to be chamfered; the preview of the resulting chamfer will be displayed. Next, click to create the chamfer. Note that by default, the first line is taken as the setback A element and the second line is taken as the setback B element. If you want to reverse the order, move the cursor over the first line. You will notice that the second line is taken as the setback A element and the first line is taken as the setback B element. Consequently, the preview will also change automatically. By default, the setback A and B are displayed in yellow color. Figure 2-23 shows the preview of the chamfer.

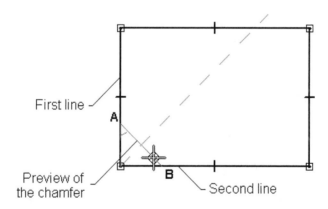

First line
A
Preview of
the chamfer
B
Second line

Figure 2-23 Preview of the chamfer

Tip. *In Solid Edge, you can create fillets or chamfers by dragging the cursor across the entities that you need to fillet or chamfer. For example, if you want to chamfer two lines, invoke the **Chamfer** tool and drag the cursor across them. The corner of these two lines will be chamfered and the angle and distances of the chamfer will depend on how far you dragged the mouse from the corner.*

SELECTING THE SKETCHED ENTITIES

When you choose the **Select Tool** button from the **Draw** toolbar, the select mode will be invoked. In this mode, you can select the sketched entities available in the drawing window by clicking on them. You can also select all entities in the drawing window by pressing the CTRL+A keys. The selected entities will be highlighted in yellow.

In addition to these methods of selection, you can also select entities by dragging a rectangular box or drawing a polygonal fence around them. You can choose the button of the rectangular box or polygonal fence from the ribbon bar. To drag the box or the fence, press and hold the left mouse button and drag the cursor in the drawing window. The entities to be selected will depend on the option selected from the **Fence Filter** drop-down list in the ribbon bar that is displayed in the select mode. The options in this drop-down list are discussed next.

Inside

This is the default selection mode and it ensures that only those entities are selected that lie completely inside the box, which is created when you hold the left mouse button and drag the cursor.

Outside

This selection mode ensures that only those entities are selected that lie completely outside the box which is created when you hold the left mouse button and drag the cursor.

Overlapping

This selection mode ensures that all entities that lie partially inside the box or even touch the box are selected.

Inside and Overlapping

This mode is a combination of the inside and the overlapping modes. This selection mode ensures that all entities that lie partially or fully inside the box are selected.

Outside and Overlapping

This mode is a combination of the outside and the overlapping modes. This selection mode ensures that all entities that are partially inside the box or completely outside the box are selected.

DELETING THE SKETCHED ENTITIES

To delete the sketched entities, select them using any one of the object selection methods discussed above. The selected entities turn yellow in color. Next, press the DELETE key; all the selected entities will be deleted.

Note
*You can also delete the sketched entities by choosing **Edit > Delete** from the **Main** toolbar.*

TUTORIALS

As mentioned in the Introduction, Solid Edge is parametric in nature. Therefore, you can draw a profile of any dimensions and then modify its size by changing the values of the dimensions. However in this chapter, you will use the ribbon bars to draw the profile with exact dimensions. This will help you in improving your sketching skills.

Tutorial 1

In this tutorial, you will draw the profile for the model shown in Figure 2-24. The profile to be drawn is shown in Figure 2-25. Do not dimension the profile because the dimensions are given only for your reference. **(Expected time: 30 min)**

Figure 2-24 Model for Tutorial 1   *Figure 2-25 Profile for Tutorial 1*

The following steps are required to complete this tutorial:

a. Start Solid Edge and then start a new file in the **Part** environment.
b. Choose the **Sketch** button and select the front plane as the sketching plane and invoke the sketching environment.
c. Draw the outer loop of the profile using the **Line** tool.
d. Fillet the sharp corners of the outer loop using the **Fillet** tool.
e. Draw the circles using the centers of the fillets to complete the profile.
f. Save the file and close it.

Starting Solid Edge and Selecting the Sketching Plane

The profile of the model will be created in the sketching environment of Solid Edge. You can invoke the sketching environment in the **Part** environment, whenever required. Therefore, you need to start a new part file first.

1. Choose the **Start** button available at the lower left corner of the screen to display a menu with additional options.

2. Choose **All Programs** (or **Programs**) > **Solid Edge V20** > **Solid Edge** from the start menu to start Solid Edge.

As Solid Edge gets started, the welcome screen is displayed. Now, you need to start a new part file to draw the sketch of the given model.

3. Click on the **Solid Part** link in the **Create** area; a new Solid Edge part file gets started.

4. Choose the **Sketch** button from the **Features** toolbar; the **Sketch** ribbon bar is displayed and you are prompted to select a planar face or a reference plane.

5. Select the front plane to draw the profile; the sketching environment is invoked and the sketch plane orients itself parallel to the screen. Also, the **Line** tool is automatically invoked.

Drawing Lines of the Outer Loop

You can draw the outer loop using the **Line** tool. The sharp corners will be rounded using the **Fillet** tool. In this chapter, you will use the ribbon bar to enter the exact values of the sketched entities.

As the **Line** tool is active, its ribbon bar is displayed on top of the **EdgeBar** and you are prompted to specify the start point of the line. You can start drawing the line from the origin, which is the point where the top, right, and front planes intersect and hence, its coordinates are 0,0,0. In the current view, the origin is the intersection point of the two planes displayed as horizontal and vertical lines.

1. Move the cursor close to the origin. One of the two planes, which are displayed as blue horizontal or vertical lines, is highlighted and the **Midpoint** relationship handle is displayed.

2. Click to specify the start point of the line.

    The point you specify is selected as the start point of the line and the endpoint is attached to the cursor. As you move the cursor on the screen, the line stretches and its length and angle values are dynamically modified in the ribbon bar .

    Next, you need to specify the other points to define the first line and the remaining lines. This will be done using the **Length** and **Angle** edit boxes in the **Line** ribbon bar.

3. Enter **200** as the value in the **Length** edit box of the **Line** ribbon bar and press ENTER. Now, enter **0** in the **Angle** edit box and press ENTER.

    You will notice that the line is drawn, but it is not completely displayed in the current display. To include it in the current display, you need to modify the drawing display area using the **Fit** tool.

4. Choose the **Fit** button from the **Main** toolbar; the current drawing display area is modified and the line is displayed completely in the current view. Also, the **Line** tool is still active and you are prompted to specify the second point of the line.

5. Enter **90** in the **Length** edit box and press ENTER. Again, enter **90** in the **Angle** edit box and press ENTER. A vertical line of 90 length is drawn.

6. Enter **40** in the **Length** edit box and press ENTER. Enter **180** in the **Angle** edit box and press ENTER. A horizontal line of 40 length is drawn toward the left of the last line.

7. Enter **40** in the **Length** edit box and press ENTER. Enter **-90** in the **Angle** edit box and press ENTER. A vertical line of 40 length is drawn downward.

8. Enter **120** in the **Length** edit box and press ENTER. Enter **180** in the **Angle** edit box and press ENTER. A horizontal line of 180 length is drawn.

9. Move the cursor vertically upward. A rubber-band line is displayed with its starting point at the endpoint of the previous line and the endpoint attached to the cursor.

10. Move the cursor once toward the vertical line of 40 length drawn earlier and then move it back in the vertical direction from the start point of this line. When the line is vertical, the vertical relationship handle is displayed.

11. Move the cursor vertically upward until the horizontal alignment indicator is displayed from the top endpoint of the vertical line of 40 length. Note that at this point, the value in the **Length** edit box is **40** and the **Angle** edit box is **90**. Now, click to specify the endpoint of this line.

12. Move the cursor horizontally toward the left and make sure that the horizontal relation-ship handle is displayed. Click to specify the endpoint of the line when the vertical alignment indicator is displayed from the vertical plane. If the alignment indicator is not displayed, move the cursor once on the vertical plane and then move it back.

13. Move the cursor vertically downward to the origin. If the first line is not highlighted in red, move the cursor over it once and then move it back to the origin. The endpoint relationship handle is displayed. This relationship ensures that this line ends at the start point of the first line.

14. Click to specify the endpoint of the line when the endpoint relationship handle is displayed. Choose the **Fit** button to fit the sketch in the drawing window.

15. Choose the **Select Tool** button to exit the **Line** tool. The sketch after drawing the lines is shown in Figure 2-26.

Filleting the Sharp Corners

Next, you need to fillet the sharp corners so that there are no sharp edges in the final model. You can fillet the corners using the **Fillet** tool.

1. Choose the **Fillet** button from the **Draw** toolbar. Note that if you had invoked the **Chamfer** tool earlier, it will now be displayed as the default tool in the **Draw** toolbar. In this case, click on the down arrow on the right side of the **Chamfer**

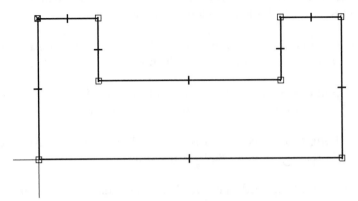

Figure 2-26 *Sketch after drawing lines*

button; a flyout will be displayed. Choose the **Fillet** button from this flyout to invoke the **Fillet** tool; the **Fillet** ribbon bar is displayed.

To fillet any sharp corner, you first need to specify the fillet radius. You can fillet the bottom left and bottom right corners first and then the remaining corners. This is because the fillet radii of the bottom left and bottom right corners are alike and those of the remaining corners are also alike.

2. Enter **15** in the **Radius** edit box in the **Fillet** ribbon bar and press ENTER. Now, move the cursor over the bottom left corner of the sketch; the two lines comprising this corner are highlighted in red.

3. Click to select this corner; the fillet is created at the bottom left corner.

4. Similarly, move the cursor over the bottom right corner and click to select it when the two lines that form this corner are highlighted in red.

    Next, you need to modify the fillet radius value and fillet the remaining corners.

5. Enter **10** as the value in the **Radius** edit box in the ribbon bar and press ENTER.

6. Select the remaining corners of the sketch one by one and fillet them with a radius of 10. The sketch after creating the fillets is shown in Figure 2-27.

Drawing the Circles

Finally, you need to draw circles to complete the profile. The circles will be drawn using the **Circle by Center** tool. You will use the center points of the fillets as the center points of the circles.

1. Choose the **Circle by Center** button from the **Draw** toolbar; the **Circle** ribbon bar is displayed and you are prompted to select the center point of the circle.

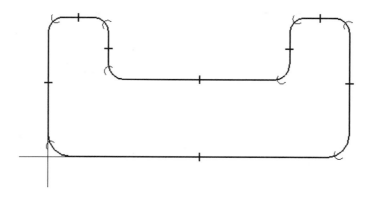

Figure 2-27 Sketch after creating fillets

2. Enter **15** in the **Diameter** edit box of the **Circle** ribbon bar and press ENTER. A circle of the specified diameter is attached to the cursor. The circle attached to the cursor moves as you move the cursor on the screen.

3. Move the cursor over the fillet on the bottom left corner once; the fillet is highlighted in red and the center point of the circle is displayed. The center point is represented by a plus sign (+).

4. Move the cursor over the center point of the fillet represented by the plus sign; the fillet is highlighted in red and the concentric relationship handle is displayed on the right of the cursor.

5. Click to specify this point as the center point of the circle; a circle is drawn at this point and you are again prompted to specify the center point of the circle.

6. Move the cursor over the bottom right fillet so that its center point is also displayed.

7. Move the cursor over the center point of the bottom right fillet and click when the concentric relationship handle is displayed. The final profile for Tutorial 1 is shown in Figure 2-28.

8. Press the ESC key to exit the **Circle** tool.

Saving the File

It is recommended that you exit the sketching environment before saving the file. This is because you cannot close a file in the sketching environment.

You can exit the sketching environment by choosing the **Return** button from the ribbon bar that is displayed in the select mode.

1. Choose the **Return** button from the ribbon bar to close the sketching environment; the

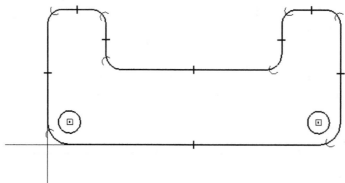

Figure 2-28 Final profile for Tutorial 1

Sketch ribbon bar is displayed. Also, the current view is automatically changed to the isometric view. Choose the **Fit** button to fit the sketch in the drawing window.

2. Enter the name of the sketch as **Base Sketch** in the **Name** edit box of the ribbon bar and choose the **Finish** button from the ribbon bar; the sketch is displayed with this name in the **EdgeBar**.

3. Choose the **Save** button from the **Main** toolbar; the **Part1 Properties** dialog box is displayed. This dialog box can be used to specify the properties of the part file.

4. Choose **OK** from the **Part1 Properties** dialog box; the **Save As** dialog box is displayed.

    It is recommended that you create a separate folder for every chapter in the textbook.

5. Browse to the *My Documents* folder and then create a folder with the name *Solid Edge* in it. Make the *Solid Edge* folder current and then create a folder with the name *c02* in this folder.

6. Make the *c02* folder current and save the file with the name *c02tut1.par*. The location of this file is given below:

    \My Documents\Solid Edge\c02\c02tut1.par

7. Choose **File > Close** from the menu bar to close the file.

Tutorial 2

In this tutorial, you will draw the profile of the model shown in Figure 2-29. The profile to be drawn is shown in Figure 2-30. Do not dimension the profile because the dimensions are given only for your reference.   **(Expected time: 30 min)**

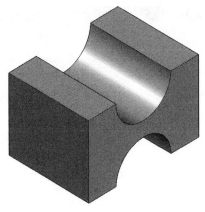

Figure 2-29 *Model for Tutorial 2*

Figure 2-30 *Profile for Tutorial 2*

The following steps are required to complete this tutorial:

a. Start a new part file.
b. Choose the sketch button and select the right plane as the sketching plane and invoke the sketching environment.
c. Draw the profile of the model using the **Line** tool.
d. Save the file and close it.

Starting a New Part File and Selecting the Sketching Plane

You can start a new part file by choosing the **New** button from the **Main** toolbar, which remains on the screen after you close all the files.

1. Choose the **New** button from the **Main** toolbar; the **New** dialog box is displayed.

2. Select **Normal.par**, as shown in Figure 2-31, and choose **OK** to start a new part file.

3. Choose the **Sketch** button from the **Features** toolbar; the **Sketch** ribbon bar is displayed and you are prompted to select a planar face or a reference plane.

4. Select the right plane to draw the profile; the sketching environment is invoked and the sketch plane orients itself parallel to the screen. Also, the **Line** tool is automatically invoked.

Drawing the Profile

As the **Line** tool is active, its ribbon bar is displayed on top of the **EdgeBar** and you are prompted to specify the start point of the line. You can start drawing the line from the origin.

1. Move the cursor close to the origin. One of the two planes, which are displayed as blue horizontal or vertical lines, is highlighted and the midpoint relationship handle is displayed.

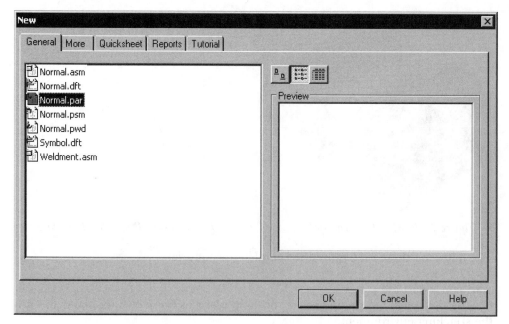

*Figure 2-31 The **New** dialog box to start a new file in Solid Edge*

2. Click to specify the start point of the line.

    The point you specify is selected as the start point of the line and the endpoint is attached
    to the cursor. When you move the cursor on the screen, the line stretches and its length
    and angle values are dynamically modified in the ribbon bar.

3. Enter **12** in the **Length** edit box of the **Line** ribbon bar and press ENTER. Enter **0** as the
    value in the **Angle** edit box and press ENTER.

    The first line is drawn and another rubber-band line is displayed with the start point at
    the endpoint of the previous line and the endpoint attached to the cursor. But as the
    next entity is an arc, you need to invoke the arc mode.

4. Press the A key to invoke the arc mode. Alternatively, you can also choose the **Arc** button
    from the ribbon bar to invoke the arc mode.

    A rubber-band arc is displayed with the start point fixed at the endpoint of the last line
    and the endpoint attached to the cursor. Also, the intent zones are displayed at the start
    point of the arc.

5. Move the cursor to the start point of the arc and then move it vertically upward through
    a small distance. Now, move the cursor toward the right. You will notice that a normal arc
    starts from the endpoint of the last line.

6. Enter **12** and **180** in the **Radius** and **Sweep** edit boxes of the ribbon bar, respectively,

The preview of the resulting arc is displayed, but the arc is still not drawn. To draw the arc, you need to specify a point on the screen with the values mentioned in the ribbon bar.

7. Move the cursor close to the horizontal plane and click when the plane is highlighted in red. The arc is drawn and the line mode is invoked again.

8. Enter **12** and **0** in the **Length** and **Angle** edit boxes, respectively. Choose the **Fit** button from the **Main** toolbar to fit the sketch in the drawing window.

9. Enter **30** and **90** in the **Length** and **Angle** edit boxes, respectively.

10. Move the cursor horizontally toward the left. Make sure the horizontal relationship handle is displayed. Click to specify the endpoint of the line when the vertical alignment indicator is displayed from the endpoint of the arc.

Next, you need to draw an arc. Therefore, you need to invoke the arc mode.

11. Press the A key to invoke the arc mode. A rubber-band arc is displayed with its start point fixed at the endpoint of the last line.

12. Move the cursor to the start point of the arc and then move it vertically downward through a small distance. When the normal arc appears, move the cursor toward the left.

13. Move the cursor over the lower arc once and then move it toward the left, in line with the upper right horizontal line from where this arc starts.

The horizontal alignment indicator is displayed originating from the upper left horizontal line. At the point where the cursor is vertically in line with the start point of the lower arc, the vertical alignment indicator appears from the start point of the lower arc, as shown in Figure 2-32.

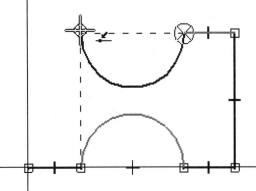

14. Click to define the endpoint of the arc when the horizontal and vertical alignment indicators are displayed. The arc is drawn and the line mode is invoked again.

15. Move the cursor horizontally toward the left and click to define the endpoint of the line when the vertical reference plane is highlighted in red.

16. Move the cursor to the first line and then move it to the start point of this line; the endpoint relationship handle is displayed.

Figure 2-32 Horizontal and vertical alignment indicators displayed to define the endpoint of the arc

17. Click to define the endpoint of this line when the endpoint relationship handle is displayed. The final profile of the model is shown in Figure 2-33.

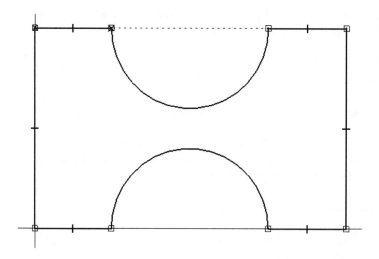

Figure 2-33 Final profile for Tutorial 2

Saving the File

1. Press the ESC key button to exit the current tool.

2. Choose the **Return** button from the ribbon bar; the sketching environment is closed and the **Sketch** ribbon bar is displayed. Also, the current view is automatically changed to the isometric view.

3. Enter the name of the sketch as **Base Sketch** in the **Name** edit box in the ribbon bar and choose the **Finish** button from the ribbon bar. The sketch will be displayed with this name in the **EdgeBar**.

4. Choose the **Save** button from the **Main** toolbar; the **Part2 Properties** dialog box is displayed. This dialog box can be used to specify the properties of the part file.

    Note that if you had started a new session of Solid Edge before starting this tutorial, the name of the dialog box will be **Part1 Properties**.

5. Choose **OK** from the **Part2 Properties** dialog box; the **Save As** dialog box is displayed.

6. Browse to the *My Documents\Solid Edge\c02* folder, if it is not the current folder. Save the file with the name *c02tut2.par*. The location of this file is given below:

    \My Documents\Solid Edge\c02\c02tut2.par

7. Choose **File > Close** from the menu bar to close the file.

Tutorial 3

In this tutorial, you will draw the profile for the base feature of the model shown in Figure 2-34. The profile to be drawn is shown in Figure 2-35. Do not dimension the profile because the dimensions are given only for your reference. **(Expected time: 30 min)**

Figure 2-34 Model for Tutorial 3   *Figure 2-35 Profile for Tutorial 3*

The following steps are required to complete this tutorial:

a. Start a new part file.
b. Choose the sketch button and select the right plane as the sketching plane and invoke the sketching environment
c. Draw the profile of the model using the **Line** tool.
d. Fillet the two corners of the outer loop and then draw the inner circle.
e. Save the file and close it.

Starting a New Part File and Selecting the Sketching Plane

As mentioned earlier, you can start a new part file by choosing the **New** button from the **Main** toolbar, which remains on the screen after you close all the files.

1. Choose the **New** button from the **Main** toolbar; the **New** dialog box is displayed.

2. Select **Normal.par** from the list box and choose **OK** to start a new part file.

3. Choose the **Sketch** button from the **Features** toolbar; the **Sketch** ribbon bar is displayed and you are prompted to select a planar face or a reference plane.

4. Select the right plane to draw the profile; the sketching environment is invoked and the sketch plane orients itself parallel to the screen. Also, the **Line** tool is automatically invoked.

Drawing the Profile

As the **Line** tool is active, its ribbon bar is displayed on the top of the **EdgeBar** and you are prompted to specify the start point of the line. You can start drawing the line from the origin.

1. Move the cursor close to the origin; one of the two planes, which are displayed as blue horizontal or vertical lines, is highlighted and the midpoint relationship handle is displayed.

2. Click to specify the start point of the line.

   The point you specify is selected as the start point of the line and the endpoint is attached to the cursor.

3. Enter **150** in the **Length** edit box of the **Line** ribbon bar and press ENTER. Enter **0** in the **Angle** edit box and press ENTER.

   The line of 150 length is drawn, but it is not completely visible on the screen. To display the complete line on the screen, you need to modify the drawing display area using the **Fit** tool.

4. Choose the **Fit** button from the **Main** toolbar; the line is now completely displayed in the current view.

5. Enter **40** and **90** in the **Length** and **Angle** edit boxes, of the ribbon bar, respectively

   Next, you need to draw a tangent arc from this point.

6. Press the A key to invoke the arc mode. Move the cursor back to the start point of the arc and then move it vertically upward through a small distance.

7. Move the cursor toward the left when the tangent arc is displayed. Enter the values **30** and **180** in the **Radius** and **Sweep** edit boxes, respectively.

8. Specify a point in the drawing window to place the arc. The arc is drawn and the line mode is invoked again.

9. Enter **20** and **-90** in the **Length** and **Angle** edit boxes, respectively.

10. Move the cursor horizontally toward the left and make sure the horizontal relationship handle is displayed. Click to define the endpoint of the line when the vertical plane is highlighted in red.

11. Move the cursor to the first line to highlight it and then move it to the start point of the first line; the first line is highlighted in red and the endpoint relationship handle is displayed.

12. Click to specify the endpoint of the line when the endpoint relationship handle is displayed. The profile after drawing the outer loop is displayed in Figure 2-36.

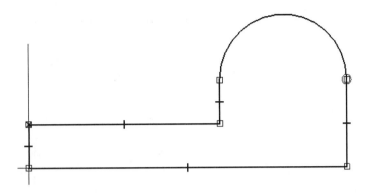

Figure 2-36 Outer loop of the profile for Tutorial 3

Filleting the Sharp Corners

Next, you need to fillet the sharp corners so that there are no sharp edges in the final model. You can fillet the corners using the **Fillet** tool.

1. Choose the **Fillet** button from the **Draw** toolbar; the **Fillet** ribbon bar is displayed.

2. Enter the value **4** in the **Radius** edit box of the **Fillet** ribbon bar and press ENTER. Now, move the cursor over the corner where the outer left vertical line and the upper horizontal line intersect; the two lines comprising this corner are highlighted in red.

3. Now, click to select this corner; the fillet is created at this corner.

4. Similarly, move the cursor over the corner where the upper horizontal line intersects the vertical line originating from the left endpoint of the arc. Click to select it when the two lines that form this corner are highlighted in red.

Drawing the Circle

Next, you need to draw a circle to complete the profile. The circle will be drawn using the **Circle by Center** tool.

1. Choose the **Circle by Center** button from the **Draw** toolbar; the **Circle** ribbon bar is displayed.

2. Enter **30** in the **Diameter** edit box; a circle of 30 mm is displayed with the cursor.

3. Move the cursor over the arc of 30 radius; the arc is highlighted in red and its center point is displayed, which is represented by a plus sign (+).

4. Move the cursor over the center point of the arc and click to define the center point of the circle when the concentric relationship handle is displayed.

    This completes the profile. The final profile for Tutorial 3 is shown in Figure 2-37.

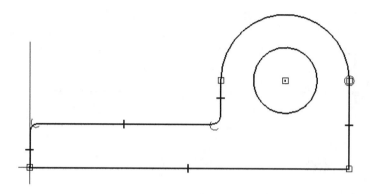

Figure 2-37 *Final profile for Tutorial 3*

Saving the File

1. Press the ESC key to exit the current tool.

2. Choose the **Return** button from the ribbon bar; the sketching environment is closed and the **Sketch** ribbon bar is displayed. Also, the current view is automatically changed to the isometric view.

3. Enter the name of the sketch as **Base Sketch** in the **Name** edit box of the ribbon bar; the sketch is displayed by this name in the **EdgeBar**.

4. Choose the **Save** button from the **Main** toolbar; the **Part3 Properties** dialog box is displayed and choose the **Finish** button from the ribbon bar. This dialog box can be used to specify the properties of the part file.

5. Choose **OK** from the **Part3 Properties** dialog box; the **Save As** dialog box is displayed.

6. Browse to the *My Documents\Solid Edge\c02* folder, if it is not current. Save the file with the name *c02tut3.par*. The location of this file is given below:

    \My Documents\Solid Edge\c02\c02tut3.par

7. Choose **File > Close** from the menu bar to close the file.

Self-Evaluation Test

Answer the following questions and then compare them to those given at the end of this chapter:

1. Most of the designs created in a solid modeling tool consist of the profile-based features, placed features, and reference features. (T/F)

2. If the base feature of a model consists of multiple closed loops, it is recommended that you draw the profile of the base feature as an independent sketch using the **Sketch** tool. (T/F)

3. You can use the ribbon bars to specify the exact values of the sketched entities. (T/F)

4. The **Sketch** button is chosen by default when you start a new part file. (T/F)

5. You can restore the original orientation of the sketching plane using the _____ tool in the **Main** toolbar.

6. You can invoke the arc mode within the **Line** tool by pressing the _____ key.

7. You can bevel the corners in the sketch using the _____ tool.

8. You can retain the sharp corners even after filleting them by choosing the _____ button from the **Fillet** ribbon bar.

9. Pressing the _____ key after defining the first edge of the rectangle results in a square.

10. You can exit the sketching environment by choosing the _____ button from the ribbon bar that is displayed when you choose the **Select Tool** button.

Review Questions

Answer the following questions:

1. Which one of the following options is selected from the **New** dialog box to start a new part file?

    (a) **Normal.asm**   (b) **Normal.dft**
    (c) **Normal.par**   (d) **Normal.psm**

2. Which one of the following tools is used to round the sharp corners in a sketch?

    (a) **Fillet**   (b) **Chamfer**
    (c) **Round**   (d) None

3.   Which edit box in the arc mode replaces the **Angle** edit box in the **Line** ribbon bar?

      (a) **Arc**   (b) **Sweep**
      (c) **Value**   (d) None

4.   In Solid Edge, how many methods are available to draw arcs?

      (a) 4   (b) 3
      (c) 6   (d) 5

5.   Which one of the following tools can be used to convert an existing sketched entity into a bezier spline curve?

      (a) **Convert to Sketch**   (b) **Convert to Arc**
      (c) **Convert**   (d) **Convert the Curve**

6.   The part file in Solid Edge is saved with a *.prt* extension. (T/F)

7.   You can select the entities by dragging a box around them. (T/F)

8.   If **Overlapping** is the current selection mode, all entities that lie inside the box or even intersect the box will be selected. (T/F)

9.   In Solid Edge, you can create fillets or chamfers by simply dragging the cursor across the entities that you want to fillet or chamfer. (T/F)

10.   You can also draw a rectangle by pressing and holding the left mouse button at a point and dragging the cursor across to define the diagonally opposite corner of the rectangle. (T/F)

Exercises

Exercise 1

Draw the profile of the base feature of the model shown in Figure 2-38. The profile to be drawn is shown in Figure 2-39. Do not dimension the profile because the dimensions are given only for your reference.   **(Expected time: 30 min)**

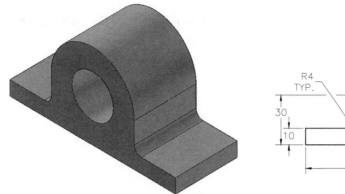

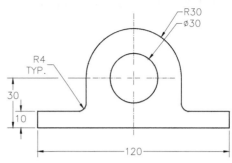

Figure 2-38 Model for Exercise 1

Figure 2-39 Profile for Exercise 1

Exercise 2

Draw the profile of the base feature of the model shown in Figure 2-40. The profile to be drawn is shown in Figure 2-41. Do not dimension the profile because the dimensions are given only for your reference.   **(Expected time: 30 min)**

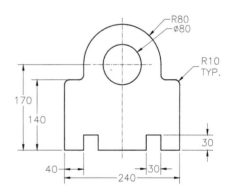

Figure 2-40 Model for Exercise 2

Figure 2-41 Profile for Exercise 2

Answers to Self-Evaluation Test

1. T, 2. T, 3. T, 4. F, 5. Sketch View, 6. A, 7. Chamfer, 8. No Trim, 9. SHIFT, 10. Finish

Chapter 3

Adding Relationships and Dimensions to Sketches

Learning Objectives

After completing this chapter, you will be able to:

- *Understand different types of geometric relationships in Solid Edge.*
- *Force additional geometric relationships to sketches.*
- *View and delete geometric relationships from sketches.*
- *Understand the methods of dimensioning in Solid Edge.*
- *Modify values of dimensions.*
- *Add automatic dimensions to the sketches while drawing them.*

GEOMETRIC RELATIONSHIPS

Geometric relationships are the logical operations performed on the sketching entities to relate them to the other sketched entities using standard properties such as collinearity, concentricity, tangency, and so on. These relationships constrain the degrees of freedom of the sketched entities and make the sketch more stable so that it does not change its shape and location unpredictably at any stage of design. Most of the relationships are automatically applied to the sketched entities while drawing.

All geometric relationships have separate relationship handles associated with them. These handles can be seen on the sketched entities when the relationships are applied to them. In the sketching environment of Solid Edge, you can add eleven types of relationships, which are discussed next.

Connect Relationship

Toolbar:	Features and Relationships > Connect

The connect relationship is used to connect the keypoints such as endpoint, midpoint, or center point of a sketched entity to another sketched entity or to its keypoints. If you connect the keypoint of the first entity to the keypoint of the second entity, it is called a two point connect. Its relationship handle is a square with a dot inside it. However, if you connect the keypoint of the first entity directly to the second entity, it is called a one point connect and its relationship handle is only a cross.

To add this relationship, choose the **Connect** button from the **Features and Relationships** toolbar and then move the cursor over the keypoint of the first sketched entity. Click to select the entity when the handle of the keypoint is displayed. After selecting the keypoint of the first entity, move the cursor over the other sketched entity. Depending on whether you connect the keypoint of the first entity to the keypoint of the second entity or to the second entity itself, the relationship will be a one point or a two point connect. Figure 3-1 shows the endpoint of a line being connected to the other line. This is a one point connect, and therefore, the relationship handle in Figure 3-2 shows just a cross.

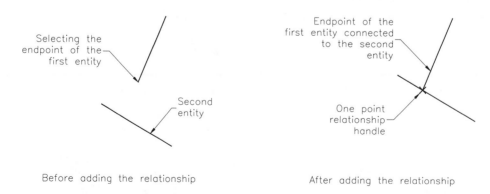

Figure 3-1 Selecting the keypoint of the first entity and then the second entity

Figure 3-2 One point connect relationship applied between the two entities

Figure 3-3 shows the endpoint of the first entity being connected to the endpoint of the second entity. This is a two point connect, and therefore, the relationship handle shows a dot inside the square, as shown in Figure 3-4.

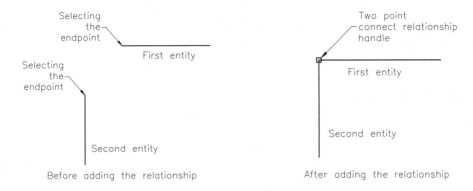

Figure 3-3 *Selecting the keypoints of the first and second entities*

Figure 3-4 *Two point connect relationship applied between the two entities*

Concentric Relationship

Toolbar: Features and Relationships > Concentric

 The concentric relationship forces two arcs, two circles, or an arc and a circle to share the same center point. If there are two arcs, two circles, or an arc and a circle with center points at different locations, this relationship will force the first selected arc or circle to move such that its center point is placed over the center point of the second arc or circle. The handle of this relationship is two concentric circles. Figure 3-5 shows two circles before and after applying this relationship.

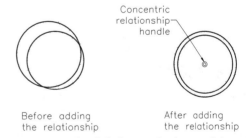

Figure 3-5 *Sketch before and after applying the concentric relationship*

Horizontal/Vertical Relationship

Toolbar: Features and Relationships > Horizontal/Vertical

This relationship forces an inclined line to become horizontal or vertical. If the angle of the inclined line is less than 45-degrees, it will become horizontal. But if the angle is equal to or greater than 45-degrees, it will become vertical. You can also select two points and force them to be placed horizontally or vertically. The handle of this relationship is a plus sign (+).

Collinear Relationship

Toolbar: Features and Relationships > Collinear

This relationship forces the selected line segments to be placed in the same line. On invoking the **Collinear** tool, you will be prompted to click on the first line. After making the first selection, you will be prompted to click on the next line. The first line segment is automatically forced to be placed in the same line as the second line segment. The handle of this relationship are the circles that appear on the collinear lines.

Parallel Relationship

Toolbar: Features and Relationships > Parallel Relationship

This relationship forces a selected line segment to become parallel to another line segment. On invoking the parallel relationship, you will be prompted to click on a line. Next, you will be prompted to click on the next line. After you click on the second line, the first line will be forced to become parallel to the second line. The handle of this relationship are two parallel lines.

Perpendicular Relationship

Toolbar: Features and Relationships > Perpendicular

This relationship forces a selected line to become perpendicular to another line, arc, circle, or ellipse. When you invoke the **Perpendicular** tool, you will be prompted to click on the first line to make it perpendicular. Next, you will be prompted to click on the second line, arc, circle, or ellipse to make perpendicular. On clicking the second entity, the first line will become perpendicular to the second entity. The handle of this relationship is a perpendicular symbol.

Lock Relationship

Toolbar: Features and Relationships > Lock

This constraint is used to fix the orientation or the location of the selected sketched entity or the keypoint of a sketched entity. If you apply this constraint to the keypoint of a sketched entity, the entity will be fixed at that keypoint and you will not be able to modify the entity from that keypoint. However, you can modify the entity from other keypoints.

Note

A keypoint that has a lock on it cannot be modified during the recomputation such as dimension value change and dragging, but it can be moved by manipulation commands such as Move, Rotate, Mirror, and so on, and will be fixed at the new location after manipulations.

Rigid Set Relationship

Toolbar: Features and Relationships > Rigid

This relationship is used to group the selected sketched entities into a rigid set. When the entities are grouped in a rigid set, they behave as a single entity. Therefore, if you drag one of the entities, all entities in the rigid set are automatically dragged. Note that you cannot include dimensions or a text entity in a rigid set.

Tangent Relationship

Toolbar: Features and Relationships > Tangent

This relationship forces a selected sketched entity to become tangent to another sketched entity, as shown in Figure 3-6. Note that one of the two entities selected should be an arc, circle, curve, or an ellipse. The handle of this relationship is a circle that appears at the point of tangency.

You can also select a curve, then press and hold the SHIFT or CTRL key and then select a chain of end to end connected tangent entities to ensure that the curve remains tangentially connected to the chain, as shown in Figure 3-7. After making the entities tangent, if you drag the curve, it will remain tangentially connected to the chain of tangent entities.

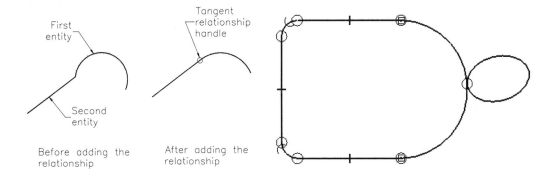

Figure 3-6 Making the entities tangent

Figure 3-7 Making a curve tangent to a chain of tangentially connected entities

Equal Relationship

Toolbar: Features and Relationships > Equal

This relationship can be used for line segments, ellipses, or arcs and circles. If you select two line segments, this relationship will force the length of the first selected line segment to become equal to the length of the second selected line segment. In case of arcs or circles, this relationship will force the radius of the first selected entity to become equal to the radius of the second selected entity. Similarly, you can force two ellipses to become equal in size using this relationship. The handle of this relationship is an equal sign (=).

Symmetric Relationship

Toolbar:	Features and Relationships > Symmetric Relationship

This relationship is used to force the selected sketched entities to become symmetrical about a symmetry axis, which can be a sketched line or a reference plane. This relationship is used in the sketches of the models that are symmetrical about a line. When you invoke the **Symmetric Relationship** tool, you will be prompted to click on the symmetry axis. Next, you will be prompted to click on an entity. Note that you can select only one entity at a time to apply this relationship. Once you have selected the first sketched entity, you will be prompted to click on the second entity. Remember that the second entity should be the same as the first element. This means that if the first element is a line, the second entity should also be a line. As soon as you select the second entity, the first selected entity will be modified such that its distance and orientation from the axis of symmetry become equal to the distance and orientation of the second selected entity. After you have applied this constraint to one set of entities, you will again be prompted to click on the next set of first and second entities. However, this time you will not be prompted to select the axis of symmetry. The last axis of symmetry will be automatically selected to add this relationship.

Figure 3-8 shows the sketched entities and the symmetry axis before applying the symmetry relationship and Figure 3-9 shows the sketch after applying the relationship.

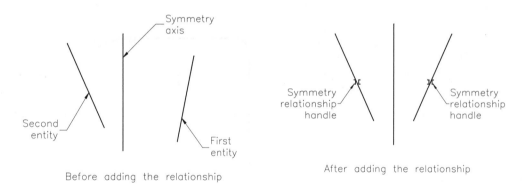

Figure 3-8 *Selecting the entities to apply the symmetry relationship*

Figure 3-9 *Entities after applying the symmetry relationship*

Setting the Symmetry Axis

Toolbar:	Features and Relationships > Symmetric Axis

In Solid Edge, you can set the symmetry axis before invoking the symmetric relationship. Therefore, when you invoke the **Symmetric Relationship** tool, you will not be prompted to select the axis of symmetry. The symmetry axis set earlier is automatically selected as the axis of symmetry. To set the axis of symmetry, choose the **Symmetry Axis** button from **Features and Relationships** toolbar. You will be prompted to click on the symmetry axis. The line that you select will automatically be changed to the symmetry axis and its linetype will also be changed.

Note
You may need to apply a number of relationships to constrain all degrees of freedom of a sketch. Generally, while applying relationships to the sketched entities, the first selected entity is modified with respect to the second one. However, if all degrees of freedom of the first entity are restricted with relationships, then the second entity is modified.

Controlling the Display of Relationship Handles

Toolbar: Features and Relationships > Relationship

In Solid Edge V20, the **Relationship Handles** button is chosen by default. As a result, the handles of all relationships are displayed in the sketch. You can turn off the display of the relationship handles by choosing this button again to clear it. Turning off the display of the relationship handles is useful while creating sketches.

CONFLICTS IN RELATIONSHIPS

Sometimes, when you apply more relationships than required, they conflict and the **Solid Edge** information box is displayed, as shown in Figure 3-10.

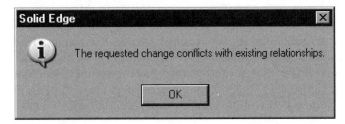

*Figure 3-10 The **Solid Edge** information box*

This box informs you that applying this relationship will create conflicts in the existing relationships. Therefore, you do not need to apply this relationship. Choose **OK** to close this information box.

DELETING RELATIONSHIPS

As mentioned earlier, whenever a relationship is applied to a sketched entity, the relationship handle is displayed on the entity. You can delete the applied relationship by selecting its handle and pressing the DELETE key.

DIMENSIONING THE SKETCHED ENTITIES

In Solid Edge, you can use the following dimension types for dimensioning the sketched entities:

1. Linear Dimensions
2. Aligned Dimensions
3. Angular Dimensions
4. Diameter Dimensions

5. Radial Dimensions
6. Linear Diameter Dimensions
7. Coordinate Dimensions
8. Angular Coordinate Dimensions

You can create these dimensions using their individual tools or using the **SmartDimension** tool. You can also use the options available in the ribbon bars that are displayed for these dimensions. As mentioned earlier, Solid Edge is parametric by nature. Therefore, irrespective of the original size of the entity, you can enter a new value in the **Dimension Value** edit box of the ribbon bar to modify the size of the entity to the required value.

The methods of dimensioning the entities using these dimensions are discussed next.

Adding Linear Dimensions

Toolbar:	Draw > SmartDimension, Distance Between

 Linear dimensions measure the linear distance of a line segment or the distance between two points. To add this dimension, you can use the **SmartDimension** tool or the **Distance Between** tool. The points that you can select to add dimension include all the keypoints such as endpoints, midpoints, and so on of lines, curves, arcs, circles, or ellipses. You can add linear dimensions to a vertical or a horizontal line by choosing the **SmartDimension** button or the **Distance Between** button and then directly selecting the line. Once you have selected the line, the linear dimension will be attached to the cursor. Now, you can place the dimension at any desired location.

To place the dimension between two points, invoke the **SmartDimension** tool or the **Distance Between** tool and select the points one by one. Now, move the cursor vertically to place the horizontal linear dimension or move the cursor horizontally to place the vertical linear dimension. Figure 3-11 shows the linear dimensioning of lines and Figure 3-12 shows the linear dimensioning between the center points of an arc and a circle.

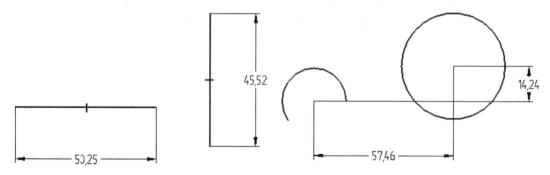

Figure 3-11   *Linear dimensioning of lines*   *Figure 3-12*   *Linear dimensioning of points*

To add linear dimensions between arcs and circles using the **SmartDimension** tool, you can directly select the arc and the circle. However, if you are creating these dimensions using the **Distance Between** tool, first you need to move the cursor over the entities to show their center points and then select the center points to create the dimensions.

You can also add the horizontal or vertical dimensions to the inclined lines, see Figure 3-13. If you select an inclined line after invoking the **SmartDimension** tool to add a linear dimension, the aligned dimension will be attached to the cursor, by default. You need to press and hold the SHIFT key to add the horizontal or vertical dimension. But if you are using the

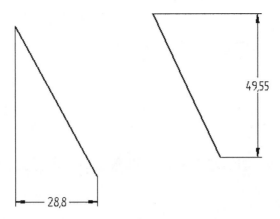

Figure 3-13 *Linear dimensioning of inclined lines*

Distance Between tool, you can select the endpoints of the inclined line and move the cursor in the horizontal or vertical direction to place the dimension.

Ribbon Bar Options

While dimensioning the sketched entities, the **Dimension** ribbon bar is displayed. This ribbon bar has some additional options and buttons, which should be set before creating the dimensions. These options are discussed next.

Dimension Style

This drop-down list shows the dimension styles available in Solid Edge, namely ANSI (inch), ANSI (mm), DIN, BSI, ISO, JIS, and UNI. You can select the required dimension style from this drop-down list.

Round-off

This drop-down list is used to set the round-off precision for the dimensions. The default round-off precision is two decimal places. You can select any other round-off precision from this drop-down list.

Driving

The driving dimensions drive the size of the entity. This means when you modify the value of a driving dimension, the size of the entity is also modified. If you clear the **Driving** button, the dimension will become driven. If you modify the value of a driven dimension, the entity will not be modified but an underscore will be placed with the dimension. The underscore implies that the dimension is driven.

Tangent

This button allows you to add a dimension between the tangent points of two entities. If you choose this button before selecting entities, the dimension will be tangent to both the entities. But, if you first select an arc or a circle, then choose this button and finally select the second arc or circle, the dimension will be tangent to only the second entity.

Note

*The **Dimension Style** drop-down list and the **Dimension Value** edit box will be activated only after selecting the dimension from the drawing window.*

Prefix

This button is chosen to add a prefix, suffix, superfix, or a subfix to the dimension. On choosing this button, the **Dimension Prefix** dialog box will be displayed, as shown in Figure 3-14. You can use this dialog box to add a special symbol or add your own text to the dimension.

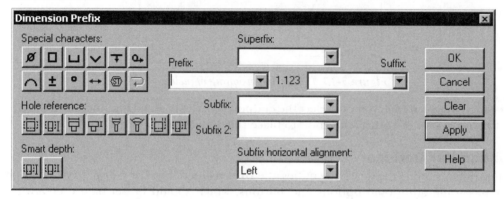

*Figure 3-14 The **Dimension Prefix** dialog box*

Dimension Type

This button is chosen to specify the type of dimension to be applied. When you choose this button, a flyout will be displayed, which provides you with the options to specify the type of dimension. For example, you can choose the **Tolerance** button from this flyout to add a tolerance dimension to the sketch. You can specify the parameters related to the type of dimension in the edit boxes displayed on the right of the ribbon bar. Similarly, you can choose the **ClassPlusMinus** button, the **Class, Upper Tolerance**, and **Lower Tolerance** edit boxes will be displayed. You can enter the class and the upper and lower tolerance values in these edit boxes. Figure 3-15 shows a sketch dimensioned using the limit and tolerance dimensions.

Inspection

This button is chosen to add an oblong around the dimension for inspection.

Note

The remaining options of the ribbon bar will be available for the other dimensioning techniques.

Adding Aligned Dimensions

Toolbar: Draw > SmartDimension

  Aligned dimensions are used to dimension the lines that are not parallel to the X-axis or the Y-axis. This type of dimensioning measures the actual distance of the

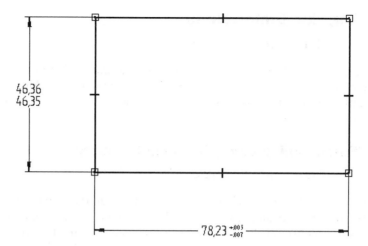

Figure 3-15 *Sketch dimensioned using the limits and tolerance dimension types*

aligned lines. You can invoke the **SmartDimension** tool and directly select the inclined line to apply this dimension. When you select the line, an aligned dimension will be attached to the cursor. Move the cursor and place the dimension at the required location.

You can also select two points to apply the aligned dimensions. The points that can be used include the endpoints of lines, curves, or arcs and the center points of arcs, circles, or ellipses. If you select these two points, the linear dimensions will be displayed by default. To add the aligned dimensions, press and hold the SHIFT key; the aligned dimension will be displayed. Move the cursor and place the dimension at the desired location. Figures 3-16 and 3-17 show the aligned dimensions applied to various objects.

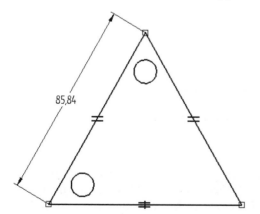

Figure 3-16 *Aligned dimensioning of lines*

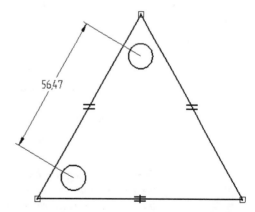

Figure 3-17 *Aligned dimensioning of points*

Adding Angular Dimensions

Toolbar: Draw > SmartDimension

Angular dimensions are used to dimension angles. You can directly select two line segments or use three points to apply the angular dimensions. You can also use angular dimensioning to dimension an arc. The options for adding angular dimensions are discussed next.

Angular Dimensioning using Two Line Segments

Toolbar: Draw > SmartDimension

You can directly select two line segments to apply angular dimensions between them. In voke the **SmartDimension** tool and then select a line segment. A linear or an aligned dimension will be attached to the cursor. Instead of placing the dimension, select the second line segment. If the linear dimension is displayed, choose the **Angle** button from the ribbon bar. Next, place the dimension to measure the angle between the two lines. While placing the dimension, you need to be careful about the point of placement of the dimension because depending on the location of the placement of dimension, the interior or the exterior angle will be displayed. Figure 3-18 shows the angular dimension between two lines and Figure 3-19 shows the external angle of the same two lines.

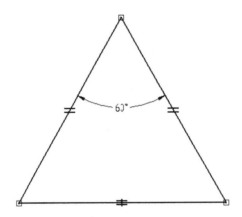

Figure 3-18 Angular dimensioning of two lines

Tip. *After placing the dimension, you can drag it to a new location. To do so, exit the dimensioning tool and then select the dimension lines. The dimension lines are the ones between which the dimension text is placed. Note that if you select the dimension text, you will not be able to move the dimension. After selecting the dimension lines, press and hold the left mouse button and drag the cursor to a new location. The dimension will be placed at the new location. Also, note that you cannot change the dimension type by dragging. For example, you cannot drag a major angle dimension to a new location to make it a minor angle dimension.*

If you want to place the angle value outside the sketch, you can choose the **Major-Minor** button from the ribbon bar to toggle between the major or minor dimensions. Figure 3-20 shows the major angle dimension between two lines.

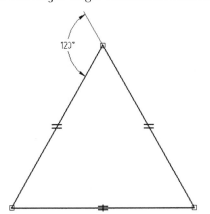

Figure 3-19 *Exterior angle between two lines*   *Figure 3-20* *Major angle between two lines*

Angular Dimensioning using Three Points

You can also add angular dimensions using three keypoints, which should be selected in the clockwise or the counterclockwise direction. Note that while selecting the points to add angular dimensions, the vertex point of the angle should be selected last. Figure 3-21 shows the angular dimensioning using three points.

Angular Dimensioning of the Sweep Angle of an Arc

You can use angular dimensions to dimension the sweep angle of an arc. To do so, invoke the **SmartDimension** tool and select the arc. Next, choose the **Angle** button from the ribbon bar; the angular dimension of the sweep angle of the arc will be displayed, as shown in Figure 3-22.

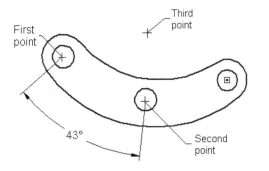

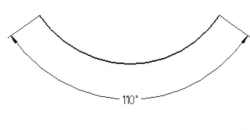

Figure 3-21 *Angular dimensioning using three points*   *Figure 3-22* *Dimensioning the sweep angle of an arc*

Adding Diameter Dimensions

Toolbar: Draw > SmartDimension

 Diameter dimensions are applied to dimension a circle or an arc in terms of its diameter. In Solid Edge, when you select a circle to dimension, the diameter dimension is applied to it by default. However, if you select an arc to dimension, the radius dimension will be applied to it. You can also apply the diameter dimension to an arc. To do so, invoke the **SmartDimension** tool and then select the arc. Now, choose the **Diameter** button from the ribbon bar to apply the diameter dimension. Figure 3-23 shows a circle and an arc with the diameter dimensions.

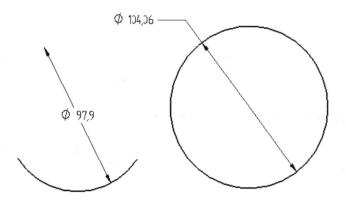

Figure 3-23 *Diameter dimensioning of an arc and a circle*

Adding Radial Dimensions

Toolbar: Draw > SmartDimension

 Radial dimensions are applied to dimension an arc, circle, curve, or an ellipse in terms of its radius. As mentioned earlier, by default, the circles will be assigned the diameter dimensions and the arcs will be applied the radius dimensions. However, you can also apply the radius dimensions to a circle. To do so, invoke the **SmartDimension** tool and then select the circle. Now, choose the **Radius** button from the ribbon bar to apply the radius dimension. Figure 3-24 shows an arc and a circle with radius dimensions.

Adding Symmetric Diameter Dimensions

Toolbar: Draw > Distance Between > Symmetric Diameter

 Symmetric diameter dimensioning is used to dimension the sketches of the revolved components. The sketch for a revolved component is drawn using the simple sketching entities. For example, if you draw a rectangle and revolve it, it will result in

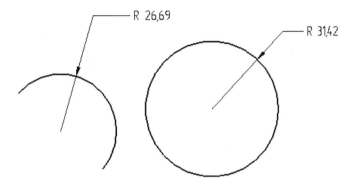

***Figure 3-24** Radial dimensioning of an arc and a circle*

a cylinder. Now, if you dimension the rectangle using the linear dimension, the same dimensions will be displayed when you generate the drawing views of the cylinder. Also, the same dimensions will be used while manufacturing the component. But these linear dimensions will result in a confusion while manufacturing the component. This is because while manufacturing a revolved component, the dimensions have to be in terms of the diameter of the revolved component. The linear dimensions will not be acceptable during the manufacturing of a revolved component.

To overcome this confusion, the sketches of the revolved features are dimensioned using the symmetric diameter dimensions. These dimensions display the distance between the two selected line segments in terms of diameter, which is double of the original length. Also, the Ø symbol is placed as a prefix to the dimension. For example, if the original dimension between two entities is 10, the symmetric diameter dimension will display it as Ø20. This is because when you revolve a rectangle with a 10 mm width, the diameter of the resultant cylinder will be 20 mm.

To add these dimensions, choose the **Symmetric Diameter** button from the **Draw** toolbar; you will be prompted to click on the dimension origin element. Note that the dimension origin element should be the line or the axis in the sketch around which the sketch will be revolved. After selecting the axis or the line, you will be prompted to select the dimension measurement element. Select the line or the keypoint in the sketch to which you want to add the linear diameter dimensions. Now, choose the **Half/Full** button from the ribbon bar. You will notice that a dimension, which is twice the measured distance is attached to the cursor. Place the dimension at the desired location. The dimension value will be displayed, preceded by the Ø symbol, indicating the symmetric diameter dimension, as shown in Figure 3-25.

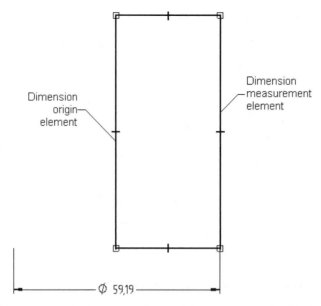

Figure 3-25 *Symmetric diameter dimensioning of a sketch*

Adding Coordinate Dimensions

Toolbar:	Draw > Distance Between > Coordinate Dimension

Coordinate dimensions are used to dimension the sketch with respect to a common origin point, which can be one of the vertices in the sketch. Figure 3-26 shows the coordinate dimensions of a sketch. In this case, the lower left corner of the sketch is taken as the common origin. The remaining entities are dimensioned with respect to this point.

To add this dimension, choose the **Coordinate Dimension** button; you will be prompted to click on the common origin element. Select a vertex, keypoint, or a line segment that you want to use as the common origin. Note that if you select a vertex or a keypoint, you can take it as a common origin for the horizontal or the vertical coordinate dimension. But in case of line segments, the vertical line will be taken as the origin for the horizontal dimensions and the horizontal line will be taken as the origin for the vertical dimensions.

After selecting the common origin, move the cursor horizontally or vertically to place the common origin dimension, which is 0; refer to Figure 3-26. If you have placed zero for the X direction, which is represented by a vertical dimension line, move the cursor in the horizontal direction and select a point or a line segment. Next, move the cursor in the direction of the zero dimension and place it. Follow this procedure to place the remaining dimensions along that direction.

Next, right-click to place the coordinate dimensions along the second direction; you will again be prompted to click on the common origin element. Select the origin element and place the dimension along the second direction and then select the points to place the coordinate dimensions along that direction.

Adding Angular Coordinate Dimensions

Toolbar: Draw > Distance Between > Angular Coordinate Dimension

As the name suggests, this tool is used to add angular coordinate dimensions with respect to a common origin point, as shown in Figure 3-27. When you invoke this tool, you will be prompted to click on the group center element. This point will be taken as the center point and the angular coordinate dimensions will be created around this point. After selecting this point, you will be prompted to select the common origin element. This is the element that will be taken as the origin of the angular coordinate dimensions. Select the origin point and move the cursor to place the zero dimension. Next, you will be prompted to click on the dimension measurement element. Select the point to which you want to add the angular coordinate dimension. After selecting the element, the preview of the angular coordinate dimension will be displayed. If the dimension is placed clockwise, you can display the counterclockwise dimension by choosing the **Counterclockwise** button from the ribbon bar. Move the cursor and place the dimension. Continue this process to add all angular coordinate dimensions.

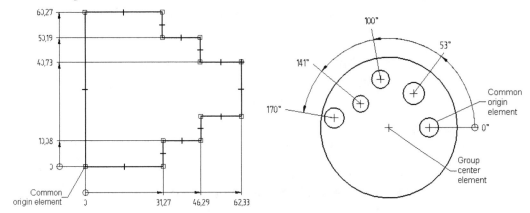

Figure 3-26 *Coordinate dimensioning of a sketch*   *Figure 3-27* *Angular coordinate dimensioning of a sketch*

ADDING AUTOMATIC DIMENSIONS

Toolbar: Main > Auto-Dimension

This tool allows you to add the dimensions to the sketched entities automatically when you draw them. This is a toggle tool that can be toggled on or off, based on the requirement of the sketch. If this tool is turned on, the sketched entities are automatically dimensioned when you draw them.

You can set the options of automatic dimensions by choosing **Tools > IntelliSketch** from the menu bar. When you do so, the **IntelliSketch** dialog box will be displayed with the **Auto-Dimension** tab active, as shown in Figure 3-28. The options available in this tab are discussed next.

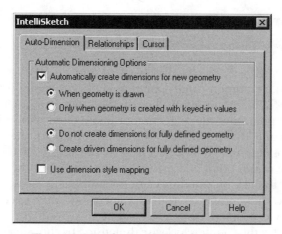

*Figure 3-28 The **IntelliSketch** dialog box*

Automatic Dimensioning Options Area

The options in this area are used to specify the automatic dimensions. These options are discussed next.

Automatically create dimensions for new geometry

This check box is used to toggle the automatic dimensions. The other options in this dialog box will be active only if this check box is selected.

When geometry is drawn

This radio button is selected by default. As a result, the automatic dimensions are applied as you draw the sketched entities.

Only when geometry is created with keyed-in values

If this radio button is selected, the automatic dimensions will be applied only to the entities that are created by entering the values in the ribbon bar.

Do not create dimensions for fully defined geometry

This radio button is selected by default. As a result, the automatic dimensions are not added if the sketch is already fully defined.

Create driven dimensions for fully defined geometry

If this radio button is selected, the automatic driven dimensions will be added for the fully defined sketches.

Use dimension style mapping

This check box is selected by default . As a result, the placed dimensions automatically inherit the dimension style specified in the **Dimension Style** table of the **Option** dialog box.

UNDERSTANDING THE CONCEPT OF FULLY CONSTRAINED SKETCHES

A fully constrained sketch is the one whose all entities are completely constrained to their surroundings using the constraints and dimensions. A fully constrained sketch cannot change its size, location, or orientation unexpectedly. Whenever you draw a sketched entity, it will be blue in color. If you add the dimensions and constraints to fully constrain it, the entities will turn black. Note that while creating the base sketch in Solid Edge, you need to relate or dimension it with respect to reference planes in order to fully constrain it.

To make sure the sketch is displayed in black after it is fully constrained, choose **Inspect > Sketch Relationship Colors** from the menu bar.

MEASURING SKETCHED ENTITIES

Menu Bar:	Inspect > Measure Distance

In Solid Edge, you can measure the distances among sketched entities, the total length of a closed loop or an open entity, and the area of a loop. You can also calculate the area properties. The techniques to measure these parameters are discussed next.

Measuring Distances

This tool allows you to measure the linear distance between any two selected points. To measure the distance, invoke this tool from the **Inspect** menu; you will be prompted to click for the first point. Select the first point to measure the linear distance; you will be prompted to click for the second point. If you move the cursor over a keypoint to select it as the second point, the linear distance, the ΔX distance, and the ΔY distance between two points will be displayed on the right of the cursor without even selecting the point, as shown in Figure 3-29. If the second point is not a keypoint, the values will not be displayed on the cursor. You need to click the left mouse button to display the distance value. In this case, the

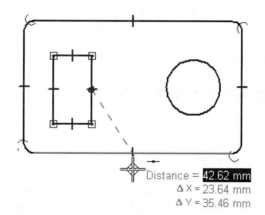

Figure 3-29 *Measuring the distance between two keypoints*

delta values will not be displayed. You can continue to select multiple points to measure the distances between the two points.

Measuring the Total Length of a Closed Loop or an Open Sketch

Menu Bar:	Inspect > Measure Total Length

This tool allows you to measure the total length of a closed loop or an open sketch. When you invoke this tool, the ribbon bar will be displayed and you will be prompted to click on the element(s) to be measured. By default, the **Chain** option is selected from the drop-down list in the ribbon bar. As a result, the complete chain of entities will be selected and the total length of the chain will be displayed. You can also select the **Single** option from this drop-down list to measure the total length of a single entity.

The total length is displayed in the **Length** edit box in the ribbon bar. If you want to measure the total length of a new set of entities, then choose the **Deselect** button from the ribbon bar. This will clear the current selection set and allow you to select a new set of entities.

Measuring Area

Menu Bar:	Inspect > Area

This tool allows you to measure the area inside a closed loop. When you invoke this tool, you will be prompted to click on the area. Click inside the closed loop; the area will be highlighted in the drawing window and the value of the area of that closed loop will be displayed on the right of the cursor. You will notice that all the closed loops inside the area selected by you get removed automatically and they will not be highlighted, as shown in Figure 3-30.

If you want to include the inner closed loops also , then press and hold the CTRL key and click inside the inner closed loop. The area inside the inner closed loop will also be highlighted and now two values will be displayed on the right of the cursor. The first value will be the area of the second loop and the other value will be the total combined area of all the selected loops. You can continue to add or remove the closed loops by pressing and holding the CTRL key and clicking inside them.

Calculating the Area Properties

Menu Bar:	Inspect > Area Properties

This tool allows you to calculate the properties of a selected area. On invoking this tool, you will be prompted to click on an area. Click inside a closed loop; the area of that loop will be highlighted. Accept the inputs in the ribbon bar and right-click in the area; the shortcut menu will be displayed. Choose the **Properties** option from it to display the **Info** dialog box. This dialog box lists all the properties of the selected area, as shown in Figure 3-31.

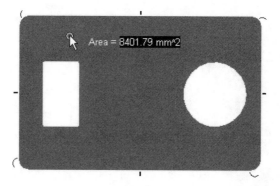

Figure 3-30 *Measuring the area of a closed loop*

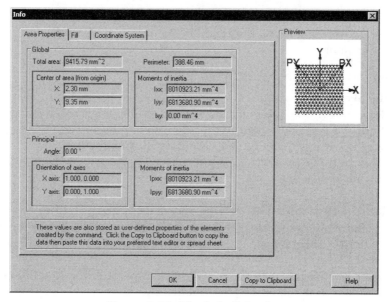

Figure 3-31 *The **Info** dialog box*

TUTORIALS

You will use the relationships and parametric dimensions to complete the model in the forthcoming tutorials..

Tutorial 1

In this tutorial, you will draw the profile of the model shown in Figure 3-32. The profile, shown in Figure 3-33, should be symmetric about the origin. You will not use the edit boxes available in the ribbon bar to enter the values of the entities. Instead, you will use the parametric dimensions to complete the sketch. **(Expected time: 30 min)**

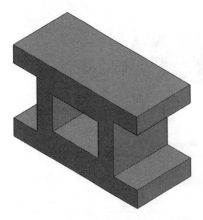

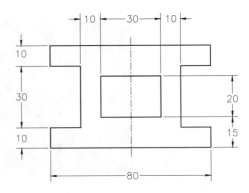

Figure 3-32 *Model for Tutorial 1*   ***Figure 3-33*** *Profile to be drawn for Tutorial 1*

Before you start working on the model, it is recommended that you outline the steps that will be used to complete this tutorial. The following steps outline the procedure to complete this tutorial:

a. Start Solid Edge and then start a new **Part** file.
b. Choose the **Sketch** button and select the front plane as the sketching plane
c. Use the **Line** tool to draw the outer loop of the profile, refer to Figure 3-34.
d. Add relationships and dimensions to the outer loop, refer to Figure 3-36.
e. Draw a rectangle inside the outer loop using the **Rectangle** tool.
f. Add dimensions to the rectangle to complete the sketch, refer to Figure 3-38.
g. Save the sketch and close the file.

Starting Solid Edge and Selecting the Sketching Plane

1. Choose the **Start** button to display the menu and choose **All Programs** (or **Programs**) > **Solid Edge V20 > Solid Edge**.

    As Solid Edge gets started, the welcome screen is displayed. Now, you need to start a new part file to draw the sketch of the given model.

2. Click on the **Solid Part** link in the **Create** area; a new Solid Edge part file is started.

3. Choose the **Sketch** button from the **Features** toolbar; the **Sketch** ribbon bar is displayed and you are prompted to select a planar face or a reference plane.

4. Select the front plane to draw the profile. The sketching environment is invoked and the sketch plane orients itself parallel to the screen. Also, the **Line** tool is automatically invoked.

Drawing the Outer Loop and Adding the Relationships

If the sketch consists of more than one closed loop, it is recommended that you draw the outer loop first and then add all the required relationships and dimensions to it. This makes it easier to draw and dimension the inner loops.

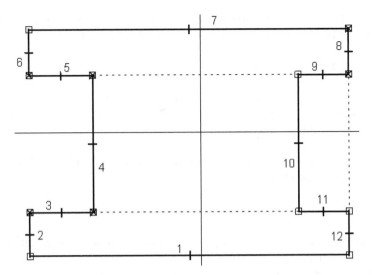

Figure 3-34 *Outer loop of the profile*

1. Draw the sketch of the outer loop using the **Line** tool, as shown in Figure 3-34. As is evident in this figure, the sketch is drawn around the origin. It is not symmetric at this stage, but it becomes so after adding all relationships and dimensions. You can use the alignment indicators to draw the sketch. For your reference, the lines in the sketch are indicated by numbers.

    Next, you need to add relationships to the sketch. You first need to apply the **Equal** relationship and then the **Symmetric** relationship.

2. Choose the **Equal** button from the **Features and Relationships** toolbar; you are prompted to click on an element.

3. Select line 2; the color of this line is changed and you are prompted to select the next line. Select line 6; the **Equal** relationship is applied to lines 2 and 6. You are again prompted to click on an element. Select line 6 as the first line and then select line 8 as the second line.

    If the **Solid Edge** information box is displayed while applying any of these constraints, choose **OK** to exit that box.

4. Similarly, select lines 8 and 12, 1 and 7, 3 and 5, 5 and 9, 9 and 11, and then lines 10 and 4. The **Equal** relationship is applied to all these pairs of lines.

    Next, you need to make this sketch symmetric about the two reference planes that appear as the vertical and horizontal lines in this view.

5. Choose the **Symmetric Relationship** button from the **Features and Relationships** toolbar; you are prompted to click on the symmetry axis.

6. Select the blue vertical line passing through the origin; a symmetry axis is created over the reference plane and you are prompted to click on an element.

7. Select lines 2 and 12. Similarly, select lines 3 and 11, 4 and 10, 5 and 9, and 6 and 8.

   Next, you need to make lines 1 and 7 symmetric about the horizontal reference plane. Note that you need to set the symmetry axis again because the vertical reference plane was set as the symmetry axis earlier.

8. Choose the **Symmetry Axis** button from the **Features and Relationships** toolbar; you are prompted to click on the symmetry axis.

9. Select the horizontal reference plane to use it as the symmetry axis.

10. Choose the **Symmetric Relationship** button from the **Features and Relationships** toolbar. Now you are not prompted to select the symmetry axis again because it was set in the previous step. Instead, you are prompted to click on an element.

11. Select lines 1 and 7 to add the **Symmetric** relationship between them.

12. Press the ESC key to exit the current tool. The sketch, after adding all relationships, is shown in Figure 3-35. Notice the handles of all relationships added to the sketch.

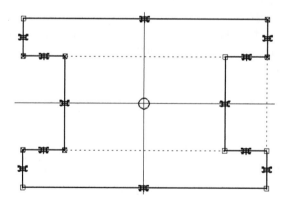

Figure 3-35   *Profile after adding relationships*

Dimensioning the Sketch

Once all the required relationships are added to the profile, you can dimension it. As mentioned earlier, when you add dimensions to the sketch and modify the value of the dimension, the entity is forced to the dimension value that you have specified.

Before you start dimensioning the sketch, it is recommended that you turn on the option to display the text in black color once it is fully constrained.

1. Choose **Inspect > Sketch Relationship Colors** from the menu bar to turn this option on.

2. Choose the **SmartDimension** button from the **Features and Relationships** toolbar; you are prompted to click on the element(s) to dimension. Select line 1.

    As soon as you select line 1; a linear dimension to measure the length of line 1 is attached to the cursor.

3. Place the dimension below line 1; the **Dimension Value** edit box in the ribbon bar is enabled. Enter **80** as the length of line 1 in this edit box and press ENTER.

    The length of the line is forced to 80 units, and because, the sketch is symmetric, it is modified symmetrically.

4. As the **SmartDimension** tool is still active, you are again prompted to click on the element(s) to dimension. Select line 2 and place the dimension on the left of this line. Enter **10** as the value in the **Dimension Value** edit box and press ENTER.

    You will notice that the length of lines 6, 8, and 12 is also forced to 10 units. This is because of the **Equal** relationship applied to all these lines.

5. Select line 3 and place the dimension below the line and enter **15** as the value in the **Dimension Value** edit box.

6. Select line 4 and place it along the previous dimension and relationships; the sketch turns black in color, suggesting that it is fully constrained. Modify the dimension value to **30** in the **Dimension Value** edit box. Notice that the length of line 10 is also modified.

    This completes the dimensioning of the outer profile. The profile, after adding these dimensions, is shown in Figure 3-36.

Drawing the Inner Loop and Adding the Relationships

Next, you need to draw the inner loop, which is a rectangle.

1. Draw the rectangle inside the outer loop using the **Rectangle** tool. Refer to Figure 3-33 for the location of the rectangle.

2. Choose the **Symmetric Relationship** button from the **Features and Relationships** toolbar; the horizontal reference plane is highlighted. This indicates that this plane is currently set as the symmetry axis.

3. Select the upper and lower horizontal lines of the rectangle to add this relationship between them.

    Next, you need to change the symmetry axis to make the vertical lines symmetrical.

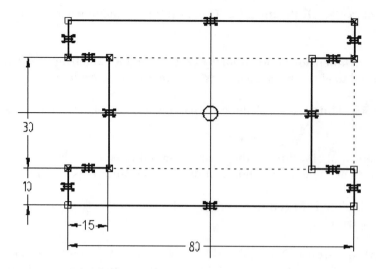

Figure 3-36 Profile after adding the relationships and dimensions

4. Choose the **Symmetry Axis** button from the **Features and Relationships** toolbar; you are prompted to click on the symmetry axis.

5. Select the vertical reference plane to use it as the symmetry axis.

6. Choose the **Symmetric Relationship** button from the **Features and Relationships** toolbar. As the symmetry axis was set in the previous step, you are not prompted to select it again. Instead, you are prompted to click on an element.

7. Select the two vertical lines of the rectangle to make them symmetrical about the vertical reference plane.

    This completes the process of adding the relationships to the inner loop. The sketch at this stage will look similar to the model shown in Figure 3-37.

Dimensioning the Inner Loop

1. Choose the **SmartDimension** button from the **Features and Relationships** toolbar and select the upper horizontal line of the inner loop.

2. Place the dimension above the sketch and enter **30** as the value in the **Dimension Value** edit box in the ribbon bar.

3. Select the left vertical line of the inner loop and line 4. Place the dimension on the left of the previous dimension and enter **10** as the value in the ribbon bar; the inner loop turns black, suggesting it is fully constrained. This completes the dimensioning of the profile. The final profile, after adding all the dimensions, is shown in Figure 3-38.

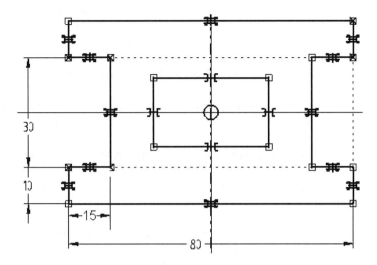

Figure 3-37 Profile after adding relationships to the inner loop

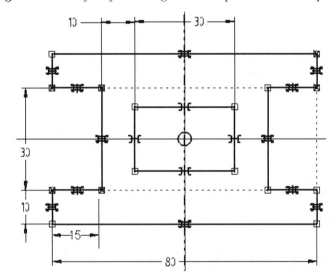

Figure 3-38 Final profile after adding all the dimensions

Saving the File

As mentioned in the previous chapter, it is recommended that you exit the sketching environment before saving or closing the file. This is because you cannot close a file in the sketching environment.

You can exit the sketching environment by choosing the **Finish** button from the ribbon bar that is displayed in the select mode.

1. Press the ESC key to exit the current tool.

2. Choose the **Return** button from the ribbon bar; the sketching environment is closed and the **Sketch** ribbon bar is displayed. Also, the current view is automatically changed to the isometric view.

3. Enter the name of the sketch as **Base Sketch** in the **Name** edit box of the ribbon bar and choose the **Finish** button. The sketch is displayed by this name in the **EdgeBar**.

4. Choose the **Save** button from the **Standard** toolbar to display the **Part1 Properties** dialog box. This dialog box can be used to specify the properties of the part file.

5. Choose **OK** from the **Part1 Properties** dialog box; the **Save As** dialog box is displayed.

    As mentioned in the previous chapter, you need to create a separate folder for every chapter in the textbook.

6. Browse to the *My Documents\Solid Edge* folder and then create a folder with the name *c03*.

7. Make the *c03* folder current and save the file with the name *c03tut1.par*. The location of this file is given below.

    \My Documents\Solid Edge\c03\c03tut1.par

8. Choose **File > Close** from the menu bar to close the file.

Tutorial 2

In this tutorial, you will create the profile for the model shown in Figure 3-39. The profile is shown in Figure 3-40. You will use the relationships and parametric dimensions to complete the sketch.   **(Expected time: 30 min)**

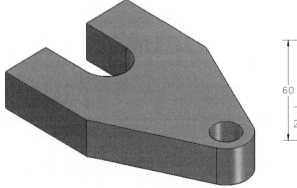

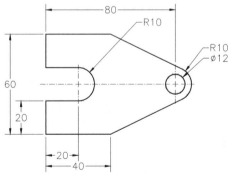

Figure 3-39 *Model for Tutorial 2*   **Figure 3-40** *Profile to be drawn for Tutorial 2*

The following steps are required to complete this tutorial:
a. Start a new part file.
b. Choose the **Sketch** button and select the top plane as the sketching plane.

c. Draw the required profile using the **Line** and **Circle by Center** tool, refer to Figure 3-41.
d. Add the required relationships and dimensions to the sketch, refer to Figure 3-43.
e. Save the file and close it.

Starting a New Part File and Selecting the Sketching Plane

1. Choose the **New** button from the **Main** toolbar; the **New** dialog box is displayed.

2. Select **Normal.par** and choose **OK** to start a new part file.

3. Choose the **Sketch** button from the **Features** toolbar; the **Sketch** ribbon bar is displayed and you are prompted to select a planar face or a reference plane.

4. Select the top plane to draw the profile.

Drawing the Profile

It is recommended that you draw the first entity in the sketch by entering its exact values in the ribbon bar. This allows you to modify the drawing display area to fit the first entity and then you can draw the other entities taking the reference of the first entity. This also helps you in dimensioning the entities at a later stage.

1. Using the **Line** tool and the ribbon bar options, draw a line of length 40 units, with its start point at the origin.

2. Taking the reference of the first line, draw the remaining entities in the profile to complete it. Use the arc mode of the **Line** tool to draw the tangent arcs in the profile.

To draw the circle, if the center point of the arc is not displayed, move the cursor over the arc once to display its center point. Use this center point to define the center point of the circle. The profile, after drawing all entities, is shown in Figure 3-41. For your reference, the entities in the sketch are indicated by numbers.

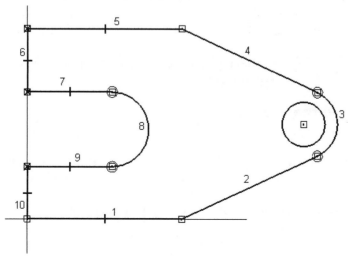

Figure 3-41 *Profile after drawing all entities*

Adding Relationships to the Profile

Next, you need to add relationships to the profile. As lines 6 and 10 overlap with the vertical reference plane, you may need to use **QuickPick** to select these lines. To use **QuickPick**, move the cursor over the entity that overlaps with some other entities and pause for a while. Three dots are displayed on the right of the cursor. Now, click to select the entities; the selection bar is displayed, which shows a separate box for each overlapping entity. Move the cursor over the boxes to highlight the entity related to that box. When the desired entity is highlighted, click to select it.

1. Choose the **Equal** button from the **Features and Relationships** toolbar and add this relationship between lines 1 and 5, 2 and 4, 6 and 10, and 7 and 9.

    Next, you need to make the two arcs in the sketch tangent to the lines to which they are connected. The tangent relationship could have been applied to the sketch while drawing. To check this relationship, see if a small circle is displayed at all points where the arcs and lines meet. The small circle is the relationship handle of the tangent relationship. Ideally, this handle must be displayed at four locations: points where arc 3 meets lines 2 and 4 and the points where arc 8 meets lines 7 and 9.

2. Choose the **Tangent** button from the **Features and Relationships** toolbar and add the tangent relationship between the entities where it is missing.

Note

*If you add a relationship that is already added, the **Solid Edge** information box is displayed, which informs you that the requested change conflicts with the existing relationships.*

Next, you need to horizontally align the center of arc 8 with the center point of the circle. This is done using the **Horizontal/Vertical** relationship.

3. Choose the **Horizontal/Vertical** button from the **Features and Relationships** toolbar. Move the cursor over the arc 8 once to display its center point. Select the center point when it is displayed. Similarly, select the center point of the circle. A horizontal dashed line is displayed between the two centers, indicating that they are aligned horizontally.

    This completes the process of adding relationships to the profile. The profile, after adding all relationships, is shown in Figure 3-42.

Dimensioning the Profile

After adding the relationships, you need to dimension the profile.

1. Choose the **SmartDimension** button from the **Features and Relationships** toolbar; you are prompted to click on the elements to dimension.

2. Select line 9 and place the dimension below the profile. Modify the value of the dimension to **20** in the ribbon bar.

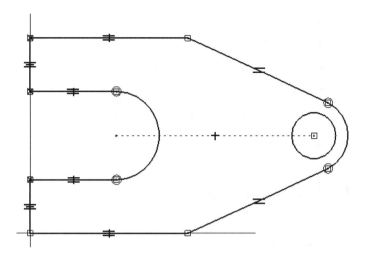

Figure 3-42 *Profile after adding all the relationships*

3.   Select line 1 and place the dimension below the previous dimension. Modify the value to **40** in the ribbon bar.

4.   Select line 6 and the circle and place the dimension above the profile. Modify the value to **80** in the ribbon bar.

5.   Select line 10 and place the dimension on the left of the profile. Modify the value to **80** in the ribbon bar.

6.   Select lines 5 and 1, and place the dimension on the left of the previous dimension. Modify the value to **60** in the ribbon bar.

7.   Select arc 3 and place the dimension on the right of the sketch. Modify the value to **10** in the ribbon bar.

8.   Select the circle and place the dimension on the right of the sketch. Modify the value to **12** in the ribbon bar.

This completes the dimensioning of the profile. The profile, after adding all the required dimensions, is shown in Figure 3-43.

Saving the File

1.   Choose the **Select Tool** button from the **Draw** toolbar to display the ribbon bar.

2.   Choose the **Return** button from the ribbon bar; the sketching environment is closed and

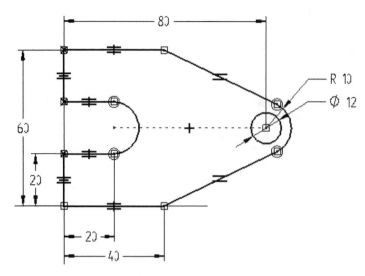

Figure 3-43 *Profile after adding all the dimensions*

the **Sketch** ribbon bar is displayed. Also, the current view is automatically changed to the isometric view.

3. Enter the name of the sketch as **Base Sketch** in the **Name** edit box in the ribbon bar and choose the **Finish** button. The sketch is displayed by this name in the **EdgeBar**.

4. Choose the **Save** button from the **Standard** toolbar to display the **Part2 Properties** dialog box.

5. Choose **OK** from the **Part2 Properties** dialog box to display the **Save As** dialog box.

6. Browse to the *My Documents\Solid Edge\c03* folder, if it is not current. Save the file with the name *c03tut2.par*. The location of this file is given below:

    \My Documents\Solid Edge\c03\c03tut2.par

7. Choose **File > Close** from the menu bar to close the file.

Tutorial 3

In this tutorial, you will create the profile for the revolved model shown in Figure 3-44. The profile is shown in Figure 3-45. You will use the parametric dimensions to complete the sketch.   **(Expected time: 30 min)**

The following steps are required to complete this tutorial:

a. Start a new part file.
b. Choose the **Sketch** button and select the front plane as the sketching plane.

Figure 3-44 Model for Tutorial 3

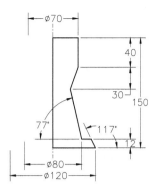

Figure 3-45 Profile to be drawn for Tutorial 3

c.   Draw the required profile using the **Line** tool, refer to Figure 3-46.

d.   Add the required dimensions to the sketch, refer to Figure 3-47.

e.   Save the file and close it.

Starting a New Part File and Selecting the Sketching Plane

You can start a new part file by choosing the **New** button from the **Main** toolbar, which remains on the screen after you close all the files.

1.   Choose the **New** button from the **Main** toolbar to display the **New** dialog box.

2.   Select **Normal.par** and choose **OK** to start a new part file.

3.   Choose the **Sketch** button from the **Features** toolbar; the **Sketch** ribbon bar is displayed and you are prompted to select a planar face or a reference plane.

4.   Select the front plane to draw the profile. The sketching environment is invoked and the sketch plane orients itself parallel to the screen. Also, the **Line** tool is automatically invoked.

Drawing the Profile

In this case, you will start drawing the sketch from the lower left corner and the bottom horizontal line will be the first entity.

1.   Move the cursor to the origin and specify the start point of the first line.

2.   Enter **60** as the length and **0** as the angle of the first line in the ribbon bar to draw the first line segment.

3.   Pan the drawing using the **Pan** tool available in the **Main** toolbar such that the origin is moved close to the middle of the bottom edge of the drawing window.

4.   Complete the sketch of the revolved model by drawing the remaining lines and taking

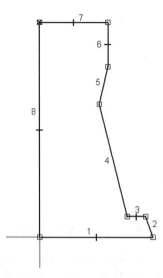

Figure 3-46 *Profile for the revolved model*

the reference of the first line; refer to Figure 3-46. For your reference, the lines in this sketch are indicated by numbers.

Adding Dimensions to the Profile

Next, you need to add dimensions to the profile. Because it is a profile for the revolved model, you need to add the symmetric diameter dimensions to define the diameter of the revolved feature, refer to Figure 3-46.

1. Make sure the **Sketch Relationship Colors** option is selected from the **Inspect** menu.

2. Choose the **Symmetric Diameter** button from the **Distance Between** flyout in the **Draw** toolbar. On invoking this tool, you are prompted to select the dimension origin element, which is the element that acts as the axis of revolution. In this profile, line 8 is the dimension origin element.

3. Select line 8 and then select the right endpoint of line 1. Choose the **Half/Full** button from the ribbon bar, if it is not already chosen.

4. Place the dimension below the sketch. You may need to modify the drawing display area by choosing the **Zoom** button.

   After placing the dimension, although it shows the value **120**, you still need to enter this value again in the **Dimension Value** edit box.

5. Enter the value of dimension as **120** in the ribbon bar.

   The line 8, which was selected as the dimension origin element, need not be selected again. You can directly select the other dimension measurement elements to add the symmetric diameter dimensions.

6. Select the lower endpoint of line 4 and place the dimension below the sketch. Modify the value of dimension to **80** in the ribbon bar.

    You will notice that as you place this dimension, the previous symmetric dimension also moves. Now, if you add the symmetric dimension to line 7 in the same sequence, the first two dimensions also move while placing the third dimension. Therefore, you need to first exit the current sequence of dimensioning.

7. Right-click to exit the current dimensioning sequence; you are again prompted to select the dimension origin element.

8. Select line 8 and then select the right endpoint of line 7; the symmetric diameter dimension is attached to the cursor.

9. Place the dimension above the sketch and modify the value to **70**.

    Next, you need to add linear and angular dimensions to the remaining entities. You can add these dimensions using the **SmartDimension** tool.

10. Choose the **SmartDimension** button from the **Features and Relationships** toolbar; you are prompted to click on the element(s) to dimension.

11. Select line 2; an aligned dimension is attached to the cursor. Press and hold the SHIFT key and move the cursor to the right of the sketch. The vertical dimension of line 2 is displayed.

12. Place the dimension on the right of the sketch and modify the value to **12** in the ribbon bar.

13. Select lines 1 and 2 and then choose the **Angle** button from the ribbon bar. Move the cursor to the right of the sketch to display the major angle dimension. Place the dimension on the right of the sketch and modify the value to **117**.

14. Select line 3 and choose the **Angle** button from the ribbon bar and then select the line 4. Next, move the cursor to the left of line 4 to display the angle dimension. Place the dimension on the left of line 4 and modify the value to **77**.

15. Select line 5 and press and hold the SHIFT key to display the vertical dimension of line 5. Place the dimension on the right of the sketch and modify the value to **30**.

16. Select line 6 and place the dimension on the right of the sketch, in line with the previous dimension. Modify the value of the dimension to **40**.

17. Select line 8 and place the dimension on the left of the sketch. Modify the dimension value to **150**.

This completes the dimensioning of the sketch. The sketch, after adding all dimensions, is shown in Figure 3-47. Notice that as the option to display the fully constrained sketch in a different color was selected from the **Inspect** menu, the sketch turns black after placing the last dimension.

Saving the File

1. Choose the **Select Tool** button from the **Draw** toolbar to display the ribbon bar.

2. Choose the **Return** button from the ribbon bar; the sketching environment is closed and the **Sketch** ribbon bar is displayed. Also, the current view is automatically changed to the isometric view.

3. Enter the name of the sketch as **Base Sketch** in the **Name** edit box of the ribbon bar and choose the **Finish** button. The sketch is displayed by this name in the **EdgeBar**.

4. Choose the **Save** button from the **Standard** toolbar to display the **Part3 Properties** dialog box.

5. Choose **OK** from the **Part3 Properties** dialog box to display the **Save As** dialog box.

6. Browse to the *My Documents\Solid Edge\c03* folder, if it is not current. Save the file with the name *c03tut3.par*. The location of this file is given below:

   \My Documents\Solid Edge\c03\c03tut3.par

7. Choose **File > Close** from the menu bar to close the file.

Self-Evaluation Test

Answer the following questions and then compare them to those given at the end of this chapter:

1. In Solid Edge, all geometric relationships have the same relationship handles associated with them. (T/F)

2. In Solid Edge, you can set the symmetry axis before invoking the symmetric relationship. (T/F)

3. The coordinate dimensions are used to dimension the sketch with respect to a common origin point. (T/F)

4. In Solid Edge, the symmetric diameter dimensions are used to dimension the sketches of the revolved components. (T/F)

5. The _____ relationship forces two arcs, two circles, or an arc and a circle to share the same center point.

6. The _____ dimensions are applied to dimension a circle or an arc in terms of its diameter.

7. The _____ dimensions are used to dimension the sketch with respect to a common origin point.

8. The _____ dimensions measure the actual distance of the aligned lines.

9. You can delete the applied relationship by selecting its handle and pressing the _____ key.

10. By default, the circles will be assigned to_____ dimensions.

Review Questions

Answer the following questions:

1. Which one of the following dimensions is applied to the arcs by default?

    (a) Radial   (b) Diameter
    (c) Angular   (d) Linear

2. Which one of the following dimensions is used to create angular coordinate dimensions with respect to a common origin point?

    (a) Angular   (b) Angular Coordinate
    (c) Linear   (d) Coordinate

3. Which one of the following relationships is used to fix the orientation or the location of a selected sketched entity or a keypoint of a sketched entity?

    (a) **Fix**   (b) **Lock**
    (c) **Hide**   (d) None

4. Which one of the following relationships is used to force the selected sketched entities to become symmetrical about a symmetry axis?

    (a) **Symmetrical**   (b) **Collinear**
    (c) **Coincident**   (d) **Horizontal**

5. Which one of the following relationships forces a selected line to become normal to another line, arc, circle, or ellipse?

    (a) **Symmetrical**   (b) **Collinear**
    (c) **Coincident**   (d) **Perpendicular**

6. After placing the dimension, you cannot modify it. (T/F)

7. While placing the angular dimensions, you can select the option to display the major or the minor angle value. (T/F)

8. You can add a prefix or a suffix to the dimension values. (T/F)

9. In Solid Edge, you can also add tolerance to the dimensions in the sketching environment. (T/F)

10. Aligned dimensions cannot be used to dimension the lines that are not parallel to the X-axis or the Y-axis. (T/F)

Exercises

Exercise 1

Draw the profile for the base feature of the model shown in Figure 3-48. The profile to be drawn is shown in Figure 3-49. Use the relationships and parametric dimensions to complete the profile. **(Expected time: 30 min)**

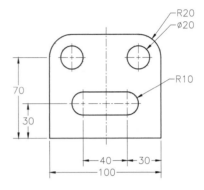

Figure 3-48 Model for Exercise 1   *Figure 3-49* Profile for Exercise 1

Exercise 2

Draw the profile for the base feature of the model shown in Figure 3-50. The profile to be drawn is shown in Figure 3-51. Use the relationships and parametric dimensions to complete the profile. **(Expected time: 30 min)**

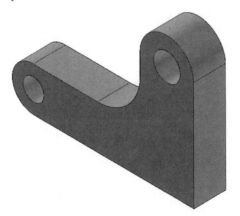

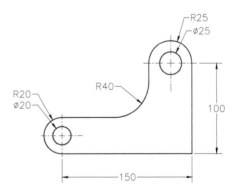

Figure 3-50 Model for Exercise 2   *Figure 3-51* Profile for Exercise 2

Answers to Self-Evaluation Test

1. F, **2.** T, **3.** T, **4.** T, **5.** Concentric, **6.** Diameter, **7.** Coordinate, **8.** Aligned, **9.** DELETE, **10.** diameter

Chapter 4

Editing, Extruding, and Revolving the Sketches

Learning Objectives

After completing this chapter, you will be able to:

* *Edit sketches using the editing tools in Solid Edge.*
* *Write text in the sketching environment.*
* *Edit sketched entities by using the ribbon bar and by dragging.*
* *Convert sketches into base features by extruding and revolving.*
* *Rotate the view of the model dynamically in 3D space.*
* *Change the view and the display type of the models.*

EDITING SKETCHES

Editing is a very important part of sketching in any solid modeling tool. You need to edit the sketches during various stages of a design. Solid Edge provides you with a number of tools that can be used to edit the sketched entities. These tools are discussed next.

Trimming the Sketched Entities

Toolbar: Draw > Trim

This tool allows you to remove a portion of a sketch by chopping off that portion. Figure 4-1 shows the sketched entities before trimming and Figure 4-2 shows the sketch after trimming the entities. Note that when used on an isolated entity, this tool deletes the entity.

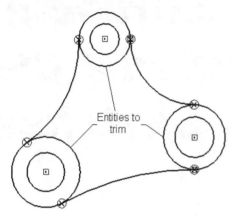

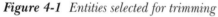

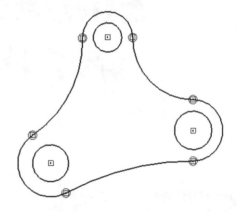

Figure 4-1 *Entities selected for trimming*   **Figure 4-2** *Sketch after trimming the entities*

To trim the entities, invoke the **Trim** tool and move the cursor over the portion to be trimmed; it will be highlighted in red. Click to trim the highlighted portion. You will again be prompted to click on the entity to trim. After trimming all the entities, press ESC to exit this tool.

Extending the Sketched Entities

Toolbar: Draw > Extend to Next

This tool allows you to extend or lengthen an open sketched entity up to the next entity it intersects. Figure 4-3 shows the sketched entities before extending and Figure 4-4 shows the sketch after extending the entities. This tool will not work on an entity that does not intersect with any existing sketched entity when extended.

Note
Sometimes while editing, some of the entities turn brown in color. These entities may need further editing such as trimming.

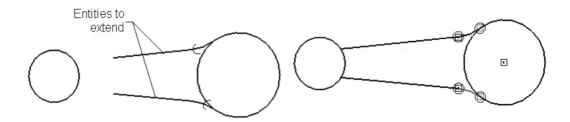

Figure 4-3 *Entities selected to be extended*   Figure 4-4 *Sketch after extending the entities*

Trimming/Extending Entities to a Corner

Toolbar: Draw > Trim Corner

This tool allows you to trim or extend two open sketched entities such that they result in a corner. Note that you can select only open entities to create a corner trim. To create a corner trim, invoke this tool and then select two open entities. They will be extended or trimmed to create a corner, as shown in Figures 4-5 and 4-6.

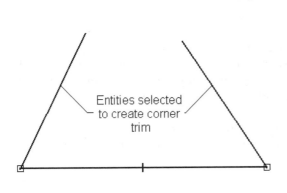

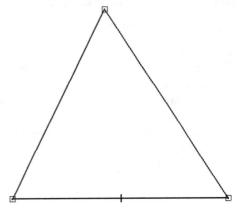

Figure 4-5 *Entities selected to create a corner trim*   Figure 4-6 *Sketch after creating the corner trim*

Creating Offset Copies

Toolbar: Draw > Offset

This tool allows you to create offset copies of a selected sketched entity or a chain defined by the selected entity. To create an offset copy, invoke the **Offset** tool from the **Draw** toolbar; the **Offset** ribbon bar will be displayed and you will be prompted to click on an element to offset. Depending on whether you want to offset a single entity or a chain of entities, select the required option from the **Select** drop-down list in the ribbon bar.

Enter the offset distance in the **Distance** edit box. After selecting the entity or the chain of entities, choose the **Accept** button; you will be prompted to click to place the offset element(s). The offset entities will be placed inside or outside the original entities, depending on where you specify the placement point. After placing the offset entities, you will again be prompted to click to place the offset element(s). This allows you to create multiple offset entities from each other. Figure 4-7 shows multiple offset triangles created by offsetting the outer triangle.

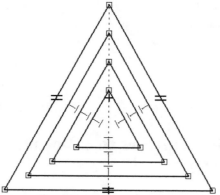

Figure 4-7 Multiple offset triangles created by offsetting the outer triangle

Creating Symmetric Offset Copies

Toolbar: Draw > Offset > Symmetric Offset

This tool allows you to create a symmetric offset on both sides of the open sketched entities or closed loops. The open sketched entity can be a center line about which you can create a symmetric offset. Figure 4-8 shows a slot created from a centerline using the **Symmetric Offset** tool. This tool is widely used to create slots in the models.

To create a symmetric offset, choose the **Symmetric Offset** button from the **Offset** flyout; the **Symmetric Offset Options** dialog box will be displayed, as shown in Figure 4-9. The options in this dialog box are discussed next.

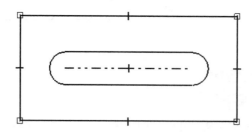

*Figure 4-8 A slot created using the **Symmetric Offset** tool*

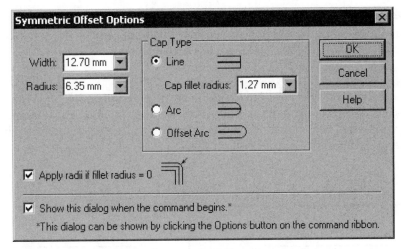

Figure 4-9 The **Symmetric Offset Options** *dialog box*

Width

The **Width** edit box is used to set the width of the slot that will be created by the symmetric offset tool. You can enter a new value in this edit box or select a preset value from the drop-down list.

Radius

If the selected entities have bends, which result in sharp corners, then this edit box will define the radius of the arc inside the resulting slot. Figure 4-10 shows the resulting slots with different radius values. If you do not want to apply arcs at the bends, enter **0** in this edit box.

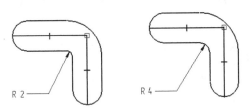

Figure 4-10 Resulting slots with different fillet radii

Note

After creating the symmetric offset entities, you cannot select the original entities and the symmetric offset entities together.

Cap Type Area

This area provides the options to specify the cap type at the end of the slots. These options are discussed next.

Line

This radio button is selected to place a line at the end of the slot. You can define a fillet at the sharp corners of the resulting slot by entering its radius in the **Cap fillet radius** edit box provided below this radio button. Figure 4-11 shows a line cap without a fillet and Figure 4-12 shows a line cap with a fillet.

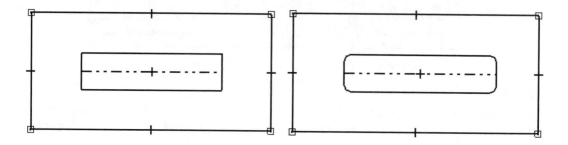

Figure 4-11 *Line cap with no fillet*   *Figure 4-12* *Line cap with a fillet*

Arc

This radio button is selected to place an arc at the end of the slot. Note that the midpoint of the arc placed using this option will be at the endpoint of the entity that is used to create the symmetric offset. The radius of the arc will be equal to half of the width value.

Offset Arc

This radio button is selected to place an offset arc at the end of the slot. Remember that the two ends of the arc will be in line with the endpoint of the entity that is used to create the symmetric offset. The radius of the arc will be equal to half of the width value.

Apply radii if fillet radius = 0

This check box is selected to create an arc at the outer corner of the resulting slot if the value **0** is entered in the **Radius** edit box. The radius of the arc will be equal to the value of the width specified in the **Width** edit box.

Show this dialog when the command begins.

This check box is selected to display the symmetric offset options dialog box whenever you invoke the **Symmetric Offset** tool.

After setting the parameters in the **Symmetric Offset Options** dialog box, choose **OK**; you will be prompted to click on the elements to offset. You can select a single entity or a chain of entities by selecting the required option from the **Select** drop-down list.

Choose the **Accept** button after selecting the entities; the symmetric offset based on the defined parameters will be created.

Moving/Copying the Sketched Entities

Toolbar:	Draw > Move

The **Move** tool is used to move the selected sketched entities from their original location to any other location in the drawing window. When you invoke this tool, the **Move** ribbon bar will be displayed and you will be prompted to click on the element(s) to modify. You can select multiple elements by dragging a box around them. After selecting the entities, you will be prompted to click for the point to move from. This is the base point from where you will hold the entities to be moved. This point can be any keypoint in the sketch or any arbitrary point in the drawing window.

When you specify the base point, you will be prompted to click for the point to move the elements to. This is the point where the base point will be placed after moving. You can specify this point by entering its X and Y coordinates in the ribbon bar or by specifying a point in the drawing window. If you are specifying the point to move in the drawing window, you can enter the step value in the **Step Distance** edit box in the ribbon bar. The step value defines the distance by which the cursor jumps while moving on the screen. Figure 4-13 shows a sketch being moved from its original location.

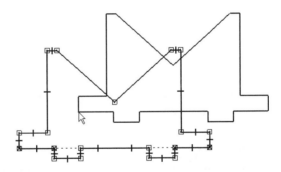

Figure 4-13 Moving the sketch from its original location

Tip. *You can also create a copy of the selected sketched entities dynamically in the drawing window. To do so, select the entities and then press and hold the CTRL key. Next, drag the cursor. A copy of the selected entities will be placed at the point where you release the left mouse button.*

By default, the **Copy** button is not chosen in the ribbon bar and therefore, the entities are only moved and not copied. If you want to create a copy of the selected entities, choose the **Copy** button; the original entities will be retained at their original location and a copy of the selected entities will be placed at the new location.

Rotating the Sketched Entities

Toolbar: Draw > Move > Rotate

The **Rotate** tool is used to rotate the selected sketched entities around a specified center point. When you invoke this tool, the **Rotate** ribbon bar will be displayed and you will be prompted to click on the element(s) to modify. Select the entities to be rotated by dragging a box around them; you will be prompted to click on the center of rotation. Select a point in the sketch or in the drawing window around which the selected entities will be rotated; you will be prompted to click on the point to rotate from. This point will define the position angle that will be taken as the base angle to rotate the selected entities. You can specify a point in the drawing window to define the position angle or enter the value of this angle directly in the **Position Angle** edit box in the ribbon bar.

After defining the position angle, you will be prompted to click on the point to rotate to. Move the cursor in the drawing window; you will notice that the preview of the rotated entities is attached to the cursor. Specify a point in the drawing window to define the rotation angle or enter the value of this angle directly in the **Rotation Angle** edit box. If you enter the value in the ribbon bar, you will be prompted to click on the side of the reference line to place the rotated object(s). You can place the rotated entities in the clockwise or the counterclockwise direction by specifying the point. Figure 4-14 shows a sketch being rotated.

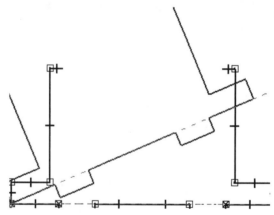

Figure 4-14 Preview of a sketch being rotated

By default, when you rotate the selected entities, their copy is created. This is because the **Copy** button is chosen by default in the ribbon bar. You can clear this button, if you do not want to create a copy of the rotated entities. You can specify the step value by which the cursor will jump to rotate the sketch using the **Step Angle** edit box in the ribbon bar.

~ring the Sketched Entities

            Draw > Move > Mirror

~ool allows you to create a mirrored copy of the selected sketched entities. To
the sketched entities, invoke this tool; the **Mirror** ribbon bar will be displayed

and you will be prompted to click on the element(s) to modify. You can select multiple entities to be mirrored by dragging a box around them. On selecting the entities, you will be prompted to click for the first point of the mirror line. You can select an existing line segment to be used as the mirror line or specify a point in the drawing window to define the first point of the mirror line. Next, you will be prompted to click for the second point of the mirror line. Move the cursor to draw a reference line. Place the cursor at the required location and specify the endpoint of the mirror line. You can also specify the angle of the mirror line by entering its value in the **Position Angle** edit box in the ribbon bar.

Once you define the mirror line, the mirrored entities will be created and highlighted. Also, you will again be prompted to specify the first point of the mirror line. This allows you to create another mirrored copy of the highlighted entities. This process continues until you terminate the current sequence by right-clicking or exit the tool by pressing the ESC key. Figure 4-15 shows the entities selected for mirroring and Figure 4-16 shows the sketch after mirroring the entities. Note that the entities are mirrored by defining a vertical line passing through the endpoint of the extreme left horizontal line.

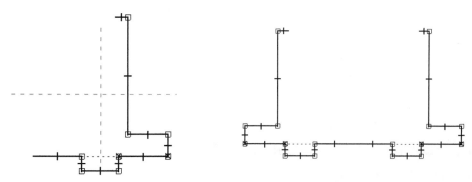

Figure 4-15 *Entities selected to mirror*   *Figure 4-16* *Resultant mirrored sketch*

When you mirror the entities, a mirrored copy of the selected entities is created and the original entities are also retained. This is because the **Copy** button is chosen by default in the ribbon bar. If this button is not chosen, the original entities are deleted after the mirrored copy is created.

> **Tip**. *If the **Copy** button is chosen in the **Mirror** ribbon bar, the symmetric offset entities will not be mirrored. They will be mirrored only if you clear the **Copy** button such that the original entities are deleted when mirrored.*

Scaling the Sketched Entities

Toolbar: Draw > Move > Scale

The **Scale** tool allows you to modify the size of the sketch maintaining its aspect ratio. You can also create a copy of the scaled sketch using this tool. To scale the sketched entities, invoke this tool; you will be prompted to click on the element(s) to modif
Select the entities that you want to scale by dragging a box around them; you will be promp'
to click for the scale center point. This is the base point which will be used to scale the en'

Next, you will be prompted to click for the new scale. You can move the cursor on the screen to scale the entities or enter the scale factor in the **Scale Factor** edit box in the ribbon bar.

The **Reference** edit box in the ribbon bar is used to set the relationship between the distance moved by the cursor and the scale factor. For example, if the value in the **Reference** edit box is entered as **50**, the scale factor will be 1 on moving the cursor 50 units away from the scale center point. Similarly, when the cursor is moved 75 units away from the scale center point, the scale factor will become 1.5. To create a copy of the selected entities while scaling, choose the **Copy** button from the ribbon bar. Figure 4-17 shows a sketch being scaled.

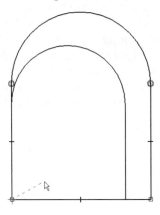

Figure 4-17 Preview of a sketch being scaled

Stretching the Sketched Entities

Menu:	Draw > Stretch

The **Stretch** tool is used to stretch objects, thereby modifying the selected portions of the objects. This command can be used to lengthen or shorten the objects and alter their shapes. When you invoke this tool, the **Stretch** ribbon bar will be displayed and you will be prompted to specify the first point of the fence. In Solid Edge, the entities you need to stretch are selected by defining a box around them. This box is termed as fence. To select the entities to be stretched, specify the first corner of the fence. Next, move the cursor and specify the diagonally opposite corner of the fence. By defining the fence, you are selecting objects and specifying the portions of those selected objects to be stretched. After defining the fence, you will be prompted to click for the point to move from. This is the base point from where you will hold the entities to be stretched. Next, you will be prompted to click for the point to move to. Move the cursor to specify the point in the drawing window. Figure 4-18 shows a fence defined to select the entities to be stretched. This figure also shows ¬tities being stretched.

e Sketched Entities by Dragging

he sketched entities by dragging them. The object will be moved or stretched ; type of entity selected, and the point of selection. For example, if you ʌy point other than the endpoints, it will be moved. If you select it at an , be stretched. Similarly, if you select an arc at its circumference, it will be

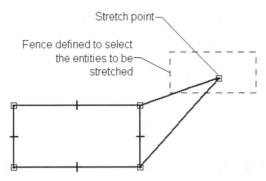

Figure 4-18 *Preview of the sketch being stretched*

moved. But if you select the arc at a keypoint, it will be stretched. Therefore, editing the sketched entities by dragging is entirely based on their selection points. Note that while editing the sketched entities using the keypoints, all related entities will also be moved or stretched. The following table gives you the details of the operation that will be performed when you drag various objects:

Object	Selection point	Operation
Circle	On circumference/center point	Move
	Keypoint on circumference	Stretch+Move
Arc	On circumference	Move
	Keypoints	Stretch
Isolated line or multiple lines selected together	Anywhere other than the endpoints	Move
	Endpoints	Stretch
Curve	Any point other than the keypoints	Move
	Keypoints	Stretch
Rectangle	All lines selected together	Move
	Any one line or any endpoint	Stretch
Ellipse	Center point or anywhere other than the keypoints	Move
	Keypoints other than the center point	Stretch

WRITING TEXT IN THE SKETCHING ENVIRONMENT

Menu: Insert > Text Profile

Solid Edge allows you to write a text in the sketching environment and use it to create features at a later stage. Based on the option that you select to place the text, you can write a straight line text or a text along a curve. To write the text, choose **Insert > Text Profile** from the menu bar; the Text dialog box will be displayed, as shown in Figure 14-19. This tool works in two steps: **Text** step and **Location** step. When you invoke this tool, the **Text** step is active.

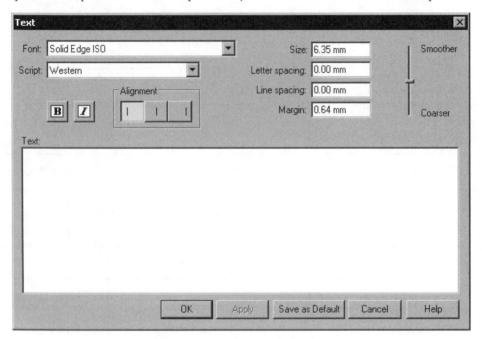

*Figure 4-19 The **Text** dialog box*

You can set the font, size, alignment, spacing, and other formatting options using the options available in this dialog box. You can also set the smoothing of the text using the vertical slider given on the upper right corner of the display box.

The preview of the text that you write will be displayed in the **Preview** display box. To write the text in the second line press ENTER. The cursor will move to the second line. After entering the required text, choose **OK**; the **Location** step will be invoked. `ou` can set the anchor for placing the text by `the` **Anchor** button. If a curve exists in the `ve` the cursor close to it; the preview of `along` the curve will be displayed. You `key` on the keyboard to toggle the `e` text. Figure 4-20 shows a text `ircle.`

Figure 4-20 Text along a circle

INSERTING IMAGES IN THE SKETCHES

Menu: Insert > Image

In Solid Edge, you can insert the external images in the sketch that can later be used as a label on the model. The images that you can insert include bitmap image (*.bmp*), jpeg image (*.jpg*), or tiff image (*.tif*). To insert an image, invoke the **Image** tool from the menu bar; the **Insert Image** dialog box will be displayed. The options in this dialog box are discussed next.

General Tab

The options in the **General** tab, as shown in Figure 4-21, are discussed next.

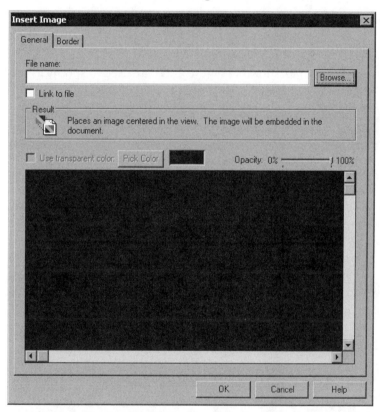

Figure 4-21 *The **General** tab in the **Insert Image** dialog box*

Browse

To select an image, choose the **Browse** button; the **Open a File** dialog box will be displayed. Browse to the image file that you want to insert using this dialog box. After selecting the fil choose **Open** from the dialog box. You will return to the **Insert Image** dialog box and image will be displayed in the preview window of the dialog box.

Link to file

Select the **Link to file** check box to create a link between the selected file and the image inserted in Solid Edge. As a result, if the original image file is changed, the image in Solid Edge can be updated to view the changes.

Use transparent color

This check box will be available only when you select the image to be inserted. When you select this check box, the **Pick Color** button will be enabled and you can choose it to set the transparency color for the image.

Opacity

You can set the opacity of the image using the **Opacity** slider bar.

Border Tab

The options in the **Border** tab, shown in Figure 4-22, are used to specify as the border color, width, and type of the selected image. After selecting the image and setting the parameters,

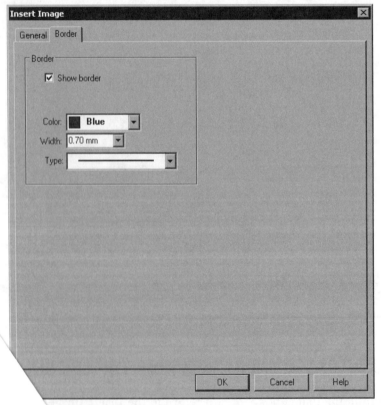

*Figure 4-22 The **Border** tab in the **Insert Image** dialog box*

box will be closed and the image will be placed in the center of the
relocate the image by selecting its edges. To resize the image, you

can use the handles at the four corners. Figure 4-23 shows an image placed in the sketching environment of Solid Edge.

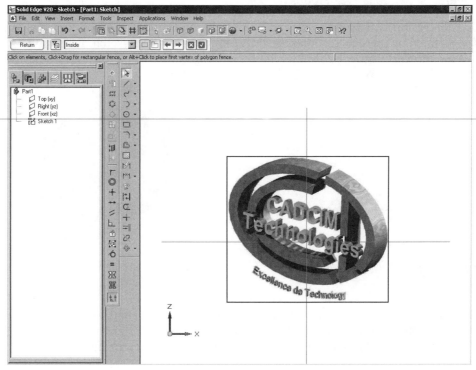

Figure 4-23 Image inserted in the sketching environment

CONVERTING SKETCHES INTO BASE FEATURES

As mentioned in the earlier chapters, most of the designs are a combination of various sketched, placed, and reference features. The first feature generally is a sketched feature. Until now, you have learned to draw sketches for these base features and add relationships and dimensions to them. After drawing and dimensioning a sketch, you need to convert it into the base feature. The base features are created in the **Part** environment. This environment is invoked when you choose **Return** from the ribbon bar.

When you exit the sketching environment and enter the **Part** environment, you will notice that the **Sketch** toolbar is replaced by the **Features** toolbar. Solid Edge provides you with a number of tools such as **Protrusion**, **Revolved Protrusion**, **Swept Protrusion**, and so on t convert these base sketches into base features. In this chapter, you will learn the use of o the **Protrusion** and **Revolved Protrusion** tools for converting the sketches into base fea The remaining tools will be discussed in later chapters.

CREATING BASE FEATURES BY PROTRUSION

Toolbar: Features > Protrusion

 Protrusion is defined as the process of creating a feature by adding the material, defined by the sketch, along the direction normal to the sketch. Figure 4-24 shows a profile and Figure 4-25 shows the protrusion feature created using this profile.

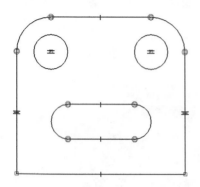

Figure 4-24 *Profile for the protrusion feature*

Figure 4-25 *Resulting protrusion feature*

All the following steps are performed using the **Protrusion** ribbon bar, which will be displayed when you invoke the **Protrusion** tool. The buttons of these steps are available on the left of the **Cancel** button in the ribbon bar. Also, the button of the current step is chosen.

Plane or Sketch Step. This step is active whenever you invoke the **Protrusion** tool. In this step, you select the plane to draw a profile. You can also select an existing sketch by selecting the **Select from Sketch** option from the **Create-From Options** drop-down list, which is available in the ribbon bar in this step.

Draw Profile Step. This step allows you to draw the profile of the base feature. This step is automatically invoked when you select a plane to draw the profile.

Side Step. If you create additional features after creating the base feature and draw an open ⌐⌐ this step will enable you to specify the side of material addition.

This step allows you to define the extents of the resulting protrusion feature ⸞ts depth.

This step allows you to define the draft angle or the crown treatment for ⸍ure.

ʼll learn about the **Plane or Sketch** step, **Draw Profile** step, and the ⸝ under various steps in the ribbon bar are discussed next.

Plane or Sketch Step

This step is active whenever you invoke the **Protrusion** tool. This is the reason you are prompted to click on a planar face or a reference plane. You can select any of the base reference planes for drawing the profile of the protrusion feature. The plane on which you click will be taken as the sketching plane and the sketching environment will be invoked.

If you have already drawn the profile using the **Sketch** tool, select the **Select from Sketch** option from the **Create-From Options** drop-down list. On doing so, the **Select** drop-down list will be available in the ribbon bar. The options in this drop-down list are discussed next.

Single

This option is chosen or selected to select a single sketched entity as a profile for creating the protrusion feature. Remember that if the single entity results in an open entity, then you cannot create the base feature using that single entity. However, you can select closed single entities such as circles and ellipses. After selecting the entity, choose the **Accept** button available on the right of this drop-down list. You can also right-click to accept the selection.

Chain

This option is used to select a chain of end-connected entities. After selecting the chain, right-click or choose the **Accept** button to accept the selection.

Draw Profile Step

The **Draw Profile** step is invoked automatically as soon as you select a reference plane to draw the profile. In this step, the sketching environment is invoked and you can draw the profile using various sketching tools.

Extent Step

The **Extent** step is automatically invoked when you exit the sketching environment after creating the profile or when you choose the **Accept** button after selecting the profile. The options available in the ribbon bar under this step are discussed next.

1-Direction Extrude

This option is chosen by default and allows you to extrude the profile in one of the directions of the sketching plane. There is no button for this option but you can make sure this option is active by not choosing the **Non-symmetric Extent** or the **Symmetric Extent** button. As this option is selected by default, the preview of the protrusion feature will be displayed on the screen. The depth of the feature will be modified dynamically as you move the cursor on the screen. You can define the depth of extrusion by entering the value in the **Distance** edit box or by clicking anywhere in the drawing area. Figure 4-26 shows the preview of a protrusion feature being created by extruding in one direction.

Non-symmetric Extent

The **Non-symmetric Extent** button is chosen to extrude the profile non-symmetrically on both sides of the plane on which the profile is created. In other words its used to specify different depths of extrusion on both the sides. When you choose this button, the **Direction 1** and **Direction 2** buttons will be displayed in the ribbon bar. These buttons are discussed next.

Direction 1

This button is automatically chosen when you choose the **Non-symmetric Extent** button and you are prompted to click to set the distance or key in a value. This button allows you to specify the depth of the extrusion in the first direction. You can click anywhere in the drawing window to specify the depth of the extrusion or enter the depth in the **Distance** edit box.

Direction 2

This button is automatically chosen when you specify the depth in the first direction. Similar to defining the depth in the first direction, you can specify the depth in the second direction by clicking anywhere in the drawing window or by entering a value in the **Distance** edit box.

Symmetric Extent

The **Symmetric Extent** button is chosen to protrude the profile symmetrically on both sides of the plane on which the profile is created. Figure 4-27 shows the preview of a protrusion feature being created with a symmetric extent.

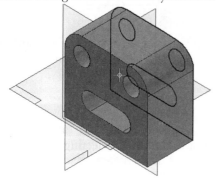

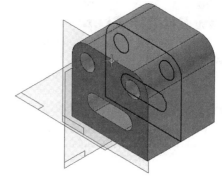

Figure 4-26 Preview of a protrusion feature being created by extruding in one direction

Figure 4-27 Preview of a protrusion feature being created with a symmetric extent

Finite Extent

This button is chosen by default to define the depth of the protrusion feature by specifying its numeric value in the **Distance** edit box.

Note
There are other options also for defining the depth of the protrusion feature. These options will be discussed in later chapters.

Distance

The **Distance** edit box is used to specify the numeric value of the depth of the protrusion feature. You can enter a value in this edit box or move the cursor on the screen to define the depth of the protrusion feature. You can also select any preset depth value from the **Distance** drop-down list.

Step

While defining the depth of the protrusion feature by moving the cursor on the screen, the value in the **Distance** edit box increases or decreases in a predefined increment. This value is specified in the **Step** edit box.

When you enter the required depth value in the **Distance** edit box or when you click in the drawing window to define the depth, most of the options in the ribbon bar are hidden. Also, the **Finish** button and the **Name** edit box will be displayed in the ribbon bar. To exit the **Protrusion** tool, choose the **Finish** button. You can change the name of the protrusion feature by entering a new name in the **Name** edit box.

You can choose the **Extent Step** button from the ribbon bar to modify the profile or the extents of the protrusion feature.

Note

Even after you choose **Finish** *from the ribbon bar to exit the* **Protrusion** *tool, this tool remains active and you can create another protrusion feature. You need to choose* **Cancel** *from the ribbon bar or press the ESC key to exit the tool.*

CREATING BASE FEATURES USING THE REVOLVED PROTRUSION

Toolbar:	Features > Revolved Protrusion

Revolved protrusion is defined as the process of creating a feature by revolving a closed sketch around an axis to add the material. Figure 4-28 shows a profile for the revolved protrusion feature and Figure 4-29 shows the revolved protrusion feature created by revolving the profile around the vertical line.

The **Revolved Protrusion** tool works in four steps: **Plane or Sketch** step, **Draw Profile** step, **Side** step, and **Extent** step. The **Side** step is not available while creating the base feature. The remaining steps are discussed next.

Plane or Sketch Step

This step is active whenever you invoke the **Revolved Protrusion** tool. As a result, you are prompted to click on a planar face or a reference plane. You can select a base reference plane for drawing the profile of the revolved protrusion feature. The plane on which you click will be taken as the sketching plane and the sketching environment will be invoked.

If you have already drawn the profile using the **Sketch** tool, select the **Select from Sketch**

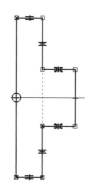

Figure 4-28 *Profile for the revolved protrusion feature*

Figure 4-29 *Resultant revolved protrusion feature*

option from the **Create-From Options** drop-down list. Note that you can select only a closed profile defined by a chain of entities to create the base revolved protrusion feature. After selecting the profile for the protrusion feature, right-click or choose the **Accept** button. You will be prompted to click on the line in the sketch to be used as the revolved feature axis. You can select any line, which is a part of the selected sketch, as the axis of revolution.

Draw Profile Step

The **Draw Profile** step is automatically invoked as soon as you select a reference plane to draw the profile of the revolved feature. In this step, the sketching environment is invoked and you can draw the profile using various sketching tools. Remember that while drawing the profile of the revolved feature, you also need to draw the axis of revolution around which the profile will be revolved. The **Axis of Revolution** tool will be available in the **Features and Relationships** toolbar when you invoke the sketching environment using this button. If you try to exit the sketching environment without drawing the axis of revolution, the **Profile Error Assistant** dialog box will be displayed. This dialog box will inform you that a revolved feature must have an axis of revolution.

Extent Step

The **Extent** step is automatically invoked when you exit the sketching environment after creating the profile or after selecting the axis of revolution of the existing sketch. The options available in the ribbon bar in this step are discussed next.

1-Direction Revolve

This option is chosen by default and allows you to revolve the profile in one of the directions of the sketching plane. There is no button for this option but you can ensure this option is active by not choosing the **Non-symmetric Extent** or **Symmetric Extent** button. As this option is chosen by default, the preview of the revolved feature is displayed on the screen. The revolution angle of the feature will be modified dynamically as you move the cursor on the screen. You can define the revolution angle by entering the value in the **Angle** edit box.

Non-symmetric Extent

The **Non-symmetric Extent** button is chosen to revolve the profile non-symmetrically on both sides of the plane on which the profile is created, or in other words, to specify different angles of revolution on both the sides. When you choose this button, the **Direction 1** and **Direction 2** buttons will be displayed in the ribbon bar that enable you to specify the revolution angle in both the directions.

Symmetric Extent

The **Symmetric Revolve** button is chosen to revolve the profile symmetrically on both sides of the plane on which the profile is drawn.

Revolve 360°

This button is chosen to revolve the profile through 360-degrees.

Finite Extent

This button is chosen by default and is used to create the revolved feature through a specified angle.

Angle

The **Angle** edit box is used to specify the angle through which the profile will be revolved to create the revolved feature. You can enter a value in this edit box or move the cursor in the drawing window to specify the angle. Note that to enter a value in this edit box, you need to move the cursor on either side of the sketching plane in the drawing window to define the direction of revolution. Figures 4-30 and 4-31 show the same sketch revolved through 180-degrees in two different directions.

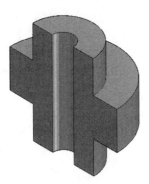

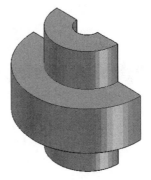

Figure 4-30 180-degrees revolved protrusion in one direction

Figure 4-31 180-degrees revolved protrusion in the other direction

Step

This edit box is used to specify the value by which the angle value will be increased or decreased when you move the cursor in the drawing window to define the angle of revolution.

Note
*The other options in the **Revolved Protrusion** ribbon bar will be discussed in later chapters.*

ROTATING THE VIEW OF A MODEL IN 3D SPACE

Toolbar: Main > Rotate

Solid Edge provides you with an option of rotating the view of a solid model freely in three-dimensional (3D) space. This makes it possible for you to visually maneuver around the solid model and view it from any direction. To invoke this tool, choose the **Rotate** button from the **Main** toolbar; a 3D indicator with three axes and the origin will be displayed at the center of the current view. The three axes of the 3D indicator represent the positive X, Y, and Z axes. This indicator allows you to rotate the view freely in 3D space or around any of these three axes.

To rotate the view freely around the center of the current view, press and hold the left mouse button and drag the cursor; the view of the model will be rotated and you can visually maneuver around it. You can also freely rotate the view around a vertex in the model by simply selecting the vertex. The 3D indicator will be relocated such that its origin will then lie at the selected vertex.

You can rotate the view around one of the axes of the 3D indicator or around an edge in the model. To do so, invoke the **Rotate** tool and select the edge or the axis. Press and hold the left mouse button down and drag the cursor; the view will be rotated around the selected edge or axis. After rotating the view, right-click to exit the **Rotate** tool.

Tip. *To rotate a view freely again in the 3D space around a vertex after rotating the view around an edge or an axis, click on a vertex or the origin of the 3D indicator.*

If you have a three-button mouse, you can use the middle button to rotate the view.

RESTORING STANDARD VIEWS

Once you have rotated the views of a model using Solid Edge, you can restore the standard views so that you can view the model from the standard orientations. To restore the standard views, choose the down arrow on the right of the **Named Views** tool in the **Main** toolbar; a drop-down list will be displayed with the standard views, as shown in Figure 4-32. You can select any standard view from this drop-down list.

You can also save any view other than the standard ones. To do so, you need to keep the model in any view other than the standard views and choose the **Click to save view** option from the drop-down list. The **New Named View** dialog box will be displayed, as shown in Figure 4-33. Enter the name of the view in the **New view name** edit box. Enter the function of the view in the **Description** edit box. The name you entered in the New view name edit box will be displayed in the main drop-down list.

SETTING DISPLAY MODES

You can set the display modes for the solid models using the buttons provided in the **Main** toolbar. The display modes that you can set for the solid models are discussed next.

Figure 4-32 The **Named Views** *drop-down list*

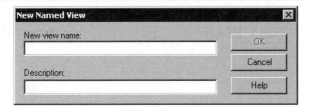

Figure 4-33 The **New Named View** *dialog box*

Shaded with Visible Edges

 This is the default display mode set for the models. In this mode, the models are displayed shaded along with all visible edges in them. Because the display is set to shaded, the model will be assigned a material and will behave as a solid model with an opaque material assigned to it.

Shaded

 In the **Shaded** display mode, the models are displayed shaded without highlighting any edge of the model.

Visible and Hidden Edges

 In this display mode, all visible and hidden edges are displayed in the model. The visible edges are displayed in black and the hidden edges are displayed in gray. You can view the entities placed behind the model in this display mode.

Visible Edges

 In this display mode, only the visible edges are displayed in the model. You cannot view the hidden edges.

Drop Shadow

This button is chosen to display the shadow of the solid model. The shadow will be displayed below the model.

IMPROVING THE DISPLAY QUALITY OF THE MODEL

In Solid Edge, you can modify the display quality of the model by improving its sharpness. To modify the sharpness, choose the down arrow on the right of the **Sharpen** button in the **Main** toolbar. The drop-down list will be displayed, select the required type of sharpness from there. Note that the sharper the image, the more time it will take to regenerate.

TUTORIALS

Tutorial 1

In this tutorial, you will create the model shown in Figure 4-34. Its dimensions are given in the drawing views shown in Figure 4-35.   **(Expected time: 30 min)**

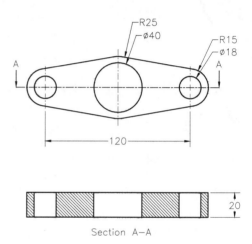

Figure 4-34 Model for Tutorial 1

Figure 4-35 Top and sectioned front view displaying the dimensions of the model

Before you start creating the model, it is recommended that you outline the steps that will be required to complete the tutorial. The following steps are required to complete this tutorial:

a. Start a new part file and then draw the profile of the outer loop, refer to Figures 4-36 and 4-37.
b. Add the required dimensions and relationships to the profile, refer to Figure 4-38.
c. Draw the inner circles and add the required dimensions to them, refer to Figure 4-39.
d. Exit the sketching environment and define the depth of the protrusion of the model, refer to Figure 4-40.
e. Increase the sharpness of the model and rotate the view in 3D space.
f. Save the file and close it.

Drawing the Sketch of the Model

The sketch of this model can be created using the **Protrusion** tool. The inner circles will be automatically subtracted from the outer profile when you protrude the sketch.

1. Start a new part file and invoke the **Protrusion** tool; you are prompted to click on a planar face or reference plane.

Note
*If the planes are not displayed in the **Feature PathFinder**, right-click in the **PathFinder** and choose **PathFinder Display > Planes** from the menu bar; the planes will then be displayed in the **Feature PathFinder**.*

2. Select the top plane; the sketching environment is invoked and the **Line** tool is active.

3. Draw the sketch using the **Circle by Center** and **Line** tools, as shown in Figure 4-36. Make sure the tangent and connect relationships are applied between the lines and the circles at all points where the lines intersect the circles. The tangent relationship is designated by a small circle and the connect relationship is designated by a cross, as shown in Figure 4-36. Also note that in this figure, because the centers of the two circles lie at the endpoints of the horizontal reference plane, a two point connect relationship is applied between the centers of the circles and the two endpoints of the horizontal reference plane.

    Next, you need to trim the unwanted portion of the circles to retain the outer profile of the model. The sketch is trimmed using the **Trim** tool.

4. Choose the **Trim** button from the **Draw** toolbar; you are prompted to select the element to trim.

5. Move the cursor over the right portion of the circle on the left; the portion that will be trimmed is highlighted in red.

6. Click on this portion of the circle to remove it, refer to Figure 4-36.

Note
If the entire circle is highlighted in red, the connect relationship is not applied between the lines and the circle. Therefore, you need to manually add this relationship to the circle and the lines.

7. Similarly, trim the unwanted portion of the other circles to get the sketch, shown in Figure 4-37.

    Next, you need to add relationships to the sketch.

8. Choose the **Equal** button from the **Features and Relationships** toolbar and make the left arc equal to the right arc. Similarly, make all the lines equal using the same relationship.

    You need to remove the connect relationship, if added between the center of the left and

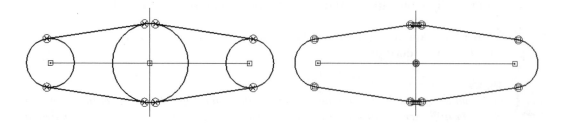

Figure 4-36 *Initial sketch for the base feature*   **Figure 4-37** *Sketch after trimming the unwanted portion of circles*

right arcs and the endpoints of the horizontal plane. This relationship is designated by the squares displayed at the two ends of the horizontal plane. You can ignore the following step if no squares are displayed at the endpoints of the reference plane in the sketch.

9. Press the ESC key to exit all tools and then select the square displayed at the left endpoint of the horizontal plane. This square is the relationship handle of the connect relationship.

10. When the relationship handle is highlighted, press the DELETE key to remove the relationship. Similarly, delete this relationship from the right endpoint of the horizontal plane.

11. Now, horizontally align the center points of the left and right arcs using the horizontal/vertical relationship. Similarly, horizontally align the center point of the left arc with the origin.

12. Add the dimensions to fully constrain the sketch, using the **SmartDimension** tool, as shown in Figure 4-38.

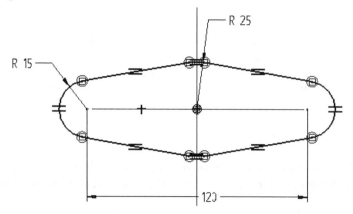

Figure 4-38 *Sketch after adding the relationships and dimensions*

Next, you need to draw the inner circles. You can use the center points of the arcs to draw them.

13. Draw three circles using the center points of arcs, refer to Figure 4-39.

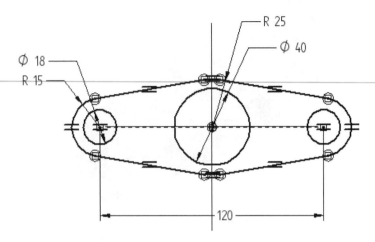

Figure 4-39 Final sketch for Tutorial 1

14. Add the **Equal** and **Concentric** relationship to the circles on the left and right. Now, add the required dimensions to the circles to complete the sketch. The final sketch of the model is shown in Figure 4-39.

Converting the Sketch into a Feature

Next, you need to convert the sketch into a feature. This is done using the **Extent** step. This step is automatically invoked when you exit the sketching environment.

1. Choose the **Return** button from the ribbon bar to exit the sketching environment. The **Protrusion** ribbon bar is displayed with the **Extent** step active. This is the reason you are prompted to click to set the distance or key in a value.

   As you move the cursor in the drawing window, the preview of the protrusion feature is displayed and its depth is modified dynamically. You will notice that you can add the depth to the sketch below or above the sketching plane. However, in this model, you need to add the depth above the sketching plane.

2. Enter **20** in the **Distance** edit box in the ribbon bar; you are prompted to select the side of extrusion.

3. Specify a point on top of the sketching plane to define the direction of extrusion; the protrusion feature is created and displayed in the drawing window.

4. Choose the **Finish** button from the ribbon bar. Again, choose **Cancel** from the ribbon bar to exit the **Protrusion** tool. The model for Tutorial 1 is shown in Figure 4-40.

Note

*In Figure 4-40, the display of the reference planes is turned off. To do this, choose the **Select Tool** button to make sure no drawing or modeling tool is active. Now, press and hold the SHIFT key down and select all the reference planes from the **EdgeBar**. Right-click to display the shortcut menu and choose **Hide**. The reference planes will no longer be displayed.*

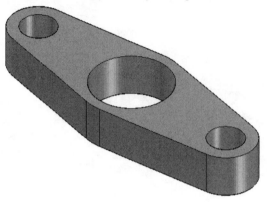

Figure 4-40 Model for Tutorial 1

Rotating the View of the Model

Next, you need to rotate the view of the model so that you can maneuver around it and view the model from different directions.

1. Choose the **Rotate** button from the **Main** toolbar to invoke this tool, the 3D indicator, along with the three axes, is displayed in the center of the current view.

2. Press and hold the left mouse button and drag the cursor in the drawing window.

    The view of the model is rotated in 3D space and you can view it from different directions. However, when you rotate the view, the circles and arcs in the model are changed to sharp-edged features because the sharpness of the model is set to the minimum value. You need to increase the sharpness of the model to make sure it remains equally sharp while rotating the view.

3. Choose the down arrow on the right of the **Sharpen** button in the **Main** toolbar to display the drop-down list, as shown in Figure 4-41.

4. From the drop-down list, select **5 Finer display**. Choose **Yes** from the **Sharpen** message box. This option increases the sharpness of the model to the maximum value.

5. Next, choose the **Rotate** button from the **Main** toolbar and rotate the view of the model. You will notice that the model remains sharp and the curved features in the model are displayed curved while rotating the view.

Figure   4-41   The ***Sharpen*** *drop-down list*

6. Right-click to exit the **Rotate** tool.

    Now, you need to restore the isometric view of the model that is changed by the **Rotate** tool. The standard views can be restored using the **Named Views** drop-down list.

7. Choose the down arrow on the right of the **Named Views** button in the **Main** toolbar to display the drop-down list.

8. From the views displayed in the drop-down list, select **iso** to change the current view to the isometric view.

9. Right-click in the drawing window and choose **Fit** from the shortcut menu. The model fits in the drawing window.

Saving and Closing the File

1. Choose the **Save** button from the **Main** toolbar to display the **Part1 Properties** dialog box.

2. Choose **OK** from the **Part1 Properties** dialog box; the **Save As** dialog box is displayed.

3. Browse to the *My Documents\Solid Edge* folder and then create a folder with the name *c04* in this folder.

4. Make the *c04* folder current and save the file with the name *c04tut1.par*. The location of this file is given below:

    \My Documents\Solid Edge\c04\c04tut1.par

5. Choose **File > Close** from the menu bar to close the file.

Tutorial 2

In this tutorial, you will open the sketch created in Exercise 1 of Chapter 3. You will then convert the sketch into a protrusion feature using the **Protrusion** tool. The depth of the protrusion is 30 units. **(Expected time: 15 min)**

The following steps are required to complete this tutorial:

a. Copy the sketch from the *c03* folder to the *c04* folder with the name *c04tut2.par*.
b. Open the sketch and extrude it to a distance of 30 units using the **Protrusion** tool, refer to Figure 4-43.
c. Rotate the view of the model in 3D space using the **Rotate** tool.
d. Save and close the file.

Opening the Sketch Drawn in Chapter 3

1. Choose the **Open** button from the **Main** toolbar to display the **Open File** option dialog box.

2. Browse to the \Solid Edge\c03 folder and open the c03exr1.par file.

Saving the Sketch with a Different Name

After opening the sketch, you need to first save it with a different name so that the original sketch drawn in Chapter 3 is not modified.

1. Choose **File > Save As** from the menu bar to display the **Save As** dialog box.

2. Browse to the \Solid Edge\c04 folder and save the sketch with the name c04tut2.par; the file is saved with the new name and is opened in the drawing window. To cross-check, refer to the name of the file on the top left corner of the screen. The name shows c04tut2.par. Figure 4-42 shows the sketch of Tutorial 2.

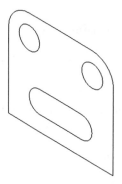

Figure 4-42 Sketch of Tutorial 2

Protruding the Sketch

Next, you need to convert this sketch into a protrusion feature using the **Protrusion** tool. The depth of protrusion is 30.

1. Choose the **Protrusion** button from the **Features** toolbar; the **Protrusion** ribbon bar is displayed and **Plane or Sketch Step** is active by default. As mentioned earlier, this step allows you to select a plane to draw the sketch of the protrusion feature or select an existing sketch. This is the reason why you are prompted to click on a planar face or reference plane.

    You need to select the sketch that you have to convert into a feature.

2. Select the **Select from Sketch** option from the **Create-From Options** drop-down list in the ribbon bar; you are prompted to click on a sketch chain.

3. One by one select the outer loop, the inner loop, and the two inner circles; the selected loops are highlighted.

4. Right-click to accept the selection; the **Extent** step is invoked and you are prompted to click to set the distance or key in a value.

5. Enter **30** in the **Distance** edit box; you are prompted to select the side for extrusion.

6. Specify a point in front of the sketching plane to define the direction of adding depth to the sketch.

7. Choose **Finish** from the ribbon bar and then choose **Cancel** to exit the **Protrusion** tool.

The protrusion feature is created, but the sketch is still displayed in the drawing window. Therefore, you need to turn off the display of this sketch using the **EdgeBar**.

8. Choose the **Select Tool** button. Right-click on **Sketch 1** in the **EdgeBar** and choose **Hide** from the shortcut menu; the display of the sketch is turned off. The protruded model is shown in Figure 4-43. Note that in this figure, the display of the reference planes is also turned off.

Figure 4-43 Model for Tutorial 2

Rotating the View of the Model

Next, you need to rotate the view of the model so that you can maneuver over it and view it from different directions.

1. Choose the **Rotate** button from the **Main** toolbar to invoke this tool. The 3D indicator, along with the three axes, is displayed in the center of the current view.

2. Press and hold the left mouse button and drag the cursor in the drawing window.

The view of the model is rotated in 3D space and you can view it from different directions.

 Tip. *While rotating the view of the model, if you select its edge or an axis in the 3D indictor the view will be rotated around that axis. To freely rotate the view again, select the origin of the 3D indictor.*

When you rotate the view, the circles and arcs in the model are changed to sharp-edged features because the sharpness of the model is set to the minimum value. You need to increase the sharpness of the model to make sure it remains equally sharp while rotating the view.

3. Choose the down arrow on the right of the **Sharpen** button in the **Main** toolbar to display the drop-down list.

4. From the drop-down list, select **5 Finer display**. The Sharpen dialog box is displayed, choose **Yes** from it. This option increases the sharpness of the model to the maximum value.

5. Now, choose the **Rotate** button from the **Main** toolbar and rotate the view of the model. You will notice that the model remains sharp and the curved features in the model are displayed as curved.

6. Right-click to exit the **Rotate** tool.

    Next, you need to restore the isometric view of the model that is changed by the **Rotate** tool.

7. Choose the down arrow on the right of the **Named Views** button in the **Main** toolbar to invoke the drop-down list.

8. From the views displayed in the drop-down list, choose **iso** to change the current view to the isometric view.

9. Right-click in the drawing window and choose **Fit** from the shortcut menu. The model fits in the drawing window.

Saving and Closing the File

1. Choose the **Save** button from the **Main** toolbar. The file is saved with the name and location given below:

    \My Documents\Solid Edge\c04\c04tut2.par

2. Choose **File > Close** from the menu bar to close the file.

Tutorial 3

In this tutorial, you will open the sketch created in Tutorial 2 of Chapter 3. You will then convert the sketch into a revolved feature using the **Revolved Protrusion** tool.

(Expected time: 15 min)

The following steps are required to complete this tutorial:

a.   Copy the sketch from the *c03* folder to the *c04* folder with the name *c04tut3.par*.
b.   Open the sketch and revolve it using the **Revolved Protrusion** tool.
c.   Rotate the model in 3D space using the **Rotate** tool.
d.   Save and close the file.

Opening the Sketch Drawn in Chapter 3

1.   Choose the **Open** button from the **Main** toolbar to display the **Open File** option dialog box.

2.   Browse to the *\Solid Edge\c03* folder and open the *c03tut2.par* file.

Saving the Sketch with a Different Name

After opening the sketch, you need to first save it with a different name so that the original sketch drawn in Chapter 3 is not modified.

1.   Choose **File > Save As** from the menu bar to display the **Save As** dialog box.

2.   Browse to the *\Solid Edge\c04* folder and save the sketch with the name *c04tut3.par*; the file is saved with the new name and is opened in the drawing window. Figure 4-44 shows the sketch for the revolved model.

Figure 4-44 Sketch for the revolved model

Revolving the Sketch

Next, you need to convert this sketch into a revolved feature using the **Revolved Protrusion** tool. Because there is no revolution axis in this sketch, you need to use the left vertical line as the axis of revolution.

1. Choose the **Revolved Protrusion** button from the **Features** toolbar; the ribbon bar is displayed and the **Plane or Sketch Step** is active. This is the reason you are prompted to click on a planar face or a reference plane.

2. Select the **Select from Sketch** option from the **Create-From Options** drop-down list in the ribbon bar and then select the sketch for the revolved feature.

3. Right-click to accept the selection; you are prompted to click on a line in the sketch to be used as the revolved feature axis.

4. Select the left vertical line of the sketch to be used as a revolution axis.

   The **Extent Step** is invoked and the **Finite Extent** button is chosen in the ribbon bar. You need to revolve the sketch through an angle of 360-degrees to create the revolved feature.

5. Choose the **Revolve 360°** button from the ribbon bar; the fully revolved feature is displayed in the drawing window.

6. Choose the **Finish** button from the ribbon bar and then choose the **Cancel** button to exit the **Revolved Protrusion** tool.

7. Right-click on **Base Sketch** in the **EdgeBar** and choose **Hide** from the shortcut menu. The revolved model for Tutorial 3 is shown in Figure 4-44.

Figure 4-44 Revolved model for Tutorial 3

Rotating the View of the Model

1. Choose the down arrow on the right of the **Sharpen** button in the **Main** toolbar to display the drop-down list.

2. From the drop-down list, select **5 Finer display**. Choose **Yes** from the **Sharpen** message box. This option increases the sharpness of the model to the maximum value.

3. Now, choose the **Rotate** button from the **Main** toolbar and rotate the view of the model.

4. Right-click to exit the **Rotate** tool.

5. Right-click in the drawing window and choose **Fit** from the shortcut menu; the model fits in the drawing window.

Saving and Closing the File

1. Choose the **Save** button from the **Main** toolbar. The file is saved with the name and location given below:

    \My Documents\Solid Edge\c04\c04tut3.par

2. Choose **File > Close** from the menu bar to close the file.

Self-Evaluation Test

Answer the following questions and then compare them to with those given at the end of this chapter:

1. In Solid Edge, you can insert the external images in the sketch that can later be used as a label on the model. (T/F)

2. You need to manually invoke the **Extent Step** in the **Protrusion** tool when you exit the sketching environment, after creating the profile, or when you choose the **Accept** button after selecting the profile. (T/F)

3. The **Extend** tool allows you to extend or lengthen an open sketched entity up to the next entity it intersects. (T/F)

4. You can set the display modes for the solid models using the buttons provided in the **Main** toolbar. (T/F)

5. In Solid Edge, you can modify the display quality of the model by improving the _____ of the model.

6. The _____ button is chosen when you want to protrude the profile symmetrically on both sides of the plane on which the profile is created.

7. The _____ tool allows you to create a mirrored copy of the selected sketched entities.

8. You can also create a copy of the selected sketched entities by pressing and holding the _____ key and dragging the cursor.

9. _____ is defined as the process of creating a feature by revolving a sketch around an axis to add the material.

10. You can restore the standard views by choosing the down arrow on the right of the _____ tool in the **Main** toolbar.

Review Questions

Answer the following questions:

1. To create a copy of the selected entities by dragging, which one of the following keys will you press and hold after selecting the enities?

    (a) ALT   (b) CTRL
    (c) SHIFT   (d) None

2. Which one of the following types of images cannot be inserted in the sketching environment of Solid Edge?

    (a) JPG   (b) BMP
    (c) PCX   (d) None

3. Which one of the following tools allows you to create a symmetric offset on both sides of open sketched entities?

    (a) **Offset**   (b) **Symmetric**
    (c) **Symmetric Offset**   (d) None

4. Which one of the following buttons is chosen from the **Revolved Protrusion** ribbon bar to revolve a profile through an angle of 270-degrees?

    (a) **Revolve 360°**   (b) **Finite Extent**
    (c) Both   (d) None

5. Which one of the following buttons is chosen from the **Mirror** ribbon bar to make sure that the original entities are also retained after creating a mirrored copy of the selected entities?

    (a) **Copy**   (b) **Mirror**
    (c) **Double**   (d) None

6. In which type of display mode, only the visible edges are displayed in the model?

    (a) **Shaded**   (b) **Visible Edges**
    (c) **Visible and Hidden Edges**   (d) None

7. After choosing **the Finish** button to exit, the **Protrusion** tool is still active and you are allowed to create another protrusion feature. (T/F)

8. When you mirror the entities, a mirrored copy of the selected entities is created by default and the original entities are deleted. (T/F)

9. In the **Shaded** display mode, the models are displayed shaded without any edge of the model. (T/F)

10. You can use the **Rotate** tool to rotate the selected sketched entities around a specified center point and create a copy of the selected entities. (T/F)

Exercises

Exercise 1

Open the profile drawn in Exercise 2 of Chapter 3 and convert it into a protrusion feature. The depth of protrusion is 40 units. After creating the model, use the **Rotate** tool to rotate the view of the model. Before saving and closing the file, restore the isometric view of the model.   **(Expected time: 15 min)**

Exercise 2

Open the profile drawn in Tutorial 1 of Chapter 3 and convert it into a protrusion feature. The depth of protrusion is 40 units. After creating the model, use the **Rotate** tool to rotate the view of the model. Before saving and closing the file, restore the isometric view of the model.   **(Expected time: 15 min)**

Answers to Self-Evaluation Test
1. T, 2. F, 3. T, 4. T, 5. sharpness, 6. Symmetric Extent, 7. Mirror, 8. CTRL, 9. Revolved protrusion, 10. Named Views

Chapter 5

Working with
Additional
Reference Planes

After completing this chapter, you will be able to:
- *Understand the use of reference geometries.*
- *Create reference planes.*
- *Control the display of reference axes.*
- *Create new coordinate systems.*
- *Use additional termination options to create protrusion features.*
- *Create protruded and revolved cutouts.*
- *Include the edges of the existing features as sketched entities in the current sketch.*
- *Work with advanced drawing display tools.*

ADDITIONAL SKETCHING AND REFERENCE PLANES

As mentioned earlier, most of the mechanical designs consist of a number of sketched, reference, and placed features that are integrated together. In the previous chapter, you learned to create the base feature, which is the first feature in a model. After creating the base feature, you need to add more features to it. Mostly, the additional features are not created on the default plane on which the base feature is created. For example, refer to the model shown in Figure 5-1.

The base feature for this model is a protrusion feature, as shown in Figure 5-2. The sketch for this protrusion feature is drawn on the front plane.

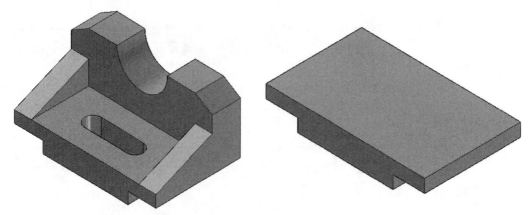

Figure 5-1 Model with multiple features   *Figure 5-2 Base feature of the model*

After creating the base feature, you need to create another protrusion feature, two rib features, and a cutout feature, refer to Figure 5-3. All these features are sketched features and require additional sketching or reference planes to draw their sketches. This is the reason you require additional sketching planes or reference planes. By default, the top, right, and front planes are available in the part file. These default planes are called the base reference planes. You can use any of these reference planes or the planar faces of the base feature to draw the sketches of the additional features.

However, you cannot use the existing planes for drawing the sketch of a feature that is at a certain offset or angle from an existing reference plane or planar face of a feature. In this case, you need to create additional reference planes.

In addition to the base reference planes, you can create two more types of reference planes, which are discussed next.

Local Reference Planes

Local reference planes are the ones that are created while defining a feature. For example, whenever you invoke a sketched feature creation tool, the ribbon bar provides the tools to create reference planes. A reference plane created at this stage will be used to create only this particular feature. Therefore, these types of reference planes are called local reference planes.

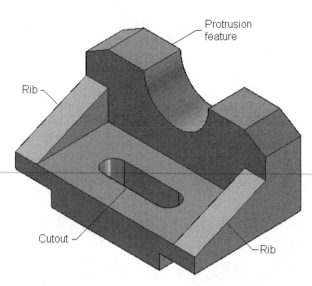

Figure 5-3 *Various features in the model*

These planes are not displayed in the drawing window and the **EdgeBar**.

Global Reference Planes

Global reference planes are the ones that are created separately as features with the help of tools available in the **Features** toolbar. These planes are displayed in the drawing window as well as in the **EdgeBar** and can be used to create multiple features.

CREATING REFERENCE PLANES

In Solid Edge, you are provided with eight options for creating global or local reference planes. You need to select the option to create a reference plane from the **Create-From Options** drop-down list available in the ribbon bar in the **Plane or Sketch** step. You can also create reference planes while creating a sketched feature. The result will be a local reference plane. But if you use the tools in the **Features** toolbar to create these features, the result will be a global reference plane. The eight methods of creating the reference planes are discussed next.

Creating a Coincident Plane

Toolbar:	Features > Coincident Plane
Ribbon Bar:	Plane or Sketch Step > Create-From Options > Coincident

 The **Coincident Plane** tool is used to create a reference plane that is coincident to a base reference plane, another reference plane, or the planar face of a model. While creating this plane, you can control the direction of the X-axis of the plane.

To create a coincident plane, invoke the **Coincident Plane** tool; you will be prompted to click on a planar face or a reference plane. Move the cursor over the reference plane or planar face on which you want to create the coincident plane; the plane will be highlighted in red and the edge that will define the X axis of the new plane will be displayed in yellow. Also, the preview of the reference plane created using the currently highlighted items will be displayed in the drawing window.

You can select the other edges of the planar face or the reference plane to define the X axis of the new plane by pressing the N or B key. Pressing the N key highlights the next edge to define the X axis of the new plane and pressing the B key highlights the previous edge to define the X axis. Figures 5-4 and 5-5 show the coincident planes being created on the same plane, but with different edges defining the X axis of the plane.

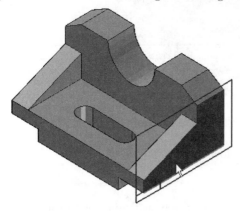
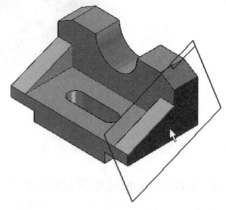

Figure 5-4 *Creating a coincident plane with the bottom edge defining the orientation of the X axis*   *Figure 5-5* *Creating a coincident plane with the inclined edge defining the orientation of the X axis*

You can also toggle the positive X axis direction of the new plane by pressing the T key. For example, if a reference plane is created, as shown in Figure 5-5, the positive X axis direction of this plane will be from the top endpoint to the bottom endpoint of the inclined edge. This is indicated by a small rectangle displayed at the origin of the plane. To reverse the direction of the positive X axis, press the T key; the direction of the positive X axis, which was pointing toward the left (Figure 5-5) will be reversed and it will now point toward the right, refer Figure 5-6. The rectangle at the origin of the plane clarifies the direction of the positive X axis.

After you have selected all the options to create a reference plane, its preview will be displayed in the drawing window. At this stage, click in the drawing area to create the plane.

Tip. *If the plane or the face that you select to define the coincident plane does not have a linear edge, the X axis direction will be defined using the base reference plane. However, you can press the N key to change the direction of the X-axis of the new plane.*

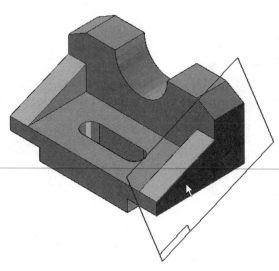

Figure 5-6 *Preview of the reference plane after reversing the positive X axis direction*

Creating a Parallel Plane

Toolbar: Features > Coincident Plane > Parallel Plane
Ribbon Bar: Plane or Sketch Step > Create-From Options > Parallel

The **Parallel Plane** tool can be used to create a reference plane parallel to a selected base reference plane, another reference plane, or a planar face. The process of creating this plane works in two steps. In the first step, you need to select the reference plane or the planar face to which the new plane will be parallel and also define the orientation of the positive X axis of the new reference plane. This step is the same as creating the coincident plane.

The second step is to define the location of the parallel plane. The location can be defined by entering the distance value or by using the keypoints such as endpoint, midpoint, center point, tangent point, and so on in the model.

To create a parallel plane, invoke the **Parallel Plane** tool; you will be prompted to click on a planar face or a reference plane. Define the orientation of the new plane and then click; the ribbon bar will be displayed with the option to define the location of the plane and you will be prompted to set the distance or the key in the value.

You can enter the offset value directly in the **Distance** edit box or use the keypoints in the model to define the location of the parallel plane. To use the keypoints in the model, choose the **Keypoints** button in the ribbon bar to display the flyout that has the keypoint options such as endpoint, midpoint, center point, tangent point, and so on. Choose the required option from this flyout and then select the corresponding keypoint in the model; the new parallel plane will be placed at the selected keypoint. Figure 5-7 shows a parallel plane being created using the center keypoint in the model and Figure 5-8 shows a parallel plane being created using the tangent keypoint in the model.

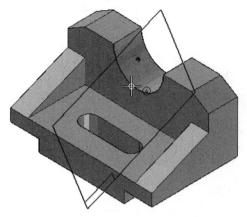
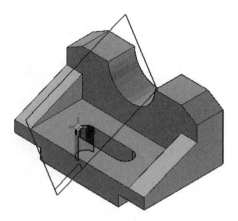

Figure 5-7 *Using the center point in the model to*
define the location of the parallel plane

Figure 5-8 *Using the tangent point in the model to*
define the location of the parallel plane

Creating an Angled Plane

Toolbar:	Features > Coincident Plane > Angled Plane
Ribbon Bar:	Plane or Sketch Step > Create-From Options > Angled

 The **Angled Plane** tool is used to create a reference plane that is at an angle to a selected plane and also passes through a specified edge, axis, or plane. On invoking this tool, you will be prompted to click on a planar face or a reference plane. The new reference plane will be defined at an angle to the selected plane. After selecting the plane, you will be prompted to click on the face, edge, or plane to form the base of the profile plane. This will define the edge or the plane through which the new plane will pass. You may need to use the **QuickPick** tool to select the required edge or plane.

Next, you need to define the direction of the positive X axis of the new plane. You will be prompted to click near the end of the axis for the reference plane orientation. As you move the cursor in the drawing window, the direction of the X axis will toggle. Click to define the positive X axis direction of the new plane.

Finally, you will be prompted to click to set the angle or the key in a value. You can enter the angle value directly in the **Angle** edit box of the ribbon bar or use the keypoints to define the angle of the plane. Note that in this case, you can use only the endpoint, midpoint, or center point to define the plane. Figure 5-9 shows various selections to create an angled plane and also the preview of the resulting plane.

Creating a Perpendicular Plane

Toolbar:	Features > Coincident Plane > Perpendicular Plane
Ribbon Bar:	Plane or Sketch Step > Create-From Options > Perpendicular

The **Perpendicular Plane** tool is used to create a reference plane that is normal to a selected plane and passes through a specified edge or axis. To create a perpendicular plane, invoke this tool; you will be prompted to click on a planar face

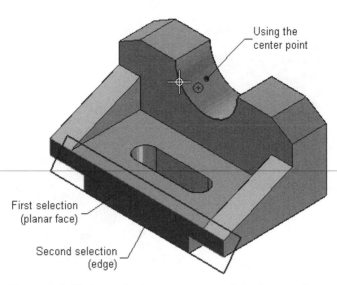

Figure 5-9 *Various selections to create angled reference plane*

or a reference plane. The new reference plane will be defined normal to the plane that you select. After selecting the plane, you will be prompted to click on a face, edge, or a plane to form the base of the profile plane. This will define the edge or the plane through which the new plane will pass. You may need to use the **QuickPick** tool to select the required edge or the plane.

Next, you need to define the direction of the positive X axis of the new plane. You will be prompted to click near the end of the axis for the reference plane orientation. As you move the cursor in the drawing window, the direction of the X axis will toggle. Click to define the positive X axis direction of the new plane.

Finally, you will be prompted to click to set the angle or the key in the value. You can move the cursor in the drawing window to define the side of the plane. Figure 5-10 shows various selections to create a perpendicular plane and the preview of the resulting plane.

Creating a Coincident Plane by Axis

Toolbar:	Features > Coincident Plane > Coincident Plane by Axis
Ribbon Bar:	Plane or Sketch Step > Create-From Options > Coincident Plane by Axis

The **Coincident Plane by Axis** tool works in the same way as the **Coincident Plane** tool. The only difference is that in this tool, after selecting the plane, you will also be prompted to select the edge to define the direction of the positive X axis and the orientation of the plane. Unlike the **Coincident Plane** tool, where you used the keyboard shortcuts to define these parameters, in this tool you need to select these parameters in the drawing window.

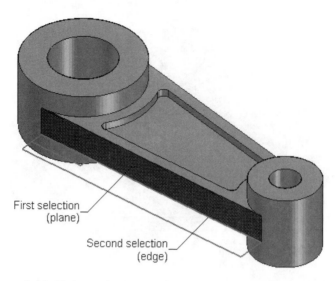

Figure 5-10 *Various selections mode to create a perpendicular reference*

Tip. *You can also define any other angle in the **Angle** edit box while creating the perpendicular plane.*

Creating a Plane Normal to an Edge or a Sketched Curve

Toolbar:	Features > Coincident Plane > Plane Normal to Curve
Ribbon Bar:	Plane or Sketch Step > Create-From Options > Plane Normal to Curve

The **Plane Normal to Curve** tool is used to create a plane that is normal to a selected sketched curve or an edge of the model. You can define a point along the curve where the normal plane needs to be placed. To create a plane normal to a curve or an edge of the model, invoke this tool; you will be prompted to click on the curve or the edge for the normal plane. Once you move the cursor close to the sketched curve or the edge of the model, the nearest endpoint of the curve or the edge will be highlighted. At this point, select the curve; the preview of the normal plane will be displayed and you will be prompted to click on a keypoint or key in the offset distance. Also, the **Position** and **Distance** edit boxes will be displayed in the ribbon bar. These edit boxes are used to specify the location of the plane along the curve. The **Position** edit box defines the position in terms of percentage. The total length of the edge or the curve is taken as 1 and you are allowed to enter any value between 0 and 1. Similarly, the **Distance** edit box defines the distance of the normal plane from the endpoint that is highlighted while selecting the edge or the curve.

You can also define the location of the normal plane by specifying a point along the edge or the curve in the drawing window. Figure 5-11 shows a plane being created normal to a sketched curve.

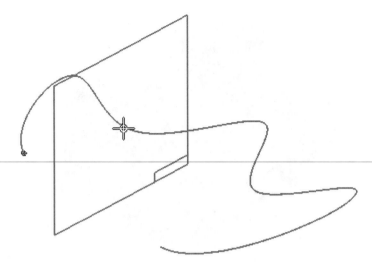

Figure 5-11 Creating a plane normal to a sketched curve

Creating a Plane Using Three Points

Toolbar:	Features > Coincident Plane > Plane by 3 Points
Ribbon Bar:	Plane or Sketch Step > Create-From Options > Plane by 3 Points

The **Plane by 3 Points** tool is used to create a reference plane by selecting three points. These three points define the origin of the plane, the direction of the positive X axis, and the direction of the positive Y axis. The length and width of the plane are determined by the distance of the second and third points from the origin.

To define a reference plane using three points, invoke the **Plane by 3 Points** tool; you will be prompted to click on a point to define the origin of the plane. Select a point in the model that you want to use as the origin of the new plane. You can use the **Keypoints** flyout from the ribbon bar to select the point. Next, you will be prompted to click on a point to define the base of the plane. Select a point that will define the direction of the positive X axis. Also, note that this point will define the length of the plane. Finally, you will be prompted to click on a point to complete the plane. Select a point that will define the direction of the positive Y axis and the width of the plane.

Figure 5-12 shows a plane being created using three points.

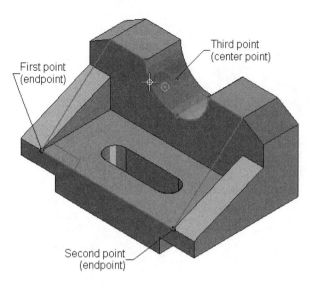

Figure 5-12 *Creating a plane using three points*

Creating a Tangent Plane

| **Toolbar:** | Features > Coincident Plane > Tangent Plane |
| **Ribbon Bar:** | Plane or Sketch Step > Create-From Options > Tangent Plane |

The **Tangent Plane** tool is used to create a reference plane that is tangent to a selected curved surface. To create a tangent plane, invoke this tool; you will be prompted to click on a curved face. Select the curved surface from the drawing area. Next, you need to click on the curved surface at the required angle or you can enter the value of angle in the **Angle** edit box in the ribbon bar; the 3D indicator with three axes and the origin will be displayed at the center of the current view. The indicator allows you to rotate the view freely in 3D space or around any of these three axes. Figure 5-13 shows the plane being created tangentially on the curved surface. The tangent plane can be created on the cylinder, sphere, cone, torus, or b-line surfaces.

Note

While selecting the option to create reference planes from the ***Create-From Options*** *drop-down list in the ribbon bar, the* ***Feature's Plane*** *and* ***Last Plane*** *options are also available. The* ***Feature's Plane*** *option uses the plane on which the profile of the selected feature was created and the* ***Last Plane*** *option uses the previous plane selected to create the feature.*

Displaying the Reference Axes

Solid Edge automatically creates reference axes when you create a revolved feature, hole feature, or any other circular or semicircular feature. However, the display of these reference axes is turned off by default. To turn on the display of the axes, choose **Tools > Show All > Reference Axes**; the reference axes of all the revolved features will be displayed in the drawing window. But the reference axes of the circular, semicircular, or hole features will not be displayed. To display the axes of these features, choose **Tools > Show All > Toggle Axes**; you will be prompted to click on the feature or the surface containing the reference axis.

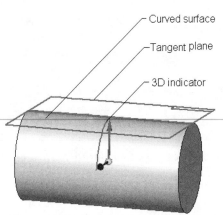

Figure 5-13 Creating a tangent plane

Select the features whose reference axes you want to display; the reference axes of the selected features will be displayed.

Similarly, you can turn off the display of the reference axes by choosing **Tools > Hide All > Reference Axes**.

Note
*Once you have toggled the display of the reference axes using the **Toggle Axes** option, you can choose **Tools > Hide All > Reference Axes** or **Tools > Show All > Reference Axes** to turn off or on the display of the reference axes.*

*You can use the options in the **Show All** or **Hide All** cascading menu to modify the display of the other entities such as reference planes.*

UNDERSTANDING COORDINATE SYSTEMS

Each part file that you start in Solid Edge has a coordinate system defined in it. This default coordinate system is called the base coordinate system. In Solid Edge, you can create additional coordinate systems according to your design requirements. These coordinate systems can be used as references to create reference planes, measure distances, copy parts, and so on.

Creating a Coordinate System

Toolbar:	Features > Coordinate System

In Solid Edge, you can create coordinate systems using two options by defining the orientations of any of the two axes using the edit boxes or by defining the orientation of any of the two axes by selecting the edges in the model. The options required to create a coordinate system can be selected from the **Coordinate System Options** dialog box , refer to Figure 5-14, which is displayed on invoking the **Coordinate System** tool.

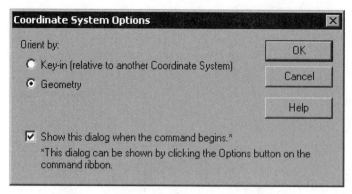

Figure 5-14   The **Coordinate System Options** *dialog box*

Select the required option from this dialog box and choose **OK**; the **Coordinate System** ribbon bar will be displayed. If you select the **Key-in (relative to another Coordinate System)** radio button, the ribbon bar will have two steps for creating the coordinate systems. But, if you select the **Geometry** Option, the ribbon bar will have three steps. If you select the **Geometry** option, this ribbon bar will have three steps for creating the coordinate system. All these steps are discussed next.

Origin Step

This step is common to both the options for creating a coordinate system and is active by default when the **Coordinate System** ribbon bar is displayed. In this step, you need to define the point where the origin of the coordinate system will be placed. To define the origin, you can select a keypoint in the model or enter the coordinates of the point in the **X**, **Y**, and **Z** edit boxes in the ribbon bar. By default, the points will be defined with respect to the default coordinate system. This is because **Model Space** is selected from the **Relative to** drop-down list in the ribbon bar. However, if there are other coordinate systems in the current drawing, they will be listed in this drop-down list and you can define the coordinates of the points with respect to them.

Orientation Step

This step is available only when you select the **Key-in (relative to another Coordinate System)** radio button. In this step, you need to define the orientation of the X, Y, and Z axes of the new coordinate system with respect to those of the default coordinate system (model space) or any other coordinate system selected from the **Relative to** drop-down list. The coordinate system will be rotated around the axis by the angle that you define in the **X**, **Y**, and **Z** edit boxes. For example, if you enter **20** as the value in the **X°** edit box, then the new coordinate system will be rotated by 20-degrees around the X axis.

Note

Solid Edge uses the right-hand thumb rule to determine the direction of the rotation of the axes. The right-hand thumb rule states that if the thumb points in the direction of the axes, then the direction of the curled fingers points toward the direction of rotation.

Enter the rotation angles in the **X°**, **Y°**, and **Z°** edit boxes and choose the **Preview** button; the preview of the resulting coordinate system will be displayed. Choose the **Finish** button to create the coordinate system.

First Axis Step

This step is available only if you select the **Geometry** radio button from the **Coordinate System Options** dialog box and will be activated automatically as soon as you define the origin of the coordinate system. In this step, you need to define the orientation of the first axis of the coordinate system. By default, the **X-Axis** button is chosen from the ribbon bar. Therefore, the axis that you define will be taken as the X axis of the coordinate system. However, if you want to define any other axis as the first axis, you can choose the button corresponding to that axis from the ribbon bar.

You can select a point, linear element, planar face, or reference plane to define the axis after selecting the corresponding option from the **Select** drop-down list. After selecting the element to define the first axis, choose the **Accept** button from the ribbon bar. You can also press ENTER or right-click to accept the selection. Next, you need to define the direction of the positive side. It is represented by an arrow along the entity that you selected to define the first axis. You can move the cursor to either side of the origin to define the direction of the positive side. Click on the desired side to accept the selection.

Second Axis Step

This step will be activated automatically as soon as you define the first axis of the coordinate system. In this step, you need to define the orientation of the second axis of the coordinate system. If you have defined the X axis of the coordinate system in the previous step, then you need to define the Y or Z axis in this step. You can choose the button corresponding to the axis that you want to define from the ribbon bar. Note that the button of the axis, which is already defined, is not enabled in the ribbon bar. The method of defining the axis is the same as that of defining the first axis.

As soon as you define the second axis, the coordinate system will be created and displayed in the model. Choose **Finish** from the ribbon bar to confirm the creation of the coordinate system. You can also choose the button of any of the steps to modify the selection made in that particular step. Figure 5-15 shows a coordinate system in the model.

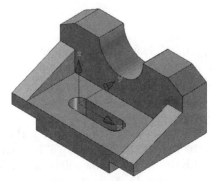

Figure 5-15 Coordinate system in the model

Note
Solid Edge uses the right-hand rule to determine the direction of the third axis. This rule states that if the thumb of the right hand points in the direction of the positive X axis and the first finger points in the direction of the positive Y axis, then the middle finger will point in the direction of the positive Z axis.

*The coordinate system is displayed as a feature in the **EdgeBar**.*

USING THE OTHER OPTIONS OF THE PROTRUSION TOOL

In the previous chapter, you have learned about some options of the **Protrusion** tool. In this chapter, you will learn the remaining options of this tool.

Side Step

 As mentioned in the previous chapter, the **Side Step** is required while creating additional features on the base feature using open sketches. In this step, you will be prompted to specify the side of the open sketch on which the material will be added. Figure 5-16 shows an open sketch and the side on which the material will be added and Figure 5-17 shows the model after creating the protrusion feature using the open sketch.

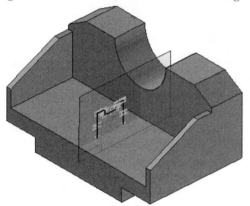
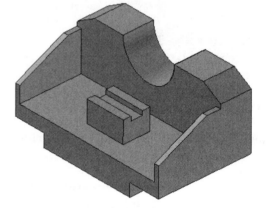

Figure 5-16 Open sketch and the side on which the material will be added

Figure 5-17 Resulting feature

Extent Step

 In the previous chapter, you learned about the symmetric and non-symmetric finite extent options to create a feature. Some other options are also available in this step. These options are discussed next.

Through All

 This option is used to create a feature by extruding the sketch through all the features available in the model. The feature will be terminated at the last face of the model. On selecting this option, an arrow will be displayed on the sketch and you will be prompted to click to select the side. You can move the cursor on either side of the sketching plane to define the direction of extrusion. Note that if you select the side in which the sketch does not intersect with any face of the model, an error message will be displayed informing you that the operation was unsuccessful. Figure 5-18 shows a sketch extruded in the downward direction using the **Through All** option.

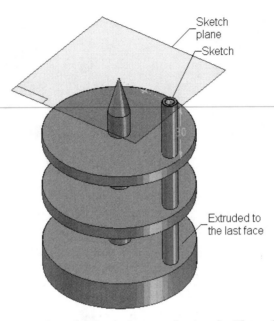

*Figure 5-18 Extruding the sketch downward using the **Through All** option*

Through Next

This option is used to create a feature by extruding the sketch up to the next surface of the model that the sketch will intersect when extruded. On selecting this option, you will be prompted to define the side of extrusion of the sketch. Figure 5-19 shows a sketch extruded in the downward direction up to the next surface.

From/To Extent

This option is used to create a protrusion feature by extruding the sketch from a selected plane to another selected plane. When you select this option, the **"From" Surface** and **"To" Surface** buttons will be displayed in the ribbon bar and you will be prompted to specify the from and to surfaces. Figure 5-20 shows a sketch extruded using this option.

You can also define the offset values from the from and to surfaces by entering the value in the **Offset** edit box. For example, if you want to use this option with an offset, choose the **From/To Extent** button from the ribbon bar; you will be prompted to select the from surface. In the **Offset** edit box, enter the offset distance for the surface from which the feature should start and then select the surface; an arrow will be displayed and you will be prompted to select the side for the offset. After selecting this side, you will be prompted to select the surface up to which the feature will be created. Again, enter the offset distance and select the surface; an arrow will be displayed and you will be prompted to select a side for the offset.

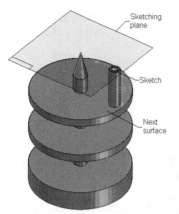

Figure 5-19 *Extruding the sketch using the* **Through Next** *option*

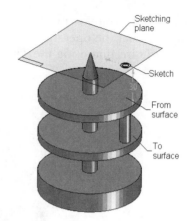

Figure 5-20 *Extruding the sketch using the* **From/To Extent** *option*

Move the cursor to define the direction of the offset. Figure 5-21 shows a protrusion feature created by defining the offset values for the from and to surfaces.

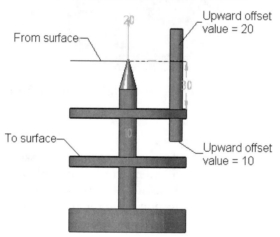

Figure 5-21 *Creating a protrusion feature by defining offset values for the from and to surfaces*

Note that you can also use the **Through All**, **Through Next**, and **From/To Extent** options to extrude the sketch on both sides of the sketching plane in combination with the **Non-symmetric Extent** option. Figure 5-22 shows a sketch extruded on both sides of the sketching plane using the **Through All** option in combination with the **Non-symmetric Extent** option.

Treatment Step

In this step, you can add a draft or a crown to the protrusion feature. These features are added to aesthetically improve the design and for an easy removal of the model from its mold. By adding a draft, you can add a linear taper to the model, as shown in Figure 5-23. This figure shows different drafts applied to both sides of a nonsymmetric

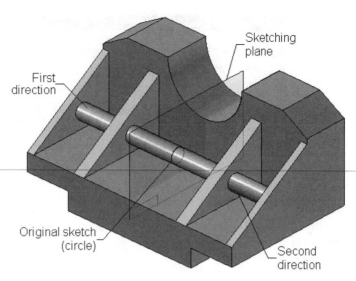

Figure 5-22 *Sketch extruded using the* **Through All** *option on both sides of the sketching plane in combination with the* **Non-symmetric Extent** *option*

feature. By adding a crown, you can add a curved taper to the model, as shown in Figure 5-24. This figure shows different crowns applied to both sides of a nonsymmetric feature. Note that in both cases, the basic sketch is a circle.

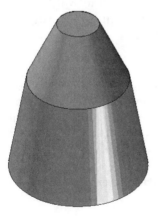

Figure 5-23 *Different drafts applied to both sides of a protrusion feature*

Figure 5-24 *Different crowns applied to both sides of a protrusion feature*

To add a treatment to the feature, choose the **Treatment Step** button from the ribbon bar. The options available in the ribbon bar in this step are discussed next.

Treatment Options

This button is chosen to display the **Treatment Options** dialog box, as shown in Figure 5-25. By default, the **Treatment** step is not invoked automatically after you complete the **Extent** step. This is because the **Never prompt for treatment parameters** radio button is selected by default in this dialog box. You can select the **Always prompt for treatment parameters** radio

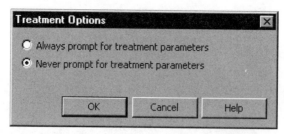

*Figure 5-25 The **Treatment Options** dialog box*

button to invoke the **Treatment** step automatically after the completion of the **Extent** step.

No Treatment

 When you invoke the **Treatment** step, this button is chosen by default. As a result, no treatment is applied to the model.

Draft

The **Draft** button is chosen to add a draft to the protrusion feature. When you choose this button, the **Angle** edit box and the **Flip 1** button will be displayed in the ribbon bar. You can enter the draft angle in the **Angle** edit box. The default direction in which the draft will be created is displayed in the preview of the model. If you want to reverse the direction of the draft, choose the **Flip 1** button. If the draft was initially inward, the preview will now show the draft outward, indicating that the draft will be applied in the reverse direction now. In case of symmetric extend extrude features, the **Angle 1**, **Angle 2**, **Flip 1**, and **Flip 2** edit boxes are displayed in the ribbon bar.

Crown

The **Crown** button is chosen to add a crown to the protrusion feature. When you choose this button, the **Crown Parameters** dialog box will be displayed. If you extrude the sketch symmetrically or nonsymmetrically on both sides of the sketching plane, the longer version of this dialog box will be displayed with the **Direction 1** and **Direction 2** areas, as shown in Figure 5-26. However, if you extrude the sketch only in one direction, the shorter version of this dialog box will be displayed with only the **Direction 1** area. The options available in both areas of the **Crown Parameters** dialog box are the same and are discussed next.

Crown Type

The **Crown Type** drop-down list is used to select the technique of applying a crown to the feature. The options available in this drop-down list are discussed next.

No Crown

This option is used when you do not want to apply the crown in any direction.

Radius

This option is used to apply the crown by defining its radius. The radius value is specified in the **Radius** edit box, which is available below the **Crown Type** drop-down list.

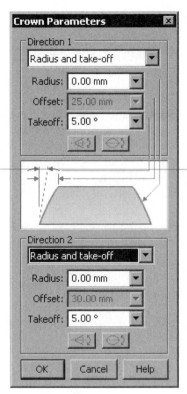

Figure 5-26 *The **Crown Parameters** dialog box*

Radius and take-off
This option is used to apply the crown by defining its radius and the take off angle. These values are specified in the edit boxes that are available below the **Crown Type** drop-down list.

Offset
This option is used to apply the crown by defining the offset value between the sections at the start and end of the crown. The offset value is specified in the **Offset** edit box available below the **Crown Type** drop-down list.

Offset and take-off
This option is used to apply the crown by defining the take off angle and offset value between the sections at the start and end of the crown. These values are specified in the edit boxes available below the **Crown Type** drop-down list.

Radius
The **Radius** edit box is used to specify the radius value of the crown and will be available only when you select the **Radius** or the **Radius and take-off** crown option.

Offset

The **Offset** edit box is used to specify the offset value of the crown and will be available only when you select the **Offset** or the **Offset and take-off** crown option.

Takeoff

The **Takeoff** edit box is used to specify the angle value of the crown and will be available only when you select the **Radius and take-off** or the **Offset and take-off** crown type.

Flip Side

This button is used to reverse the side on which the crown is applied. If the crown is applied inside the feature, choosing this button will apply the crown outside the feature.

Flip Curvature

The **Flip Curvature** button is used to reverse the curvature of the crown.

Preview Window

The **Preview** window displays the preview of various crown parameters that you define using the **Crown Parameters** dialog box.

Figures 5-27 and 5-29 show different previews of the crown features and Figures 5-28 and 5-30 show the resulting crown features created using the offset and take-off crown types, respectively.

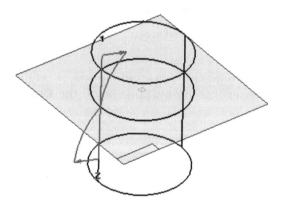

Figure 5-27 Preview of the crown displaying the side of the crown

Figure 5-28 Feature with the resulting crown

Crown Parameters

The **Crown Parameters** button is chosen to display the **Crown Parameters** dialog box again for modifying the crown parameters.

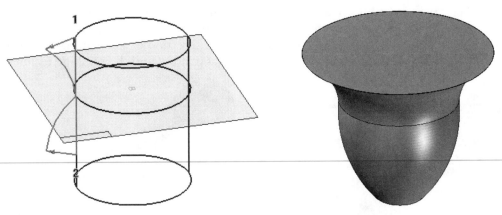

Figure 5-29 *Preview of the crown displaying the side of the crown*

Figure 5-30 *Feature with the resulting crown*

CREATING CUTOUT FEATURES

Cutouts are created by removing the material, defined by a profile, from one or more existing features. In Solid Edge, you can create various types of cutouts such as extruded cutouts, revolved cutouts, swept cutouts, and so on. In this chapter, you will learn about the extruded or revolved cutouts. The remaining types of cutouts will be discussed in the later chapters.

Creating Extruded Cutouts

Toolbar: Features > Cutout

Extruded cutouts are created by extruding a profile to remove the material from one or more features. Figure 5-31 shows the base feature and the sketch that will be used to create a cutout and Figure 5-32 shows the rotated view of the model after creating the cutout.

Figure 5-31 *Base feature and the sketch for the cutout*

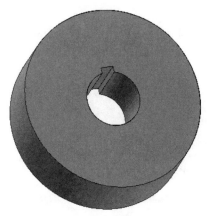

Figure 5-32 *Rotated view of the model after creating the cutout*

In Solid Edge, the cutouts are created using the **Cutout** tool. This tool works in the same manner as the **Protrusion** tool. Note that while creating the cutouts, you can create close profiles and use the **Side Step** extensively to define the direction of the material removal. Figures 5-33 through 5-36 show the side of the material removal and the resulting features.

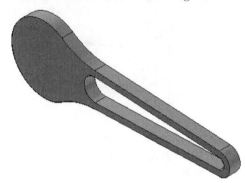

Figure 5-33 Sketch for the cutout and the direction for the cutout pointing inside the sketch

Figure 5-34 Resulting cutout created by removing the material inside the sketch

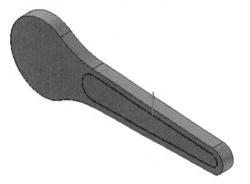

Figure 5-35 Sketch for the cutout and the direction for the cutout pointing outside the sketch

Figure 5-36 Resulting cutout created by removing the material outside the sketch

You can also use open profiles to create the cutouts. However, you need to carefully define the side of the material removal for the cutout, see Figures 5-37 through 5-40.

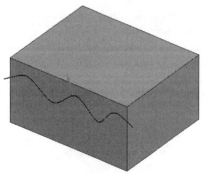

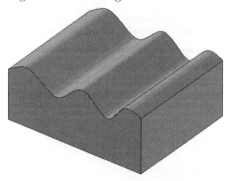

Figure 5-37 Open profile and the side of material removal

Figure 5-38 Resulting cutout created by removing the material above the open profile

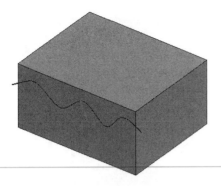

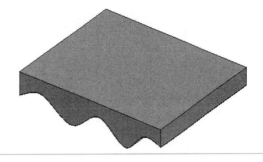

Figure 5-39 *Open profile and the side of the material removal*

Figure 5-40 *Resulting cutout created by removing the material below the open profile*

Creating Revolved Cutouts

Toolbar:	Features > Revolved Cutout

The **Revolved Cutout** tool is used to create a revolved cutout by removing the material defined by the sketch. This tool will be active only when a feature exits in the modeling window. This tool works in the same manner as the **Revolved Protrusion** tool. The only difference is that the **Revolved Cutout** tool removes the material only from an existing feature. Similar to the extruded cutouts, you can also use the **Side** step extensively in the revolved cutouts to specify the side of material removal. Figures 5-41 through 5-44 show the side of material removal and the resulting models after creating a symmetric semicircular revolved cutout.

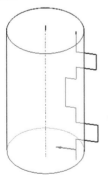

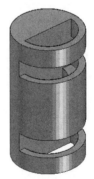

Figure 5-41 *Open profile and the side of the material removal*

Figure 5-42 *Resulting revolved cutout created by removing the material on the left of the profile*

INCLUDING THE EDGES OF THE EXISTING FEATURES IN THE SKETCH

Toolbar:	Draw > Include

Sometimes, while drawing the profiles of some features, you may need to use the edges of the existing features as the sketched entities in the current profile. In Solid Edge, you can do this using the **Include** tool in the sketching environment. You can

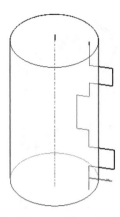
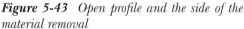

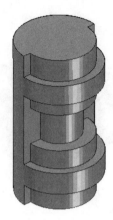

Figure 5-43 *Open profile and the side of the material removal*

Figure 5-44 *Resulting revolved cutout created by removing the material on the right of the profile*

copy the edges of the existing features by projecting them exactly as they are on the current sketching plane or by copying them with some offset. Note that because you are projecting the entities that are already used in the model, you do not need to add dimensions to the projected entities. They will automatically take the dimensions from the original entities.

To project the geometries, invoke the sketching environment in the model with some existing features. Choose the **Include** button from the **Draw** toolbar; the **Include Options** dialog box will be displayed, as shown in Figure 5-45. The options available in this dialog box are discussed next.

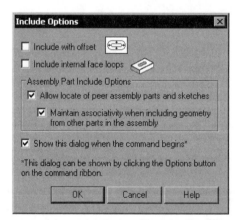

Figure 5-45 *The **Include Options** dialog box*

Include with offset

This check box is used to project the geometries with some offset value. If this check box is selected, the offset options will be displayed in the ribbon bar after you select the edges.

Include internal face loops

If this check box is selected, the geometries of all the internal loops on a face will also be projected when you select a face to project the edges.

Assembly Part Include Options Area

The options available in this area are used in the assembly modeling environment. These options are discussed next.

Allow locate of peer assembly parts and sketches

If this check box is selected, you will be allowed to select the geometries from the other parts in the assembly.

Maintain associativity when including geometry from other parts in the assembly

If this check box is selected, the geometries that you project from the other parts in the assembly will be associative.

After setting the options in this dialog box, choose the **OK** button to display the **Include** ribbon bar. Depending on whether you have selected the option to include with an offset, this tool works in one or two steps, which are discussed next.

Select Step

This step allows you to select the geometries that you want to include in the profile. You can set the option for selecting the geometries using the **Select** drop-down list. Depending on the selected from this list, you may need to choose the **Accept** button after selecting the entities. If you have not selected the option to include the geometries with an offset, then exit this tool after selecting the entities. As mentioned earlier, you do not need to dimension the projected entities. The dimensions are adopted from the original geometries that are projected.

Offset Step

This step will be available only if you select the option that allows you to include the geometries with an offset. In this case, select the geometries in the **Select** step and then choose the **Accept** button from the ribbon bar; the **Offset** step will be invoked and the **Distance** edit box will be displayed in the ribbon bar. Enter the offset distance in this edit box and then move the cursor in the drawing window to specify the side for the offset. After selecting the side, click to project and offset the selected geometry.

Figure 5-46 shows a model after projecting some of the geometries from the existing features on a reference plane created at an offset from the top face of the model.

ADVANCED DRAWING DISPLAY TOOLS

In the earlier chapters, you learned about some of the basic drawing display tools. In this chapter, you will learn about the advanced drawing display tools, which are discussed next.

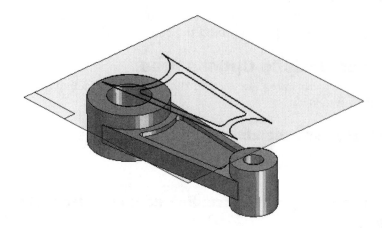

Figure 5-46 *Geometries projected on a reference plane*

Creating User-defined Named Views

As mentioned earlier, you can use the **Named Views** drop-down list in the **Main** toolbar to invoke the standard named views. In Solid Edge, you can also create user-defined standard views that are automatically added to the **Named Views** drop-down list. As a result, you can invoke these views whenever required.

To create the user-defined named views, set the current view to the view that you want to save using the **Rotate** tool or any other drawing display tool. After setting the view, choose **View > Named Views** from the menu bar; the **Named Views** dialog box will be displayed with six standard named views. Enter the name of the new user-defined view in the **Name** column of the seventh row of the **Named Views** dialog box. You can also enter a brief description about the view in the **Description** column. After entering the information, exit the dialog box. The view that you defined will be displayed in the **Named Views** drop-down list and can be selected from this list.

USING COMMON VIEWS

Toolbar:	Main > Rotate > Common Views

Solid Edge provides you with the **Common Views** tool, which is a very user-friendly tool to set the current view to some standard common views. You can also invoke this tool by right-clicking in the drawing window when the **Select** tool is active. From the shortcut menu, choose **Common Views**; the **Common Views** dialog box will be displayed with a cube in it. You can use the vertices or the faces of this cube to rotate the view of the model. As you move the cursor over any vertex or face of the cube in the **Common Views** dialog box, a message will be displayed in this dialog box that will inform you about the direction of rotation of the view. While working with the **Common Views** tool, you can press the HOME key at any point of time to invoke the standard isometric view.

TUTORIALS

Tutorial 1

In this tutorial, you will create the model shown in Figure 5-47. The dimensions of the model are given in Figure 5-48. After creating the model, save it with the name
Solid Edge\c05\c05tut1.par. **(Expected time: 45 min)**

Figure 5-47 *Model for Tutorial 1*

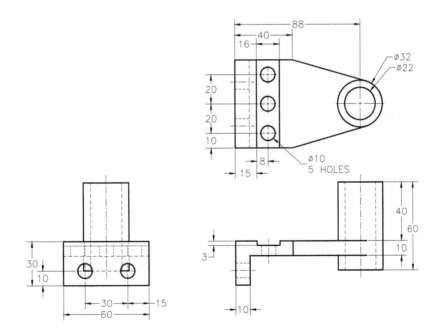

Figure 5-48 *Dimensions of the model*

Whenever you start creating a model, you first need to determine the number of features in it and then the sequence in which they will be created. The model for Tutorial 1 is a combination of three protrusion features and three cutouts to define the holes. The base feature will be created on the right plane. The second feature will be created on the top face of the base feature. The third feature will be created by defining a reference plane at an offset of 10 units from the bottom face of the second feature. The cutouts will be created on the planar face of the protrusion features.

The following steps are required to complete this tutorial:

a. Create the base feature on the right plane, refer to Figure 5-50.
b. Select the top planar face of the base feature as the sketching plane and then create the second feature, refer to Figure 5-53.
c. Define a reference plane at an offset of 10 units from the bottom face of the second feature and use it to create the third feature, refer to Figure 5-54.
d. Create two holes on the left face of the base feature using the **Cutout** tool, as shown in Figure 5-56.
e. Similarly, create the remaining cutouts to complete the model, refer to Figure 5-57.

Creating the Base Feature

As mentioned earlier, the base feature is a protrusion feature and so the profile of this feature will be created on the right plane.

1. Start a new part file and then select the right plane as the sketching plane for the protrusion feature.

2. Draw the profile for the base feature using various sketching tools.

3. Add the required relationships and dimensions to the sketch, as shown in Figure 5-49.

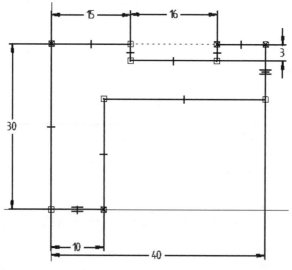

Figure 5-49 *Dimensioned profile for the base feature*

4. Exit the sketching environment and choose the **Protrusion** button from the **Features** toolbar.

   Select the sketch from the drawing area; the **Extent** step is automatically invoked and you are prompted to click for specifying the distance or key in the value.

5. Choose the **Symmetric Extent** button and then enter **60** as the value in the **Distance** edit box in the ribbon bar; the preview of the base feature is displayed.

6. Choose **Finish** from the ribbon bar. The base feature of the model is shown in Figure 5-50.

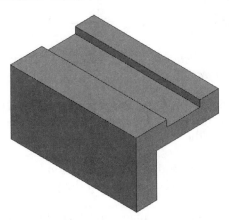

Figure 5-50 Base feature of the model

Creating the Second Feature

As mentioned earlier, the second feature is a protrusion feature and its profile is created on the top face of the base feature. Note that you did not exit the **Protrusion** command, therefore this command is still active. Select the **Coincident Plane** option from the **Create-From Options** drop-down list, if it is not already selected. Now you are prompted to click on the planar face or the reference plane.

1. Move the cursor over the top face of the base feature and then press the N key to orient the sketching plane, as shown in Figure 5-51.

2. Draw the profile for the second feature using various sketching tools and then add the required dimensions and relationships to the profile, as shown in Figure 5-52. Note that you do not need to draw the vertical line on the left to close the sketch. While creating the feature, you can define the side of material addition to complete the feature.

3. Exit the sketching environment. Because the profile for the second feature is open from the left, the **Side Step** is automatically invoked and you need to click to accept the displayed side or select the other side in the view.

   You need to add the material inside the profile. Therefore, you need to ensure that the arrow points inside the sketch to create this feature.

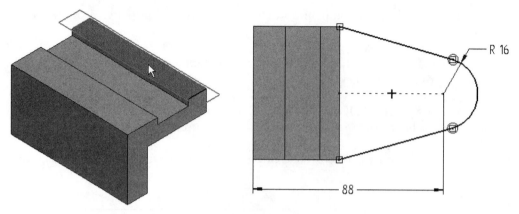

Figure 5-51 *Specifying the orientation of the sketching plane for the second feature*

Figure 5-52 *Open profile for the second feature*

4. Move the cursor inside the profile to ensure that the arrow points inside. Click to define the direction and exit this step; the **Extent Step** is automatically invoked and you are prompted to click to set the distance or key in the value.

5. Choose the **From/To Extent** button from the ribbon bar; you are prompted to select the "from" surface or right-click to extrude from the profile plane.

    You can right-click and select the plane on which the profile is created for starting the extrusion.

6. Right-click to select the profile plane as the plane from which the extrusion will start; you are prompted to select the "to" surface.

7. Invoke the **QuickPick** tool and then select the immediate bottom face of the base feature that is at a distance of 10 units from the top face.

    The preview of the model is displayed in the drawing window.

8. Choose **Finish** from the ribbon bar to complete the feature. The model, after creating the second feature, is shown in Figure 5-53.

Creating the Third Feature

The third feature is also a protrusion feature and its profile is created on a reference plane created at an offset of 10 units from the bottom face of the second feature.

1. Select the **Parallel Plane** option from the **Create-From Options** drop-down list in the ribbon bar and then invoke the **QuickPick** tool to select the bottom face of the second feature.

2. Enter the value **10** in the **Distance** edit box. Move the cursor to the lower half portion of the drawing window and click to define the plane; the sketching environment is invoked.

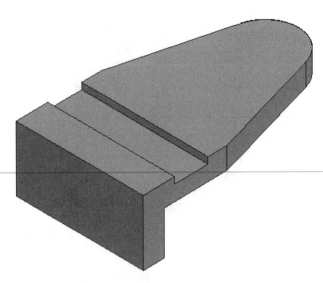

Figure 5-53 *Model after creating the second feature*

The profile for the third feature is a circle with the diameter equal to the diameter of the arc in the second feature.

3. Draw a circle concentric with the arc in the second feature with diameter 32. You can locate the center of the arc by moving the cursor once over it.

4. Exit the sketching environment and choose the **Finite Extent** button if it is not already chosen from the ribbon bar.

5. Enter the value **60** in the **Distance** edit box. Move the cursor in the upper half portion of the drawing window and click to define the feature.

6. Choose **Finish** and then choose **Cancel** to create the feature and exit the **Protrusion** tool. The model, after creating the third protrusion feature, is shown in Figure 5-54.

Creating a Cutout on the Left Face of the Base Feature

The fourth feature is a cutout that is required to define a hole on the left face of the base feature. The profile of this cutout is created on the left face of the base feature.

1. Choose the **Cutout** button from the **Features** toolbar, the **Cutout** ribbon bar is displayed with the **Plane or Sketch Step** active. The **Coincident Plane** option is selected from the **Create-From Options** drop-down list in the ribbon bar.

2. Select the left face of the base feature to define a sketching plane on this face; the sketching environment is invoked.

3. Draw the profile for the cutout. The profile consists of two circles each with a diameter of 12, as shown in Figure 5-55.

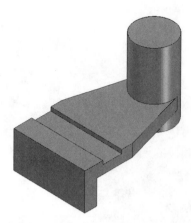

Figure 5-54 *Model after creating the third feature*

4. Exit the sketching environment and choose the **Through Next** button from the ribbon bar.

5. Move the cursor to the right of the model and left-click to specify the direction of the cutout feature. The model, after creating the cutout feature, is shown in Figure 5-56.

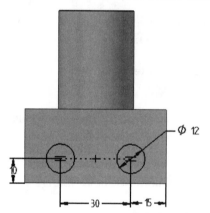

Figure 5-55 *Profile for the cutout*

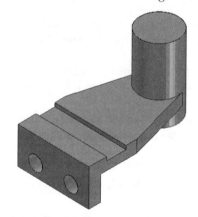

Figure 5-56 *Model after creating the cutout feature*

Creating the Remaining Features

1. Similarly, create the remaining two cutouts. The model, after creating all features, is shown in Figure 5-57.

Saving the Model

1. Save the model with the name given below and then close the file.

    Solid Edge\c05\c05tut1.par

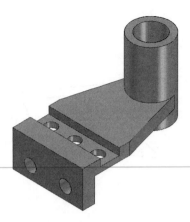

Figure 5-57 *Final model for Tutorial 1*

Tutorial 2

In this tutorial, you will create the model shown in Figure 5-58. The dimensions of the model are given in Figure 5-59. After creating the model, save it with the name and location given */Solid Edge\c05\c05tut2.par*. **(Expected time: 45 min)**

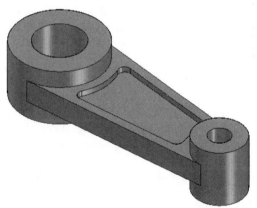

Figure 5-58 *Model for Tutorial 2*

The model for Tutorial 2 is a combination of three protrusion features and one cutout. The base feature will be created on the top plane and extruded symmetrically. The second feature will also be created on the top plane and extruded symmetrically. Next, you will create a sketch on the top plane that will be used to create a cutout as well as a protrusion feature in the second feature.

The following steps are required to complete this tutorial:

a. Create the base feature on the top plane, refer to Figure 5-61.
b. Create the second feature also on the top plane, refer to Figure 5-63.
c. Invoke the **Sketch** tool and draw a sketch on the top plane, refer to Figure 5-64.

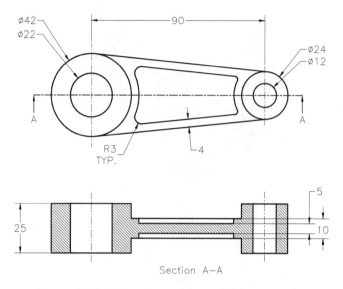

Figure 5-59 *Dimensions of the model for Tutorial 2*

d. Create a cutout in the second feature using the sketch, refer to Figure 5-65.

e. Create a protrusion feature using the same sketch to complete the model, refer to Figure 5-66.

Creating the Base Feature

1. Start a new part file and then select the top plane as the sketching plane for the protrusion feature.

2. Draw the profile for the base feature using various sketching tools.

3. Add the required relationships and dimensions to the sketch, as shown in Figure 5-60.

4. Exit the sketching environment and then extrude the sketch symmetrically through a distance of 10 units. The base feature of the model is shown in Figure 5-61.

Creating the Second Feature

The second feature is also created on the top plane. To draw the profile of this feature, you need to project the outer circles of the base feature and then draw tangent lines on those circles.

1. Select the top plane as the sketching plane and draw the profile for the second feature using various sketching tools.

2. Add the required relationships and dimensions to the sketch, as shown in Figure 5-62.

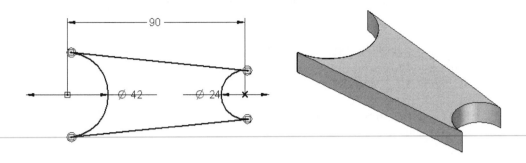

Figure 5-60 Profile for the base feature   *Figure 5-61* Base feature of the model

3. Exit the sketching environment and then extrude the sketch symmetrically through a distance of 25 units. The model, after creating this feature, is shown in Figure 5-63.

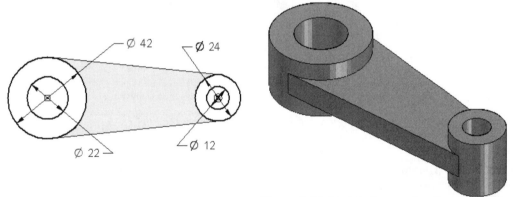

Figure 5-62 Profile for the second feature   *Figure 5-63* Model after creating the second feature

Creating the Sketch for the Third and Fourth Features

Now, you need to create a sketch that will be used as a profile for the third and fourth features. This sketch is also created on the top plane. To create this sketch, you need to project the edges of the second feature at an offset of 4 units.

1. Choose the **Sketch** button from the **Features** toolbar and select the top plane as the sketching plane.

2. Choose the **Include** button from the **Draw** toolbar; the **Include Options** dialog box is displayed.

3. Select the **Include with offset** check box and make sure that the **Include internal face loops** check box is cleared.

4. Exit the dialog box and then select **Loop** from the **Select** drop-down list.

5. Move the cursor close to the upper inclined edge of the second feature and click when the complete loop, defined to create the second feature, is highlighted; the complete loop is projected.

6. Right-click to proceed to the **Offset** step. Enter the value **4** in the **Distance** edit box and move the cursor to the center of the model. Click when the offset arrow points inside the model; the outer loop is projected with an offset of 4 units.

7. Add a fillet of radius 3 to the vertices of the projected loop. The sketch after adding the fillet is shown in Figure 5-64.

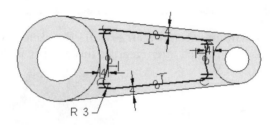

Figure 5-64 *Sketch after adding the fillet*

8. Exit the sketching environment and then exit the **Sketch** tool. This sketch is saved as **Sketch 1** in the **EdgeBar**.

Creating the Cutout

Next, you need to create a cutout using the sketch created in the previous step.

1. Choose the **Cutout** button from the **Features** toolbar.

2. Select the **Select from Sketch** option from the **Create-From Options** drop-down list in the ribbon bar.

3. Select the sketch and then right-click to proceed to the **Extent** step.

4. Choose the **Symmetric Extent** button from the ribbon bar and then enter the value **10** in the **Distance** edit box.

5. Exit the **Cutout** tool. The model, after creating the cutout, is shown in Figure 5-65. This figure also shows the sketch because its display is not turned off.

Creating the Protrusion Feature

1. Choose the **Protrusion** button from the **Features** toolbar and then select the **Select from Sketch** option from the **Create-From Options** drop-down list.

2. Select the sketch and then right-click to proceed to the **Extent** step.

3. Choose the **Symmetric Extent** button from the ribbon bar and then enter the value **5** in the **Distance** edit box.

4. Choose **Finish** and then choose **Cancel** from the ribbon bar to exit the **Protrusion** tool.

    Before you save and close the file, it is recommended that you turn off the display of the sketches in the model.

5. Right-click on **Sketch 1** in the **EdgeBar** and choose **Hide** from the shortcut menu; the display of the sketch is turned off. The final model for Tutorial 2 is shown in Figure 5-66.

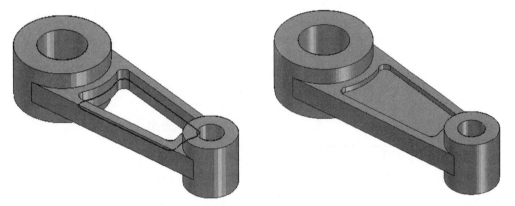

Figure 5-65 *Model after creating the cutout*   *Figure 5-66* *Final model for Tutorial 2*

Saving the Model

1. Save the model with the name given below and then close the file.

    \Solid Edge\c05\c05tut2.par

Tutorial 3

In this tutorial, you will create the model shown in Figure 5-67. Its dimensions are given in Figure 5-68. After creating the model, save it with the name and locaton given below:
\Solid Edge\c05\c05tut3.par.   **(Expected time: 45 min)**

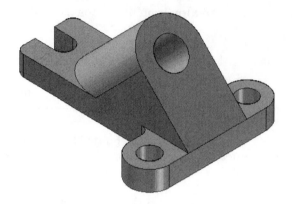

Figure 5-67 *Model for Tutorial 3*

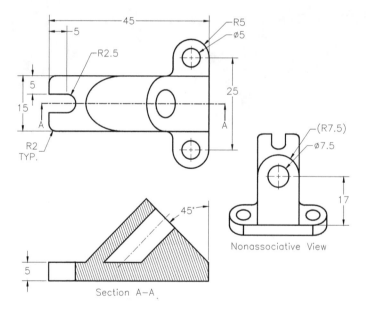

Figure 5-68 *Dimensions of the model for Tutorial 3*

Whenever you start creating a model, you first need to determine the number of features in it and then the sequence in which they will be created. The model for Tutorial 3 is a combination of two protrusion features. The base feature will be created on the top plane. The second feature will be created at an angled plane created at 45-degrees.

The following steps are required to complete this tutorial:

a. Create the base feature with two holes on the top plane, refer to Figure 5-70.
b. Define a new reference plane at an angle of 45-degrees to the right edge of the base feature and use it to draw the profile for the second feature, refer to Figure 5-73.
c. Extrude the profile up to the next face to complete the feature, refer to Figure 5-74.

Creating the Base Feature

As mentioned earlier, the base feature is a protrusion feature whose profile will be created on the top plane.

1. Start Solid Edge in the **Part** environment and then choose the **Protrusion** button. Next, select the top plane as the sketching plane for the protrusion feature.

2. Draw the profile for the base feature using various sketching tools.

3. Add the required relationships and dimensions to the sketch, as shown in Figure 5-69.

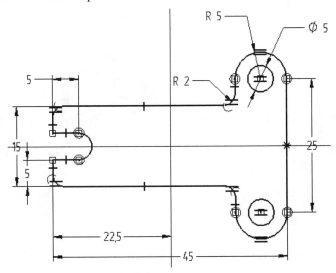

Figure 5-69 Dimensioned profile for the base feature

4. Exit the sketching environment; the **Extent** step is automatically invoked and you are prompted to click for specifying the distance or key in the value.

5. Enter the value **5** in the **Distance** edit box in the ribbon bar and click anywhere in the drawing window above the top plane to specify the side of the feature creation; the preview of the base feature is displayed.

6. Choose **Finish** and then choose **Cancel** from the ribbon bar. The base feature of the model is shown in Figure 5-70.

Creating the Second Feature

The second feature needs to be created using an angled reference plane, which in turn will be created using the right edge of the top face of the base feature. It is recommended that you create this plane from within the **Protrusion** tool, because this angled reference plane will be used to create only one feature,

1. Invoke the **Protrusion** tool to display the **Protrusion** ribbon bar.

2. Select the **Angled Plane** option from the **Create-From Options** drop-down list; you are prompted to click on a planar face or a reference plane.

   To create an angled plane, you first need to select a reference plane or a planar face of the model from which the new plane will be at an angle. In this case, you need to select the top face of the base feature to define the angled plane.

3. Select the top face of the base feature, as shown in Figure 5-71; the face is highlighted and you are prompted to click on the face, edge, or plane to be the base of the profile plane. You need to select an edge through which the angled plane will pass. In this case, the right edge of the top face of the base feature will be selected as the edge through which the plane will pass.

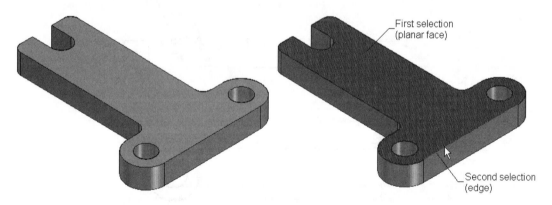

Figure 5-70 *Base feature of the model*   **Figure 5-71** *Making selections to create an angled plane*

4. Select the edge through which the angled plane will pass, refer to Figure 5-72.

   Next, you are prompted to click near the end of the axis for the reference plane orientation.

5. Click in the lower half portion of the drawing window to make sure that the orientation of the positive X axis is from the left to the right.

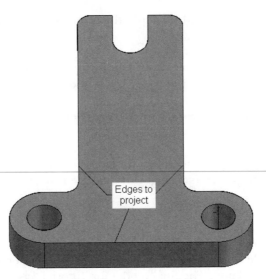

Figure 5-72 Selecting the entities to project

As soon as you specify the orientation of the plane, a preview of the resulting plane is displayed and the **Angle** and **Step** edit boxes are displayed in the ribbon bar. When you move the cursor in the drawing window, the preview of the resulting plane is modified accordingly.

6. Enter the value **45** in the **Angle** edit box and then click close to the right face of the base feature to define the plane.

    The plane is defined and is selected as the sketching plane. Also, the sketching environment is invoked where you can draw the profile for the second feature.

    To create the profile for the second feature, you can project the entities from the base feature and then modify them to complete the profile.

7. Choose the **Include** button from the **Draw** toolbar; the **Include Options** dialog box is displayed.

8. Make sure the **Include with offset** and **Include internal face loops** check boxes are cleared in this dialog box. Choose **OK** from this dialog box and then select the edges to project, as shown in Figure 5-73.

9. Trim and extend the projected entities using the sketching tools and then draw a tangent arc to complete the profile of the second feature, refer to Figure 5-73.

    Note that if you use the projected entities in the form in which they are projected, you do not need to dimension them. However, if you modify them by trimming and extending, you need to add dimensions to them.

10. Add a circle to the profile and then add the required dimensions to the profile and the circle, as shown in Figure 5-73.

11. Exit the sketching environment; the **Extent Step** is automatically invoked and you are prompted to click to set the distance or key in the value.

12. Choose the **Through Next** button from the ribbon bar; you are prompted to click and select the side.

13. Click below the angled plane to define the side of the feature creation; the preview of the second feature is displayed merging with the base feature.

14. Choose **Finish** and then choose **Cancel** from the ribbon bar.

15. Press and hold the SHIFT key and then select the three base reference planes from the **EdgeBar**. Right-click and choose **Hide** from the shortcut menu to turn off the display of the base reference planes. The final model for Tutorial 3 is shown in Figure 5-74.

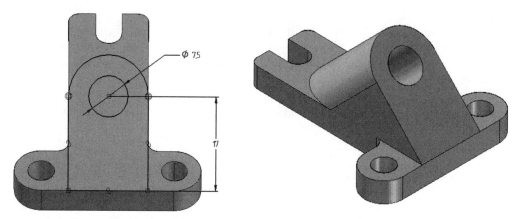

Figure 5-73 Profile for the second feature   *Figure 5-74 Final model for Tutorial 3*

Saving the Model

1. Save the model with the name given below and then close the file.

    \Solid Edge\c05\c05tut3.par

    Note
    *The holes shown in the model for Tutorial 3 can also be drawn directly using the **Hole** tool. The use of this tool will be discussed in the later chapters.*

Self-Evaluation Test

Answer the following questions and then compare them to those given at the end of this chapter:

1. The **Treatment** step is automatically invoked while creating the protrusion features. (T/F)

2. The reference planes that are available by default are called the base reference planes. (T/F)

3. The **Parallel Plane** tool can be used to create a reference plane parallel to a selected base reference plane, an other reference plane, or planar face of the model. (T/F)

4. Cutouts are created by removing the material, defined by a profile, from one or more existing features. (T/F)

5. While creating the cutouts, you can create open profiles and use the _____ extensively to define the direction of the material removal.

6. The _____ tool is used to create a plane normal to a selected sketched curve or an edge of the model.

7. In Solid Edge, you can create coordinate systems using _____ options.

8. The _____ tool is used to create a revolved cutout by removing the material defined by the sketch.

9. If the plane that you select to define the coincident plane does not have a linear edge, the _____ direction is defined using the base reference plane.

10. While creating the protrusion feature, you can use the _____ to add a draft or a crown to the protrusion feature.

Review Questions

Answer the following questions:

1. In Solid Edge, which of the following tools can be used to project the edges of the existing features on the current sketching plane?

    (a) **Project**   (b) **Include**
    (c) **Insert**   (d) None

2. In Solid Edge, which of the following dialog boxes can be used to create user-defined standard views that are automatically added to the **Named Views** drop-down list?

    (a) **Views**   (b) **Named Views**
    (c) **Drawing Views**   (d) None

3. Which one of the following is not a type of reference plane?

    (a) Base reference planes   (b) Global reference planes
    (c) Local reference planes   (d) Sample reference planes

4. Which reference planes are created separately as features using the tools available in the **Features** toolbar to create reference planes?

    (a) Base reference planes   (b) Global reference planes
    (c) Local reference planes   (d) Sample reference planes

5. Which rule is used by Solid Edge to determine the direction of rotation of the axes?

    (a) Right-hand thumb   (b) Right-hand
    (c) Left-hand thumb   (d) Left-hand

6. Which two of the following options are also available while selecting the option to create reference planes from the **Create-From Options** drop-down list in the ribbon bar?

    (a) Feature's Plane   (b) Base Plane
    (c) Last Plane   (d) Blank Plane

7. The **Coincident Plane** tool is used to create a reference plane that is coincident to a base reference plane, another reference plane, or a planar face of the model. (T/F)

8. You cannot use open profiles to create cutouts. (T/F)

9. The **Plane by 3 Points** tool is used to create reference planes by selecting three points. (T/F)

10. Solid Edge automatically creates reference axes when you create a revolved feature, hole feature, or any other circular or semicircular feature. (T/F)

Exercises

Exercise 1

Create the model shown in Figure 5-75. The dimensions of the model are given in the views shown in Figure 5-76. After creating the model, save it with the name given below:

\Solid Edge\c05\c05exr1.par   **(Expected time: 30 min)**

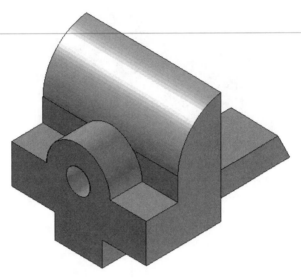

Figure 5-75 Model for Exercise 1

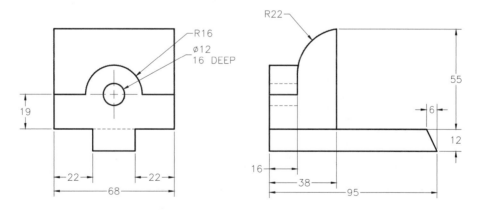

Figure 5-76 Dimensions of the model for Exercise 1

Exercise 2

Create the model shown in Figure 5-77. Its dimensions are given in the views shown in Figure 5-78. After creating the model, save it with the name given below:

　　\Solid Edge\c05\c05exr2.par　　　　　　　　　　　　　**(Expected time: 30 min)**

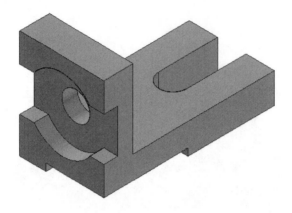

Figure 5-77 *Model for Exercise 2*

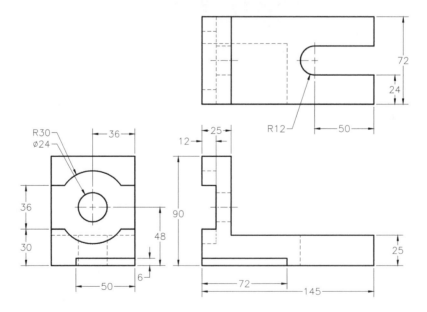

Figure 5-78 *Dimensions of the model for Exercise 2*

Answers to Self-Evaluation Test
1. F, 2. T, 3. T, 4. T, 5. Side Step, 6. Plane Normal To Curve, 7. two, **8. Revolved Cutout, 9.** X axis, **10. Treatment Step**

Chapter 6

Advanced Modeling Tools-I

ADVANCED MODELING TOOLS

Most of the designs on which you work consist of advanced features such as counterbore/ countersink holes, ribs, webs, shells, and so on. Solid Edge provides you with a number of advanced modeling tools that assist you in creating these advanced features. These features are parametric by nature and can be modified or edited at any point of time. The advanced modeling tools appreciably reduce the time taken in creating the features in the models, thereby reducing the designing time.

In this chapter, you will learn about some advanced modeling tools. The remaining advanced modeling tools will be discussed in later chapters.

CREATING HOLES

Toolbar:	Features > Hole
Menu bar:	Features > Holes > Hole

Holes are circular cut features that are generally provided for the purpose of assembling the model. In an assembly, components such as bolts and shafts are inserted into the hole. In Solid Edge, holes are created by first specifying the type of hole that you require and then specifying the location of the hole feature in the model using the sketching environment.

To create a hole, invoke the **Hole** tool; the **Hole** ribbon bar will be displayed. As mentioned earlier, you first need to specify the type of hole you want to create and its related settings.

To specify the hole options, choose the **Hole Options** button from the ribbon bar; the **Hole Options** dialog box will be displayed, as shown in Figure 6-1. The preview of the hole that will be created using the options you select in this dialog box is displayed in the preview window available in this dialog box. The options available in this dialog box are discussed next.

Saved settings

This drop-down list is used to select the saved hole settings. By default, this drop-down list does not have any option. But if you want to use some hole settings frequently, you can select and save them with a particular name. This name will then be displayed in this drop-down list. Whenever you select this name, the settings configured under it will automatically be set in the **Hole Options** dialog box.

Save

Choose this button to save the hole settings with the some name. Enter the name in the **Saved Settings** edit box and then choose this button. The current hole settings defined in the **Hole Options** dialog box will be saved with the specified name.

Note
*The saved settings are also available in the drop-down list that will be displayed when you choose the down arrow on the right of the **Hole Options** button in the **Hole** ribbon bar.*

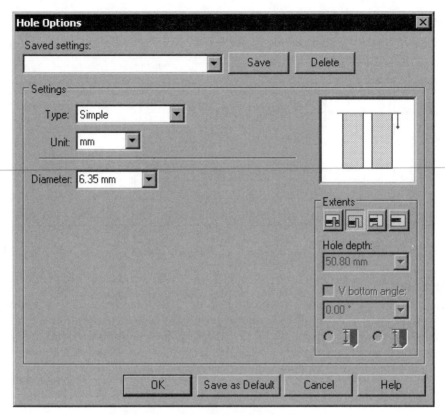

*Figure 6-1 The **Hole Options** dialog box*

Delete

Choose this button to delete the saved hole setting that is currently in the **Saved settings** drop-down list.

Type

This drop-down list is used to specify the type of hole that you want to create. The options available in this drop-down list are discussed next.

Simple

This option is selected to create a simple hole. A simple hole is the one that has a uniform diameter throughout its length. The diameter and the depth of the hole need to be specified in the **Settings** and **Extents** areas. Figure 6-2 shows the section view of a simple hole.

Threaded

This option is selected to create a threaded hole. Note that the threaded surface can be shown with a predefined depiction standard in the drafting environment.

Tapered

This option is selected to create a tapered hole, as shown in Figure 6-3.

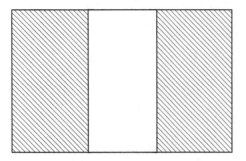
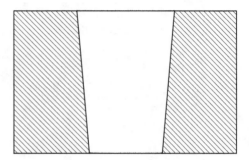

Figure 6-2 *Section view of a simple hole*   *Figure 6-3* *Section view of a tapered hole*

Counterbore

This option is selected to create a counterbore hole. A counterbore hole is a stepped hole and has two diameters: the counterbore diameter and the hole diameter. In this type of hole, you also need to specify two depths. The first depth is the counterbore depth, which is the depth up to which the bigger diameter will be defined. The second depth is the depth of the hole. Figure 6-4 shows the section view of a counterbore hole.

Countersink

This option is used to create a countersink hole. A countersink hole has also two diameters, but the transition between the bigger diameter and the smaller diameter is in the form of a tapered cone. In this type of hole, you will need to define the countersink diameter, hole diameter, countersink angle, and depth of the hole. Figure 6-5 shows the section view of a countersink hole.

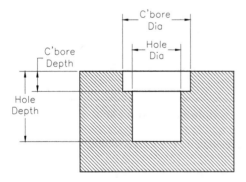
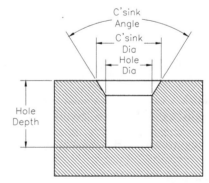

Figure 6-4 *Section view of a counterbore hole*   *Figure 6-5* *Section view of a countersink hole*

Unit

This drop-down list is used to specify the units for creating a hole. You can select the millimeter (mm) or inches (inch) unit for creating a hole.

Settings Area Options (For Simple Hole)

The remaining options in the **Settings** area depend on the type of hole selected from the **Type** drop-down list. For the simple hole type, this area provides the following option:

Diameter

The **Diameter** drop-down list is used to set the diameter of the hole. You can select the diameter from the predefined values available in this drop-down list or enter a value in this edit box. Note that the units of the diameters in this drop-down list depend on the type of unit selected from the **Unit** drop-down list.

Note

*The default hole diameters available in the **Diameter** drop-down list are based on the diameters available in the HOLES.TXT file. This file is available in the C:\Program Files\Solid Edge V20\Program folder.*

Settings Area (For Threaded Hole)

In addition to the **Diameter** drop-down list, the **Settings** area provides the following options for the threaded hole type:

Thread

The **Thread** drop-down list is used to set the thread type for the selected hole diameter. You can select any predefined thread type from this drop-down list.

Standard thread

On selecting this radio button, a standard thread is created for the hole.

Straight pipe thread

On selecting this radio button, a straight pipe thread is created for the hole.

Tapered pipe thread

On selecting this radio button, a straight pipe thread is created for the hole.

To hole extent

The **To hole extent** radio button is selected to create threads throughout the length of the hole. Note the change in the preview window when you select this radio button.

Finite extent

The **Finite extent** radio button is selected to create threads up to a specified depth. The depth is specified in the edit box available below this radio button.

Settings Area (For Tapered Hole)

The **Settings** area provides the following options for the tapered hole type:

Profile at bottom

 The **Profile at bottom** radio button is the first button on the right of the **Diameter** drop-down list. If this radio button is selected, all tapering parameters will be set based on the bottom diameter of the hole.

Profile at top

 The **Profile at top** radio button is selected to set all the tapering parameters based on the top diameter of the hole.

Decimal (R/L)

This radio button is selected to specify the taper angle value that is calculated by dividing the radius of the hole by its length.

Ratio (R:L)

This radio button is selected to specify the taper angle value that is calculated by the ratio of the radius of the hole to its length.

Angle

This radio button is selected to specify the value of the taper angle for creating a tapered hole.

Settings Area (For Counterbore Hole)

In addition to the **Diameter** drop-down list, the **Settings** area provides the following options for the counterbore hole type:

Profile at top

 If this radio button is selected, then the plane you define to place the hole will be taken as the plane from where the counterbore depth starts. This is the top face of the hole feature.

Profile at bottom

 If the **Profile at bottom** radio button is selected, then the plane you define to place the hole will be taken as the plane at which the counterbore depth ends. This is also the plane from where the hole diameter starts; refer to the preview of the hole shown in the preview window in the dialog box.

Counterbore diameter

The **Counterbore diameter** drop-down list is used to specify the counterbore diameter. You can select the diameter from this drop-down list or enter a value in this edit box.

Counterbore depth

The **Counterbore depth** drop-down list is used to specify the depth up to which the counterbore diameter will be defined in the hole. You can select the depth from this drop-down list or enter a value in this edit box.

V bottom angle

The **V bottom angle** check box is selected to create a tapered cone transition on the face where the counterbore depth ends; refer to the preview in the preview window. The angle for the V bottom is specified in the edit box available on the right of this check box. Figure 6-6 shows the section view of a counterbore hole with a V bottom for the counterbore.

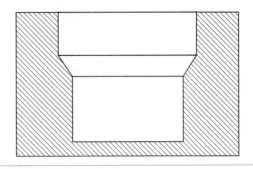

Figure 6-6 *Section view of a counterbore hole with V bottom defined for counterbore*

Note
*You can also create a threaded counterbore hole by selecting the threading options available in this area. Remember that the option to create threads will be available only for the standard hole diameters that are available in the **Diameter** drop-down list.*

Settings Area (For Countersink Hole)

In addition to the **Diameter** drop-down list and the thread options, the **Settings** area provides the following options for the countersink hole type:

Countersink diameter

The **Countersink diameter** drop-down list is used to specify the countersink diameter. You can select the diameter from this drop-down list or enter a value in this edit box.

Countersink angle

The **Countersink angle** drop-down list is used to specify the countersink angle. You can select the depth from this drop-down list or enter a value in this edit box.

Extents Area

Most of the options available in the **Extents** area are the standard termination options that are discussed in the **Protrusion** tool. If you choose the **Finite Extent** option to terminate the hole, the following options will be available in this area.

V bottom angle

If the **V bottom angle** check box is selected, the end of the hole will be tapered and it will be converged on to a point, refer to the preview in the preview window of the dialog box. The angle for the V bottom is specified in the edit box available below this check box. Figure 6-7 shows the section view of a countersink hole with a V bottom.

Dimension to flat

 The **Dimension to flat** radio button is selected to define the depth of the hole up to the flat face of the hole.

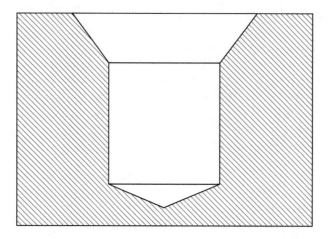

Figure 6-7 *Section view of the countersink hole with V bottom*

Dimension to V

 The **Dimension to V** radio button is selected to define the depth of the hole up to the tip of the bottom V of the hole.

After setting parameters in the **Hole Options** dialog box, this tool works in three steps, which are discussed next.

Plane Step

 The **Plane Step** allows you to select the plane on which the profile of the hole will be placed. This step is active when you invoke this tool. Therefore, you are prompted to click on a planar face or a reference plane. You can also use the **Create-From Options** drop-down list to create a new reference plane to place the hole profile.

Hole Step

 The **Hole Step** will automatically be invoked as soon as you specify the plane to place the hole profile. In this step, you need to define the location of the hole profile. This is the reason the sketching environment is invoked. Depending on the type of hole selected from the **Hole Options** dialog box, single or two concentric circles are attached to the cursor in the sketching environment. You can place single or multiple hole profiles by specifying their locations in the model. You can use relationships and dimensions to specify the exact location of the hole. After adding dimensions and relationships to the hole profiles, choose the **Hole Circle** button to place more hole profiles. Figure 6-8 shows

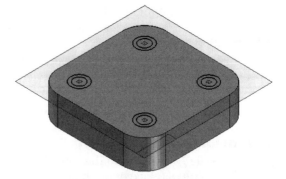

Figure 6-8 *Profiles for four counterbore holes placed in the sketching environment*

Tip. *You can also invoke the **Hole Options** dialog box to change the hole parameters while defining its location in the sketching environment. To do so, make sure the **Hole Circle** button is chosen. Next, choose the **Hole Options** from the ribbon bar to invoke the **Hole Options** dialog box. The changes that you make in this dialog box will be reflected in the hole profiles that are already placed and also in the new ones that have to be placed.*

the profiles of four counterbore holes placed in the sketching environment in the **Hole Step**. After placing the hole profile, choose the **Return** button from the ribbon bar.

Extent Step

The **Extent Step** will automatically be invoked as soon as you choose the **Finish** button from the ribbon bar in the sketching environment of the **Hole** step. The ribbon bar in this step provides the standard option for terminating the hole. By default, the extent option that you have selected in the **Hole Options** dialog box is selected in the ribbon bar and you are prompted to select the side for the feature. Move the cursor in the direction in which you want to create the hole feature and then click to accept the direction. The preview of the hole feature will be displayed. Choose the **Finish** button and then choose the **Cancel** button to exit this

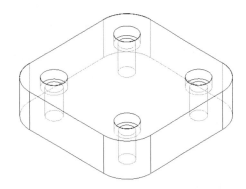

Figure 6-9 *Model after creating four counterbore holes*

tool. Figure 6-9 shows a model with four holes created using the hole profiles shown in Figure 6-8.

Tip. *Even if you create multiple holes by placing more than one hole profile using a single sequence of the **Hole** tool, they will be displayed as a single hole feature in the **EdgeBar**.*

CREATING ROUNDS

Toolbar:	Features > Round
Menu bar:	Features > Edge Treatments > Round

In Solid Edge, you can add fillets or rounds to the sharp edges of the models using the **Round** tool. This tool allows you to create four different types of rounds. You can select the type of round that you want to create from the **Round Options** dialog box shown in Figure 6-10. This dialog box is invoked by choosing the **Round Options** button from the **Round** ribbon bar.

In this chapter, you will learn to create the first two types of rounds. The remaining two types of rounds will be discussed in later chapters.

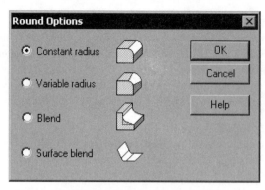

*Figure 6-10 The **Round Options** dialog box*

Creating Constant Radius Round

To create this type of round, select the **Constant radius** radio button from the **Round Options** dialog box.

When you invoke the **Round** tool or exit the **Round Options** dialog box after selecting the **Constant radius** radio button, the **Select Step** will be activated and you will be prompted to click on an edge chain. The options available in the ribbon bar in this step are discussed next.

Select

The **Select** drop-down list provides various selection types for selecting the entities to fillet. These selection types are discussed next.

Edge/Corner

This option is used to select an individual edge or a corner defined by multiple edges. Note that you may need to use the **QuickPick** tool to select the corner.

Chain

This is the default option and is used to select the chain of tangentially continuous edges.

Face

This option is used to select a face, thus selecting all its edges. As you move the cursor close to a face, all its edges will be highlighted. Click anywhere on the face to select all the edges of that face.

Loop

This option is used to select a specified loop on a selected face. When you select this option, you will be prompted to select a face containing loops. After selecting the face, you will be prompted to select a loop. You can select any loop on the face.

Feature

This option is used to fillet all the edges of a selected feature. You can select the feature from the drawing window or from the **EdgeBar**.

All Fillets

This option is used to fillet all the internal edges of the model. The fillets result in concave surfaces and are created by adding material to the model. When you select this option, you will be prompted to click on the part to accept the selection. Select the part; all the edges to which the fillet is added will be highlighted. Figure 6-11 shows a model with fillets added to all the possible edges.

All Rounds

This option is used to add rounds to all the external edges of the model. The rounds result in convex surfaces and are created by removing the material from the model. When you select this option, you will be prompted to click on the part to accept. Select the part; all the edges to which the rounds are added will be highlighted. Figure 6-12 shows a model with rounds added to all the possible edges.

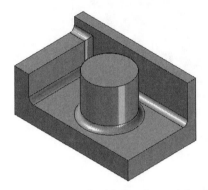

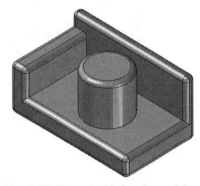

Figure 6-11 *Round added to the model using the **All Fillets** option*

Figure 6-12 *Round added to the model using the **All Rounds** option*

Radius

The **Radius** edit box is used to specify the radius value.

After selecting the edges to round and specifying the radius, choose the **Accept** button on the right of the **Select** drop-down list; the preview of the resulting fillet will be displayed.

In Solid Edge, you can modify the round parameters using the **Round Parameters** dialog box shown in Figure 6-13. To invoke this dialog box, choose the **Round Parameters** button available on the right of the **Select Step** button in the ribbon bar.

The options available in the **Round Parameters** dialog box are discussed next.

Roll across tangent edges

If the round in the model comes across the tangent edges, then selecting this check box will roll the round across these tangent edges. If you clear this check box, the round will terminate as soon as it comes across a tangent edge. Figure 6-14 shows the model before adding the round. Figure 6-15 shows a round rolled across the tangent edges by selecting the check box and Figure 6-16 shows a round terminated by clearing the check box.

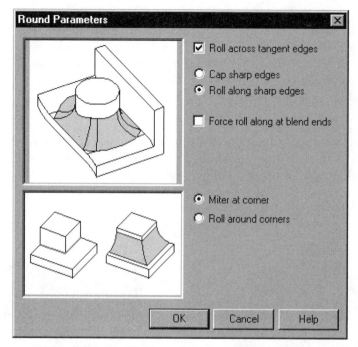

Figure 6-13 The **Round Parameters** *dialog box*

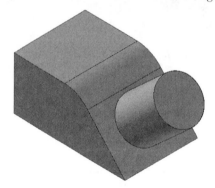

Figure 6-14 Model before creating the round

Cap sharp edges
If the round in the model comes across the sharp edges, then selecting this radio button will extend the face defined by the sharp edges to maintain the round, as shown in Figure 6-17.

Roll along sharp edges
If the round in the model comes across the sharp edges, then selecting this radio button will terminate the round such that the sharpness of the edges is retained, as shown in Figure 6-18.

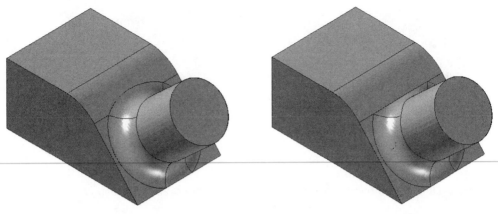

Figure 6-15 *Round rolled across the tangent edge* **Figure 6-16** *Round terminated at the tangent edge*

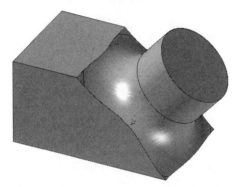

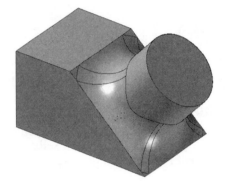

Figure 6-17 *Round created by capping the sharp edges*

Figure 6-18 *Round created by rolling along the sharp edges*

Force roll along at blend ends

This check box is selected to force the round at the blend ends to retain the sharp edges.

Miter at corner

This radio button is selected to create a miter at the sharp corner.

Roll around corner

This radio button is selected to roll the round around the corners.

If you select the three edges that form a corner, the **Soften Corner Step** button will be available on the right of the **Round Parameters** button in the ribbon bar. By choosing this button, you can invoke the **Soften Corner Step**. This step allows you to add a setback to the selected corner. Figures 6-19 and 6-20 show rounds in the model without and with the setback added to the corner, respectively.

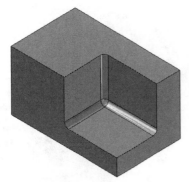

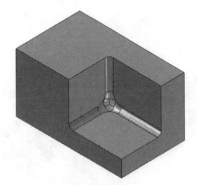

Figure 6-19 *Edges rounded without setback*   *Figure 6-20* *Edges rounded with setback*

The options available in the ribbon bar in the **Soften Corner** step are discussed next.

Select

This drop-down list enables you to select the corner to soften. By default, the **Corner** option is selected from this drop-down list. This option allows you to select the individual corner to soften. If you select the **All Corners** option, all corners of the feature will be selected.

Method

This drop-down list is used to specify the method of adding a setback to the corner. You can specify a numeric value for the setback by selecting the **Distance** option. If you select the **Multiple of radius** option, you can specify the setback value in terms of multiples of the fillet radius.

Value

This edit box is used to specify the setback value.

 Tip. *If you return to the **Soften Corner Step** and you had earlier selected the corner to add a setback, then that selected corner will be displayed in the **Select** drop-down list. The name of that corner will be suffixed by the value of the setback.*

 Tip. *If you return to the **Soften Corner Step** and you had earlier specified a unique edge value setback, the edges that comprised the corner will be displayed as **Edge-Corner** in the **Select** drop-down list. The value suffixed to the corner is the setback value along that edge.*

Unique Edge Values

This button is chosen when you want to specify different setback values along every edge that forms the corner. When you choose this button, the **Edge Setbacks** dialog box will be displayed. You can enter the setback for each edge in this dialog box. Figure 6-21 shows round edges setback of different values along each edge.

Creating Variable Radius Round

In this type of round, you can specify multiple radius values along the length of the edge selected to be filleted, as shown in Figure 6-22.

To create this type of round, select the **Variable radius** radio button from the **Round Options** dialog box.

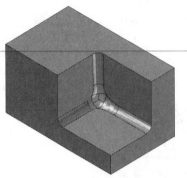

Figure 6-21   Setback with different values along each edge

Figure 6-22   Variable radius round

When you exit the **Round Options** dialog box, the **Select Step** will be activated and you will be prompted to click on an edge chain. You can use the other options available in the **Select** drop-down list to select the entities to fillet. These selection types were discussed in the **Creating Constant Radius Round** section.

After selecting the edge, choose the **Accept** button to invoke the **Select Vertices** step. This step is used to select the vertices along the edge to define different radius values. When this step is invoked, the **Point** option will be selected in the **Select** drop-down list and you will be prompted to click on the point to edit. Select the first point on the edge to enable the **Radius** edit box. Enter the radius value at this vertex in the **Radius** edit box. Note that you can select only the keypoints along the edge, such as the endpoints and the midpoint. To define some intermediate points, you need to sketch them using the **Sketch** tool.

As soon as you press the ENTER key after specifying the radius value at a selected vertex, the **Radius** edit box will be disabled. Now, again select a vertex and then enter the radius at the vertex. Continue this procedure until you select all the vertices and also specify their corresponding radii. Next, choose the **Preview** button to display the preview of the resultant round and then choose the **Finish** button to create it. You can click on the radius value in the preview to modify it.

CREATING CHAMFERS

Toolbar:	Features > Round > Chamfer
Menu bar:	Features > Edge Treatments > Chamfer

 Chamfering is defined as the process of beveling the sharp edges of a model to reduce the area of stress concentration. In Solid Edge, the chamfers are created using the **Chamfer** tool. When you invoke this tool, the **Chamfer** ribbon bar will be displayed. Before you proceed with creating the chamfer, you first need to specify the type of chamfer that you want to create. You can do so using the **Chamfer Options** dialog box, as shown in Figure 6-23. This dialog box is displayed by choosing the **Chamfer Options** button from the ribbon bar. The options available in this dialog box are discussed next.

Equal setbacks

This radio button is selected to create a chamfer with equal setback values of the selected edges from both the faces. The chamfer thus created will be at 45-degrees. This is the default option. Therefore, on invoking this tool, you will be prompted to select the edge to be treated. The setback value can be specified in the **Setback** edit box. Figure 6-24 shows a model without adding the setback and Figure 6-25 shows a model after adding the equal setback chamfer.

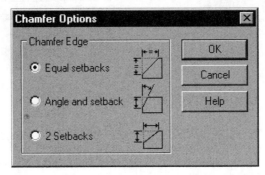

Figure 6-23 The **Chamfer Options** dialog box

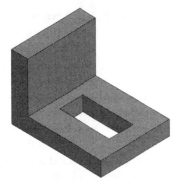
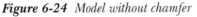

Figure 6-24 Model without chamfer

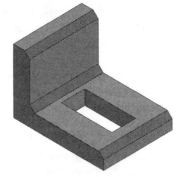

Figure 6-25 Model after creating the chamfer

Angle and setback

This is the second method of creating chamfers. This option is used to create a chamfer by defining one setback distance value and one angle value. When you exit the **Chamfer Options** dialog box after selecting this option, you will be prompted to select the face containing the edges to be chamfered. This is the face against which the angle will be measured. After selecting the face, choose the **Accept** button from the ribbon bar. You will be prompted to select the face edges to be chamfered. Note that you can select only the edges that are part of the selected face. The setback distance and the angle value can be specified in their respective edit boxes in the ribbon bar. Figure 6-26 shows the face to measure the angle and also the edge selected to be chamfered and Figure 6-27 shows the model after chamfering the selected edges with a setback value 10 and angle value 50-degrees.

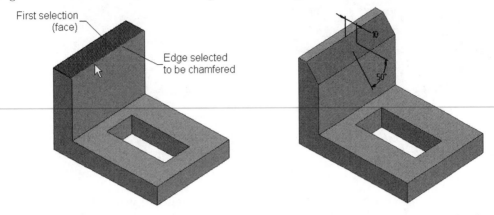

Figure 6-26 *Selecting the face and edge to chamfer*   *Figure 6-27* *Model after creating the chamfer*

2 Setbacks

This radio button is selected to create a chamfer using two different distances. When you exit the **Chamfer Options** dialog box after selecting this option, you will be prompted to select the face containing the edges to be chamfered. This is the face along which the first setback distance will be measured. After selecting the face, choose the **Accept** button. You will be prompted to select the face edges to be chamfered. Note that you can select only those edges that are part of the selected face. The two setback distances can be specified in the **Setbacks 1** and **2** edit boxes in the ribbon bar.

CREATING RECTANGULAR AND CIRCULAR PATTERNS

Toolbar: Features > Pattern

Most of the mechanical designs consist of multiple copies of some features arranged in a rectangular or circular fashion. For example, the grooves on the base of the pedestal bearing, as shown in Figure 6-28 or the holes on a particular bolt circle diameter on a flange, as shown in Figure 6-29.

Creating such features individually is very tedious and time consuming. To make the process easier and faster, Solid Edge provides you with the **Pattern** tool. This tool can be used to create rectangular as well as circular patterns.

Creating Rectangular Patterns

The process of creating a rectangular pattern is completed in three steps: **Select** step, **Plane or Sketch Step**, and **Draw Profile Step**. The first two steps are the same for creating the rectangular pattern and the circular pattern. In the **Draw Profile** step, you specify whether you need to create a rectangular pattern or a circular pattern by drawing a rectangular or a circular profile. All these steps and their corresponding options are discussed next.

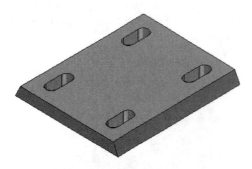 

Figure 6-28 *Model with features arranged in a rectangular fashion*

Figure 6-29 *Model with features arranged in a circular fashion*

When you invoke the **Pattern** tool, this step will be activated and you will be prompted to click on a feature. Select the feature that you want to pattern and then choose the **Accept** button; the **Plane or Sketch** step will be invoked.

Plane or Sketch Step

This step is used to select the plane on which the profile of a rectangular or a circular pattern will be drawn. You can select the option from the **Create-From Options** drop-down list to specify the plane on which the profile will be drawn. As soon as you select the plane, the **Draw Profile** step will be activated and the sketching environment will be invoked.

 Tip. *If you have created the profile of a pattern using the **Sketch** tool, then you can select that profile using the **Select from Sketch** option available in the **Create-From Options** drop-down list.*

Draw Profile Step

This step is used to draw the profile of a pattern that you want to create. The third tool in the **Features and Relationships** toolbar in the sketching environment is the **Rectangular Pattern** and it is chosen when the sketching environment is invoked. This tool allows you to create the profile of a rectangular pattern, which is a rectangle. This rectangle is drawn by specifying the opposite corners. The occurrences of the pattern are represented by small crosses (x). The rectangle profile may not necessarily pass through the feature selected to be patterned because the rectangle is used just for reference. Note that the profiles of the patterns are just like any other sketched entities and so it is recommended that you add dimensions and relationships to them to make them stable. The options available in the ribbon bar for the rectangular pattern are discussed next.

Pattern Type Drop-down List

This drop-down list is used to specify the method of defining the placement of occurrences in the rectangular pattern. These methods are discussed next.

Fit

If this option is selected, then the occurrences you specify along the X and Y directions are fitted inside the width and height of the rectangle.

Fill

This option allows you to specify the individual spacing between the occurrences along the X and Y directions and the length and width of the rectangle. The total number of occurrences along the X and Y directions are automatically determined by the values of the individual spacing and the length and width of the rectangle.

Fixed

This option is selected when you want to specify the total number of occurrences along the X and Y directions and also the individual spacing between the occurrences.

X/Y

These edit boxes are used to specify the occurrences along the X and Y directions and are available only for the **Fit** and **Fixed** pattern types.

X space/Y space

These edit boxes are used to specify the individual spacing between the occurrences along the X and Y directions. These edit boxes are available only for the **Fill** and **Fixed** pattern types.

Width/Height

These edit boxes are used to specify the width and height of the rectangle and are available only for the **Fit** and **Fill** pattern types.

Stagger Options

In Solid Edge, you can create a rectangular pattern in which every alternate row or column is offset from its original location. This is done using the **Stagger Options** dialog box, as shown in Figure 6-30. This dialog box is displayed on choosing the **Stagger Options** button.

To create a staggered rectangular pattern, you need to select an option from the drop-down list available in the **Stagger** area. You can specify whether you want to stagger the row or the column. By default, the staggering distance is half of the offset value. However, you can also specify any other numeric value by selecting the **Stagger** radio button. The **Include last column** check box is selected to specify that you want to create the last row or column in the staggered pattern. Figure 6-31 shows a rectangular pattern staggered along the row and Figure 6-32 shows the same pattern staggered along the column.

Reference Point

While defining a pattern, the reference point plays an important role in determining the direction in which the pattern elements will be placed. By default, the first corner of the rectangle is taken as the reference point and is designated by a bold cross (**x**). The pattern is created from this first point in the direction in which the rectangle is drawn. If you want to change the reference point, choose the **Reference Point** button from the ribbon

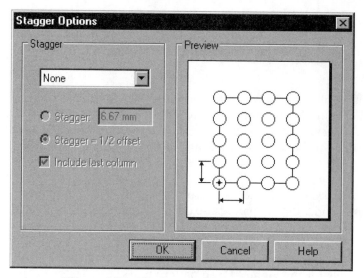

Figure 6-30 *The **Stagger Options** dialog box*

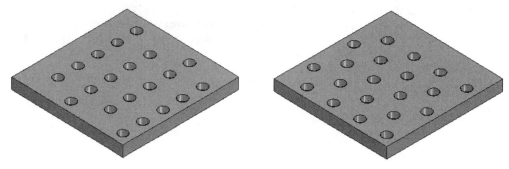

Figure 6-31 *Pattern staggered along the row*   *Figure 6-32* *Pattern staggered along the column*

bar and then select the point you want to use as the reference point. For example, refer to Figure 6-33.

In this figure, the reference point is at the lower left corner of the rectangle that is at the center of the circular cut feature. Figure 6-34 shows the resulting pattern.

In Figure 6-35, the reference point is at the lower right corner of the rectangle and Figure 6-36 shows the resulting pattern.

Suppress Occurrence

This button is chosen to suppress some of the occurrences in the rectangular pattern. To suppress the occurrences, choose this button and then select the cross (x) of the occurrence that you do not want in the pattern. You can unsuppress the occurrences by selecting them. After suppressing the occurrences, right-click to continue. Figure 6-37 shows a pattern without suppressing the occurrences and Figure 6-38 shows the same pattern with some occurrences suppressed.

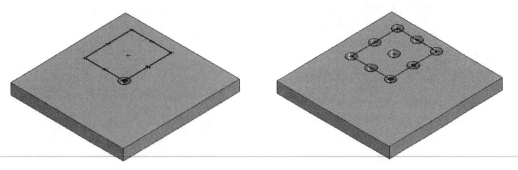

Figure 6-33 *Selecting the lower left corner*   *Figure 6-34* *Resulting rectangular pattern*
of the rectangle as the reference point

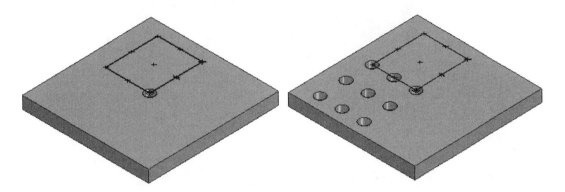

Figure 6-35 *Selecting the lower right corner of*   *Figure 6-36* *Resulting rectangular pattern*
the rectangle as the reference point

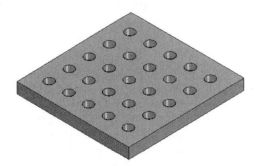 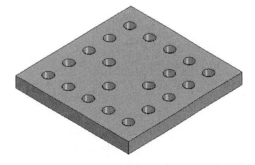

Figure 6-37 *Pattern without suppressing*   *Figure 6-38* *Pattern with some occurrences*
the occurrences   *suppressed*

After specifying the parameters of the pattern in the sketching environment, choose the **Finish** button to display the preview of the resulting pattern.

In addition to the buttons of various steps, the ribbon bar provides two more buttons, **Smart** and **Fast**. The functions of these two buttons are discussed next.

Smart/Fast

The **Smart** button is chosen to create patterns that require more complex situations. For example, refer to Figure 6-39. This figure shows a staggered pattern in which the occurrences in the last column do not lie completely inside the model. Such cases cannot be handled by the **Fast** option. You need to necessarily use the **Smart** option to create the pattern. If you try to create this pattern using the **Fast** option, the last column will not be created.

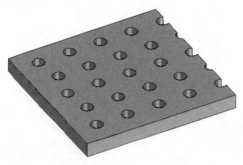

Figure 6-39 Model with a complex pattern situation

Note

*Generally, the coplanar features can be patterned using the **Fast** pattern option and the features that are not coplanar can be patterned using the **Smart** pattern option.*

Creating Circular Patterns

As mentioned earlier, the process of creating circular patterns is the same as that of creating rectangular patterns. The only difference is in the **Draw Profile Step**. To invoke this step, you first need to select the feature to pattern and then select the plane or the planar face on which the profile of the circular pattern will be drawn.

Profile Step

To create a circular pattern, you need to draw its profile, which is a circle or an arc. This circle or arc acts as the reference to arrange the occurrences in a circular fashion. In the sketching environment, choose the **Circular Pattern** button from the **Features and Relationships** toolbar. You will be prompted to click for the center point of the arc. Specify the center point of the circular pattern; you will be prompted to specify the start point of the arc. Specify a point to define the radius of the circle for the circular pattern. Finally, you will be prompted to click for a point on the arc. By defining this point, you can define the direction of the pattern. You will notice that an arrow is displayed at the point you defined as the start point of the arc. You can move the cursor to either sides of the start point to define the circular pattern in the clockwise direction or in the counterclockwise direction. The options available in the ribbon bar for the circular pattern are discussed next.

Reference Point

This button is chosen to change the reference point of the pattern.

Suppress Occurrence

This button is chosen to suppress some of the occurrences in the circular pattern. To suppress the occurrences, choose this button and then select the cross (x) of the occurrence that you do not want in the pattern. After suppressing them, right-click to continue.

Pattern Type Drop-down List

This drop-down list is used to specify the method of defining the placement of occurrences in the circular pattern. These options are discussed next.

Fit

If this option is selected, then the occurrences that you specify in the count edit box are fitted inside the profile of the circular pattern.

Fill

This option allows you to specify the individual spacing between the occurrences along the profile of the circular pattern.

Fixed

This option is available only when you select the **Partial Circle** button. This option is selected when you want to specify the total number of occurrences and the individual spacing between them.

Partial Circle

This button is chosen when you do not want to create a circular pattern through a complete circle. You can specify the angle of sweep for the partial circle in the **Sweep** edit box. Figure 6-40 shows a circular pattern of eight holes arranged around a partial circle of 270-degrees angle. In this case, the original feature is the circle at the bottom and the remaining occurrences are placed in the counterclockwise direction. Figure 6-41 shows the same pattern, but the occurrences are placed in the clockwise direction.

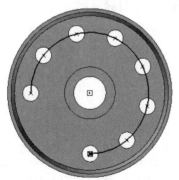   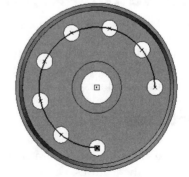

Figure 6-40 Circular pattern placed along a partial circle in the counterclockwise direction   *Figure 6-41 Circular pattern placed along a partial circle in the clockwise direction*

Full Circle

This button is chosen to create a circular pattern through a complete circle, as shown in Figure 6-42.

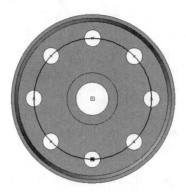

Figure 6-42 *Circular pattern through a complete circle*

Radius

This edit box is used to specify the radius of the profile of the circular pattern.

Sweep

This edit box is available only when you choose the **Partial Circle** button and is used to specify the angle of the partial circle. This edit box is available only for the **Fit** and **Fill** pattern types.

Count

This edit box is available only for the **Fit** and **Fixed** pattern types and is used to specify the occurrences in the circular pattern.

Spacing

This edit box is available only for the **Fill** and **Fixed** pattern types and is used to specify the individual spacing between the occurrences in the circular pattern.

CREATING THE PATTERN ALONG A CURVE

Toolbar: Features > Pattern > Pattern Along Curve

 In Solid Edge, you can also pattern the selected features along an existing curve or an edge using the **Pattern Along Curve** tool. This tool works in four steps, which are discussed next.

Select Step

This step is active when you invoke the **Pattern Along Curve** tool. In this step, you are prompted to click on a feature to pattern. You can select one or more features to pattern. After selecting the features, choose the **Accept** button to invoke the **Select Curve** step.

Select Curve Step

This step is used to select the curve, along which the pattern will be created. You will be allowed to specify other options such as the anchor point and the total number of occurrences in the pattern. The options available in the ribbon bar of this step are discussed next.

Pattern Curve

This button is automatically chosen when the **Select Curve** step is invoked. This button enables you to select the curve along which the selected feature will be patterned. You can select an existing sketched entity or an edge as the curve for creating the pattern. After selecting the curve, you need to set the other options such as **Pattern Type**, **Count**, and **Spacing**. After setting these options, choose the **Accept** button.

Anchor Point

This button will be automatically chosen when you choose **Accept** after selecting the pattern curve. This button enables you to select the anchor point in the selected curve to specify the alignment of the pattern occurrences. You can select any of the endpoints of the curve or the joining points of a chain of entities. As soon as you select the anchor point, an arrow will be displayed at that point and you will be prompted to click to accept the displayed side or select the other side in the view. This arrow defines the direction in which the occurrences will be placed along the curve. While defining the anchor point, you can also specify the distance by which the occurrences will be offset from the anchor point in the **Offset** edit box. This edit box is available while defining the anchor point. Figures 6-43 and 6-44 show the preview of a pattern of counterbore holes along the curve with different anchor points.

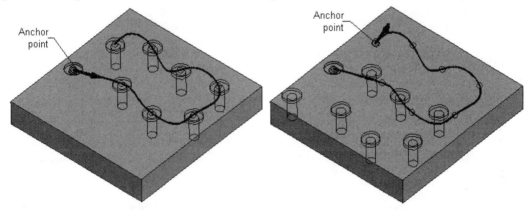

Figure 6-43 *Preview of the pattern along the curve*

Figure 6-44 *Preview of the pattern with different anchor points*

Note
*The other options in the **Select Curve Step** are similar to those discussed in the rectangular and circular patterns.*

Path Curve Step

The **Path Curve Step** is not invoked automatically. You need to choose the button of this step to invoke it. This step is used to select a path curve that defines the second direction along which the occurrences will be arranged. The curve you define in this step will define the direction and the total distance between all occurrences along the second direction. After selecting the path curve, select the anchor point. The options available in this step are the same as those discussed in the **Select Curve Step**. Figure 6-45 shows the preview of a pattern along a curve with the second direction defined using the path curve, which is a line. Note that the number of occurrences in the path curve direction is 2.

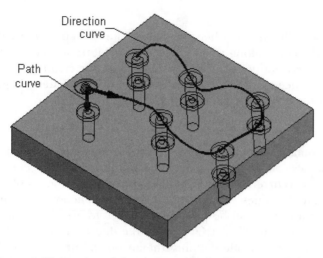

Figure 6-45 *Preview of the pattern with the direction and the path*

Advanced Definition Step

This step is used to specify the advanced parameters of the pattern along the curve. The options available in the ribbon bar of this step are discussed next.

Transformation Type

This drop-down list is used to specify the types of transformation of occurrences in the resulting pattern. The options available in this drop-down list are discussed next.

Linear

If you select this option, the occurrences of the pattern will have the same orientation as that of the original occurrence, as shown in the preview of the pattern in Figure 6-46.

Full

If you select this option, the occurrences of the pattern will be oriented along the direction of the selected curve at a particular point, as shown in the preview of the pattern in Figure 6-47.

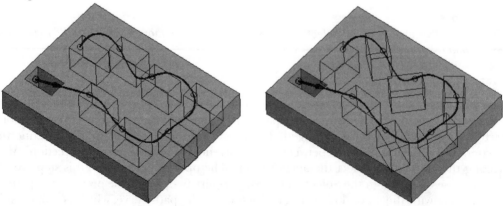

Figure 6-46 *Pattern with linear transformation*   **Figure 6-47** *Pattern with full transformation*

From Plane

This option allows you to select a plane on which the original occurrence and a pattern occurrence are projected and the measured angle defines the orientation of the pattern occurrence.

Rotation Type

This drop-down list is used to specify the types of rotation of the occurrences in the resultant pattern. The options available in this drop-down list are discussed next.

Curve Position

If you select this option, the curve position will determine the rotation of the occurrences, as shown in the preview of the pattern in Figure 6-48.

Feature Position

If you select this option, the feature position will determine the rotation of occurrences, as shown in the preview of the pattern in Figure 6-49.

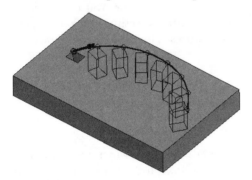 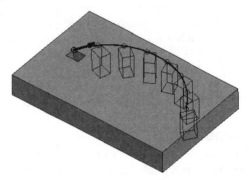

Figure 6-48 *Pattern with curve position rotation*   *Figure 6-49* *Pattern with feature position rotation*

Reference Point

This button is chosen to change the reference point of the pattern.

Suppress Occurrence

This button is chosen to suppress some of the occurrences of the pattern.

Insert Occurrence

This button is chosen to insert additional occurrences in the pattern. By default, the occurrence is inserted at a keypoint. However, you can use the **Offset** edit box to define the offset of the occurrence from the keypoint. You can specify a negative or a positive offset value, based on whether you want to offset the occurrence to the left or to the right of the keypoint.

MIRRORING FEATURES AND BODIES

Similar to mirroring the sketched entities in the sketching environment, you can also mirror selected features or the entire body in the part modeling environment. As mentioned in introduction, a body is the entire model consisting of all features created until now. The methods of mirroring features and bodies are discussed next.

Mirroring Selected Features

Toolbar:	Features > Mirror Copy Feature

 The **Mirror Copy Feature** tool enables you to mirror the selected features about a selected reference plane or planar face. This helps in saving a lot of time in modeling a symmetric feature. The **Mirror Copy Feature** tool works in two steps, which are discussed next.

Select Features Step

This step enables you to select the features that you want to mirror. You can select these features from the drawing window or from the **EdgeBar**. After selecting the features, choose the **Accept** button or right-click to accept the selected features. The **Plane** step will be invoked.

 Note

You can also press and hold the CTRL key, select the features to mirror and then invoke the ***Mirror Copy Feature*** *tool. In this case, the* ***Select Features*** *step will not be invoked.*

Plane Step

This step enables you to select a reference plane or a planar face to mirror the selected feature. You can also use the **Create-From Options** drop-down list to create a new reference plane to mirror the features. As soon as you select the plane, the preview of the mirror feature will be displayed. Note that if an error message is displayed, you need to change the fast mirror to the smart mirror by choosing the **Smart** button from the ribbon bar.

Figure 6-50 shows a model before mirroring the features and Figure 6-51 shows the same model after mirroring the features about the reference plane passing through the center of the model.

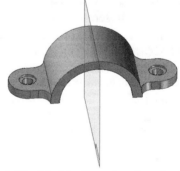

Figure 6-50 Model before mirroring the features

Figure 6-51 Model after mirroring the features about the reference plane passing through the center of the model

Mirroring Bodies

Toolbar: Features > Mirror Copy Feature > Mirror Copy

The **Mirror Copy** tool enables you to mirror the selected body about a selected reference plane or a planar face. This tool also works in two steps, which are discussed next.

Select Step

This step allows you to select the body that you want to mirror. You need to select the body in the drawing window. As soon as you move the cursor over the body, it will be highlighted. Click to accept the body; the **Plane** step will be invoked.

Plane Step

This step allows you to select a reference plane or a planar face to mirror the selected feature. As soon as you select the plane, the preview of the mirror body will be displayed.

Figure 6-52 shows a body selected to mirror and a planar face being selected as the mirror plane. Figure 6-53 shows the same model after mirroring the body.

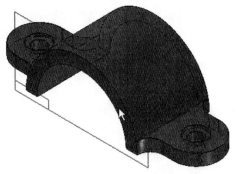

Figure 6-52 Body selected to mirror and the mirror plane

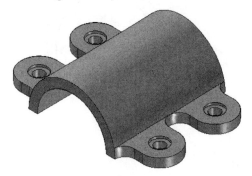

Figure 6-53 Model after mirroring the body

TUTORIALS

Tutorial 1

In this tutorial, you will create the model shown in Figure 6-54. The dimensions of this model are given in the drawing, as shown in Figure 6-55. After creating the model, save it with the name and location given below:

    \Solid Edge\c06\c06tut1.par   **(Expected time: 30 min)**

The following steps are required to complete this tutorial:

a. Start Solid Edge in the **Part** environment. Create the profile for the base revolved feature on the front plane and revolve it through 360-degrees, refer to Figure 6-57.

Figure 6-54 *Model for Tutorial 1*

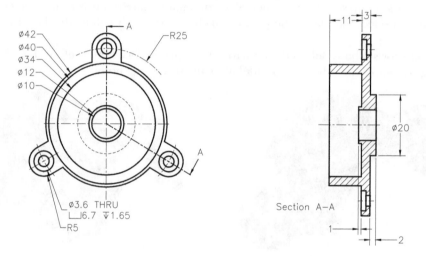

Figure 6-55 *Dimensions of the model for Tutorial 1*

b. Create the next join feature, refer to Figure 6-60.
c. Create a counterbore hole on the new feature, refer to Figure 6-61.
d. Create a circular pattern of the second feature and a hole, refer to Figure 6-62.
e. Save the model and then close the file.

Creating the Base Feature

As mentioned earlier, the base feature is a revolved protrusion feature and its profile will be created on the front plane.

1. Start Solid Edge in the **Part** environment and then select the front plane as the sketching plane for the revolved feature.

2. Draw the profile for the revolved feature using various sketching tools, as shown in Figure 6-56.

3. Add the required relationships and dimensions to the sketch.

4. Exit the sketching environment and then revolve the sketch through 360-degrees to create the base feature, as shown in Figure 6-57.

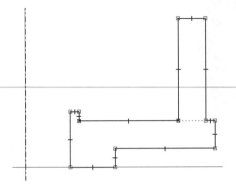

Figure 6-56 *Sketch for the revolve feature*

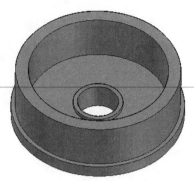

Figure 6-57 *Base revolved feature*

Creating the Second Feature

The second feature is a protrusion feature and will be created on the bottom of the base feature. Note that to get a proper orientation of the model, you need to be careful in defining the sketching plane for this feature.

1. Set the top view using the **Named Views** drop-down list in the **Main** toolbar. Right-click in the drawing window and choose **Fit** to fit the model in the drawing window.

2. Invoke the **Rotate** tool and then rotate the model around the vertical edge of the rotate tool such that the bottom face of the model is displayed, refer to Figure 6-58.

3. Invoke the **Protrusion** tool and then select the bottom face of the base feature as the sketching plane, refer to Figure 6-58.

4. Draw the sketch of the protrusion feature and then add the required relationships and dimensions to it, as shown in Figure 6-59.

5. Exit the sketching environment and then extrude the sketch up to the next plane using the **From/To Extent** option. The top view of the model, after creating the protrusion feature, is shown in Figure 6-60.

Creating the Counterbore Hole

Next, you need to create a counterbore hole on the protrusion feature by using the **Hole** tool.

1. Choose the **Hole** button from the **Features** toolbar to display the **Hole** ribbon bar.

2. Choose the **Hole Options** button from the ribbon bar to display the **Hole Options** dialog box.

Figure 6-58 *Selecting the bottom face of the model as the sketching plane*

3. Select the **Counterbore** option from the **Type** drop-down list. Enter **3.6** in the **Diameter** edit box of the **Settings** area.

4. Enter **6.7** in the **Counterbore diameter** edit box and **1.65** in the **Counterbore depth** edit box.

5. Accept the remaining default options and choose **OK** from this dialog box. You are prompted to click on a planar face or a reference plane.

6. Select the top face of the second feature to place the hole. The sketching environment is invoked and two concentric circles that are the profiles of the hole feature are attached to the cursor.

7. Place the profiles of the hole concentric to the arc of the second feature. Exit the sketching environment to invoke the **Extent Step**.

8. Specify the side of the feature downward to display the preview of the feature. Choose the **Finish** button from the ribbon bar to complete the feature and then exit the **Hole** tool by choosing the **Cancel** button. The model, after creating the counterbore hole, is shown in Figure 6-61. Note that the view shown in this figure is not the isometric view of the model.

Creating a Circular Pattern of the Features

Next, you need to create a circular pattern of the second feature and the hole. As mentioned earlier, you need to draw the profile of the circular pattern in the sketching environment. The sketching environment is invoked in the **Profile** step of the **Pattern** tool.

1. Choose the **Pattern** button from the **Features** toolbar to display the **Pattern** ribbon bar.

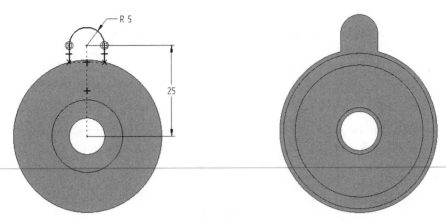

Figure 6-59 *Sketch for the protrusion feature* **Figure 6-60** *Top view of the model after creating the protrusion feature*

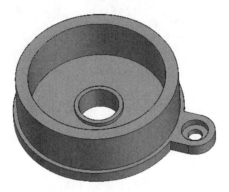

Figure 6-61 *Model after creating the counterbore hole*

2. Select the **Protrusion 2** and **Hole 1** features from the **EdgeBar**; the selected features are highlighted. Right-click to accept the features; the **Plane or Sketch Step** button is invoked and you are prompted to click on a planar face or a reference plane.

3. Select the top face of the second feature to draw the profile of the circular pattern.

    The sketching environment is invoked and the **Circular Pattern** button is automatically chosen from the **Features** toolbar in the sketching environment. You are prompted to click for the center point of the arc.

4. Select the center of the model as the center point of the arc. You are prompted to click for the start point of the arc.

5. Move the cursor to the center of the hole and click when the handle of the center point is displayed. An arrow is displayed at this point and you are prompted to click for a point on the arc.

6. Move the cursor to the top of the start point of the arc and then click to define the direction of the pattern in the counterclockwise direction.

7. Enter **3** in the **Count** edit box to specify three occurrences in the pattern. Exit the sketching environment; the **Pattern_1** dialog box is displayed and you are informed that errors have been detected and no patterns can be created.

8. Choose **OK** from the dialog box and then choose the **Smart** button from the ribbon bar to display the preview of the pattern. Choose the **Finish** button to complete the pattern.

The isometric view of the final model, after creating the pattern, is shown in Figure 6-62.

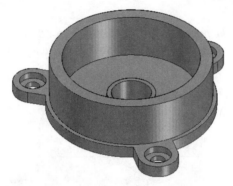

Figure 6-62 Final model for Tutorial 1

Saving the Model

1. Save the model with the name given below and then close the file.

   \Solid Edge\c06\c06tut1.par

Tutorial 2

In this tutorial, you will create the model of the Guide bracket shown in Figure 6-63. Its dimensions are given in the drawing shown in Figure 6-64. After creating the model, save it with the name given below:

   \Solid Edge\c06\c06tut2.par   **(Expected time: 30 min)**

   The following steps are required to complete this tutorial:

a. Create the profile of the base feature on the top plane and then extrude it symmetrically to the sketching plane, refer to Figure 6-65.
b. Create a reference plane at an offset of 20 in the downward direction from the top planar face of the base feature. Use this reference plane to create the second protrusion feature, refer to Figure 6-66.
c. Mirror the second feature about the top plane.

Figure 6-63 Model for Tutorial 2

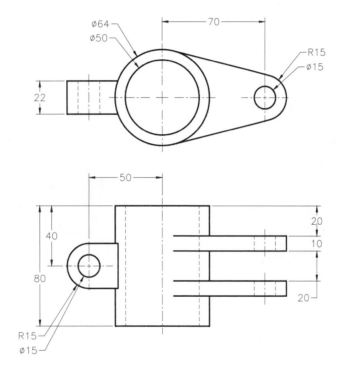

Figure 6-64 Dimensions of the model for Tutorial 2

d. Create the fourth feature on the front plane and extrude it symmetrically through a distance of 22, refer to Figure 6-69.

e. Create simple holes on the second feature and the fourth feature to complete the model, as shown in Figure 6-70.

Creating the Base Feature

1. Start a new part file and then draw the sketch for the base protrusion feature on the top plane. The sketch for the base feature consists of two concentric circles of diameters 64 and 50, respectively.

2. Exit the sketching environment and extrude the sketch symmetrically through a distance of 80. The isometric view of the base feature of the model is shown in Figure 6-65.

Creating the Second Feature

The second feature is a protrusion feature that is created using an open profile. This profile is drawn on a parallel plane created in the downward direction of the top planar face of the base feature.

1. Invoke the **Protrusion** tool, if it is not active, and then define a plane parallel to the top planar face of the base feature at a distance of 20 units in the downward direction.

2. Create the open profile of the second protrusion feature and then add the required dimensions and relationships to the profile.

Figure 6-65 *Base feature of the model*   *Figure 6-66* *Model after creating the second feature*

3. Exit the sketching environment and then extrude the profile through a distance of 10 in the downward direction. The model, after creating this feature, is shown in Figure 6-66.

Mirroring the Second Feature

Since the base feature was created symmetrically to the top plane, you can create the third feature by mirroring the second feature about the top plane.

1. Choose the **Mirror Copy Features** button from the **Features** toolbar to invoke the **Mirror** ribbon bar. The **Select Features** step is active and you are prompted to select the features to be included in the mirror feature.

2. Select the second feature and then right-click to accept the selection. The **Plane** step is invoked and you are prompted to click on a planar face or a reference plane.

3. Select the top plane from the drawing window or from the **EdgeBar** to display the preview of the mirror feature.

4. Choose the **Finish** button to create the feature. The model, after mirroring the feature, is shown in Figure 6-67.

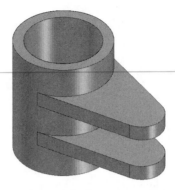

Figure 6-67 Model after mirroring the second feature

Creating the Fourth Feature

1. Create an open profile on the front plane for the fourth feature and then add the required dimensions and relationships to the profile, as shown in Figure 6-68.

2. Exit the sketching environment and then extrude the profile symmetrically through a distance of 22 mm. The model, after creating this feature, is shown in Figure 6-69.

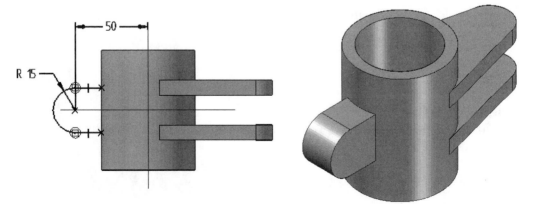

Figure 6-68 Open profile for the fourth feature   *Figure 6-69* Model after creating the fourth feature

Creating Holes

Next, you need to create simple holes. Note that if you create a through hole on the second feature, it will automatically be created on the mirrored feature. Therefore, you need to create two holes, one for the second and third features, and other for the fourth feature.

1. Invoke the **Hole** tool and then choose the **Hole Options** button from the ribbon bar to display the **Hole Options** dialog box.

2. Enter **15** in the **Diameter** edit box of the **Settings** area.

3. Choose the **Through All** button from the **Extents** area and then choose **OK** to exit the dialog box.

4. Move the cursor to the top face of the second feature and select it as the sketching plane.

5. Place the profile of the hole concentric to the arc in the second feature and then exit the sketching environment.

6. Define the direction of the feature creation in the downward direction. The preview of the feature passing through the mirrored feature is also displayed.

7. Choose the **Finish** button from the ribbon bar to complete the feature. The **Hole** tool is still active and you are prompted to click on a planar face or a reference plane.

8. Select the front planar face of the fourth feature as the sketching plane. Invoke the **Hole Options** dialog box and modify the diameter of the hole to **15** in the **Diameter** edit box. Choose the **Through All** button from the **Extents** area.

9. Place the hole concentric to the arc in the feature and then exit the sketching environment.

10. Create the hole by specifying the side of feature creation and exit the **Hole** tool. The final model of the Guide bracket is shown in Figure 6-70.

Saving the Model

1. Save the model with the name given below and then close the file.

   \Solid Edge\c06\c06tut2.par

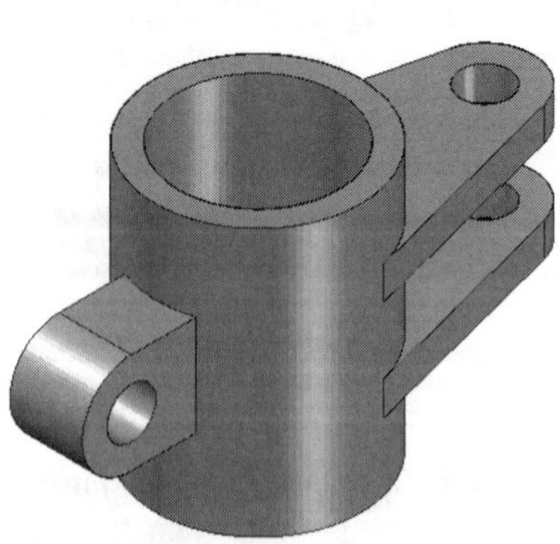

Figure 6-70 *Final model of the Guide bracket for Tutorial 2*

Tutorial 3

In this tutorial, you will create the model shown in Figure 6-71. Its dimensions are given in the drawing shown in Figure 6-72. After creating the model, save it with the name given below:

  \Solid Edge\c06\c06tut3.par   **(Expected time: 30 min)**

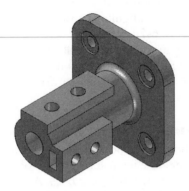

Figure 6-71 *Model for Tutorial 3*

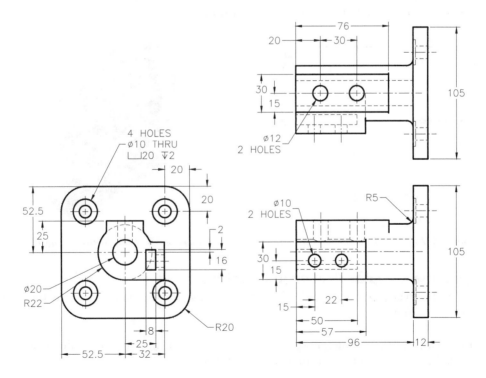

Figure 6-72 *Dimensions of the model for Tutorial 3*

The following steps are required to complete this tutorial:

a. Create the base feature on the front plane, refer to Figure 6-74. The sketch for the base feature consists of a square with a fillet on all the four corners.

b. On the front face of the base feature, create the circular protrusion feature, refer to Figure 6-75.

c. Add two rectangular join features to the cylindrical feature, refer to Figure 6-77, and then create the rectangular cut feature on one of the rectangular join features.

d. Create all simple holes on the rectangular features by defining the sketch plane on the required planes, refer to Figure 6-79.

e. Create one counterbore hole on the front face of the base feature.

f. Create a rectangular pattern of the counterbore hole, refer to Figure 6-80.

g. Create the fillet on the circular protrusion feature to complete the model, refer to Figure 6-81.

Creating the Base Feature

1. Start a new part file and then draw the sketch for the base protrusion feature on the front plane. The sketch for the base feature is a square of side 105. It has all four corners filleted with a radius of 20, as shown in Figure 6-73. As evident in this figure, the sketch is symmetric about the origin of the sketching plane.

2. Exit the sketching environment and extrude the sketch to a distance of 12. The isometric view of the base feature of the model is shown in Figure 6-74.

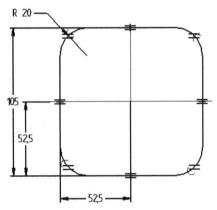

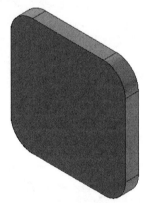

Figure 6-73 Sketch for the base feature   *Figure 6-74* Base feature of the model

Creating the Circular Protrusion Feature

1. Invoke the **Protrusion** tool and select the front face of the base feature as the sketching plane.

2. Draw a circle as the profile of the second feature and add the required dimensions to it. Remember that the center of the circle is at the origin.

3. Exit the sketching environment and extrude the sketch through a distance of 96 units in the forward direction. The model, after creating this feature, is shown in Figure 6-75.

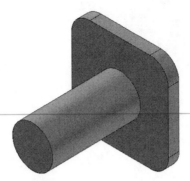

Figure 6-75 *Model after creating the circular protrusion feature*

Creating the Rectangular Protrusion Features

Next, you need to create two rectangular protrusion features on the circular feature. Both these features will be created by defining parallel planes from the base reference planes and then extruding the sketch up to the circular protrusion feature.

1. Invoke the **Protrusion** tool and define a parallel plane at a distance of 25 mm from the top plane in the upward direction.

2. Draw the profile of the rectangular join feature and add the required dimensions and relationships to it.

3. Exit the sketching environment and then extrude the profile up to the circular protrusion feature using the **Through Next** option. The model, after creating this feature, is shown in Figure 6-76.

4. Similarly, define a parallel plane at a distance of 32 mm from the right plane toward the right and use it to draw the profile of the next rectangular protrusion feature.

5. Exit the sketching environment and then extrude the profile up to the circular protrusion feature. The model, after creating this feature, is shown in Figure 6-77.

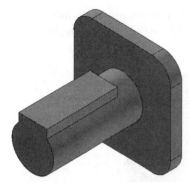

Figure 6-76 *Model after creating the top rectangular join features*

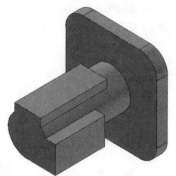

Figure 6-77 *Model after creating the side rectangular join features*

Creating the Cutout

1. Invoke the **Cutout** tool and define the front face of the circular protrusion feature as the sketching plane.

2. Draw the profile of the cut feature and add the required dimensions to it.

3. Exit the sketching environment and specify the depth of the cut as 50 units.

Creating Simple Holes

Next, you need to create the simple holes. You need to use three different sequences of the **Hole** tool to create simple holes on the circular protrusion features and the two rectangular protrusion features. First, you need to create a simple hole on the circular protrusion feature because this hole will be used to terminate the hole on the top rectangular protrusion feature.

1. Invoke the **Hole** tool and then choose the **Hole Options** button from the ribbon bar to display the **Hole Options** dialog box.

2. Enter **20** as the value in the **Diameter** edit box in the **Settings** area.

3. Choose the **From/To Extent** button from the **Extents** area and then choose **OK** to exit the dialog box.

4. Move the cursor to the front face of the circular protrusion feature and select it as the sketching plane.

5. Place the profile of the hole concentric to the circular feature and then exit the sketching environment.

   Since you selected the **From/To Extent** termination option for the hole from the **Hole Options** dialog box, you are prompted to select the to surface. The planar face that you have selected to place the hole is automatically taken as the from surface.

6. Select the front planar face of the base feature as the plane to terminate the hole. Terminate this sequence of the **Hole** tool by choosing the **Finish** button from the ribbon bar.

    Next, you need to create a hole on the planar face of the top rectangular feature. The **Hole** tool is still active and you are prompted to click on a planar face or a reference plane. For the next hole sequence, you need to change the dimensions of the hole. You can also change the dimensions of the hole while placing the hole profile in the sketching environment.

7. Select the planar face of the top rectangular protrusion feature to invoke the sketching environment.

8. Choose the **Hole Options** button from the ribbon bar. Enter **12** as the value of the hole diameter in the **Diameter** edit box and then exit the dialog box.

9. Place two instances of the hole profile and add the required dimensions and relationships, as shown in Figure 6-78.

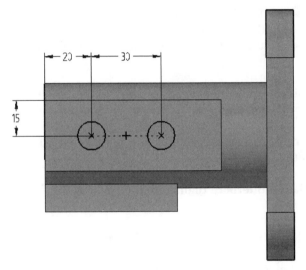

Figure 6-78 Dimensioned hole profiles

10. Choose the **Return** button to exit the sketching environment and specify the side of the feature creation downward. The holes are created and automatically terminated at the central hole feature.

11. Similarly, select the planar face of the side rectangular protrusion feature.

12. In the sketching environment, modify the hole diameter to 10 units and then place two instances of the hole profile.

13. Add the required dimensions and relationships to the hole profiles and then exit the sketching environment.

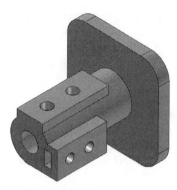

Figure 6-79 *Model after creating simple holes*

14. Specify the side of the hole creation inside the model to terminate the sequence of the **Hole** tool. The isometric view of the model, after creating simple holes, is shown in Figure 6-79.

Creating the Counterbore Hole

The next feature is the counterbore hole. This hole will be created on the front planar face of the base feature and will be concentric to the fillet on the top left corner of the base feature.

1. Invoke the **Hole** tool, if it is not already active, and then choose the **Hole Options** button from the ribbon bar to invoke the **Hole Options** dialog box.

2. Select **Counterbore** from the **Type** drop-down list. Enter **10** as the value of the diameter of the hole in the **Diameter** edit box.

3. Enter **20** in the **Counterbore diameter** edit box and **2** in the **Counterbore depth** edit box.

4. Choose the **Through All** button from the **Extents** area and then exit the dialog box.

   You are prompted to click on a planar face or reference plane.

5. Select the front planar face of the base feature. The sketching environment is invoked and the hole profile is attached to the cursor.

6. Place the hole profile concentric to the center of the fillet on the top left corner of the base feature. Exit the sketching environment and specify the side of the hole creation toward the back of the model. Exit the **Hole** tool to complete the creation of the hole.

Creating the Rectangular Pattern of the Counterbore Hole

Next, you need to create the rectangular pattern of the counterbore hole. The rectangular pattern will have two rows and two columns and the profile of the pattern will be drawn on the front face of the base feature.

1. Choose the **Pattern** button from the **Features** toolbar and select the counterbore hole as the feature to pattern.

2. Right-click to accept the feature; the **Plane or Sketch** step is invoked and you are prompted to click on a planar face or reference plane.

3. Select the front planar face of the base feature to draw the profile of the rectangular pattern. The sketching environment is invoked and the **Rectangular Pattern** button is chosen from the **Features** toolbar. You are prompted to click for the first point.

4. Move the cursor to the center of the counterbore hole and click when the handle of the concentric relationship is displayed.

5. Move the cursor to the bottom right fillet on the base feature and then move it to its center point. Click when the handle of the concentric relationship is displayed. The **Width** and **Height** edit boxes displays the value of 65.00.

6. Accept the other default options in the ribbon bar and exit the sketching environment. The preview of the pattern is displayed. Choose **Finish** from the ribbon bar and then exit the **Pattern** tool. The model, after creating the rectangular pattern, is shown in Figure 6-80.

Creating the Round

To complete the model, you need to create the round on the edge where the circular protrusion feature connects with the base feature. The fillet will be created using the constant radius fillet.

1. Choose the **Round** button from the **Features** toolbar and select the circular edge of the circular protrusion feature where it connects with the base feature.

2. Enter **5** in the **Radius** edit box and then choose the **Preview** button to display the preview of the fillet.

3. Choose the **Finish** button and then choose the **Cancel** button to exit the **Round** tool. The final model for Tutorial 3 is shown in Figure 6-81.

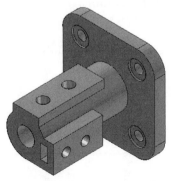

Figure 6-80 *Model after creating the pattern of the counterbore hole*

Figure 6-81 *Final model for Tutorial 3*

Saving the Model

1. Save the model with the name given below and then close the file.

    \Solid Edge\c06\c06tut3.par

Self-Evaluation Test

Answer the following questions and then compare them to those given at the end of this chapter:

1. Holes are the circular cut features that are generally provided for the purpose of assembling the model. (T/F)

2. The advanced modeling tools considerably reduce the time taken in creating the features in the models, thus reducing the designing time. (T/F)

3. If you have created the profile of the pattern using the **Sketch** tool, you can select that profile using the **Select from Sketch** option. (T/F)

4. You can press and hold the CTRL key and first select the features to be mirrored and then invoke the **Mirror Copy Feature** tool. (T/F)

5. In Solid Edge, you can also pattern the selected features along with an existing curve or an edge using the _____ tool.

6. The _____ button is chosen from the **Pattern** ribbon bar to create patterns that require more complex situations.

7. _____ is defined as the process of beveling the sharp edges of a model to reduce the area of stress concentration.

8. You can select the type of round to be created from the _____ dialog box.

9. The _____ radio button is selected from the **Chamfer Options** dialog box to create a chamfer with equal setback values of the selected edge from both the faces.

10. The **Round** tool allows you to create _____ different types of rounds.

Review Questions

Answer the following questions:

1. Which one of the following is not a type of hole in Solid Edge?

    (a) **Counterbore**   (b) **Countersink**
    (c) **Simple**   (d) **Sectional**

2. Which one of the following is not a type of pattern in Solid Edge?

   (a) **Circular**   (b) **Elliptical**
   (c) **Rectangular**   (d) **Pattern along curve**

3. Which one of the following is not a type of round in Solid Edge?

   (a) **Constant radius**   (b) **Variable radius**
   (c) **Point**   (d) **Blend**

4. Which one of the following tools is used to mirror bodies in Solid Edge?

   (a) **Mirror Copy**   (b) **Mirror Feature**
   (c) Both   (d) None

5. Which one of these options is used to create a chamfer by defining one setback distance value and one angle value?

   (a) **Equal setbacks**   (b) **2 Setbacks**
   (c) **Angle and setback**   (d) None

6. In which type of round can you specify multiple radius values along the length of the edge selected to fillet?

   (a) **Constant radius**   (b) **Variable radius**
   (c) **Point**   (d) **Blend**

7. The saved hole settings are also available in the drop-down list that is displayed when you choose the down arrow on the right of the **Hole Options** button in the ribbon bar. (T/F)

8. A counterbore hole is the one that has a uniform diameter throughout the length of the hole. (T/F)

9. If the **V bottom angle** check box is selected while creating a hole, the end of the hole will be tapered and it will converge into a point. (T/F)

10. If you have created the profile of the pattern using the **Sketch** tool, you can select that profile using the **Select from Sketch** option. (T/F)

Exercises

Exercise 1

Create the model shown in Figure 6-82. Its dimensions are given in the views shown in Figure 6-83. After creating the model, save it with the name given below:

\Solid Edge\c06\c06exr1.par   **(Expected time: 30 min)**

Figure 6-82 *Model for Exercise 1*

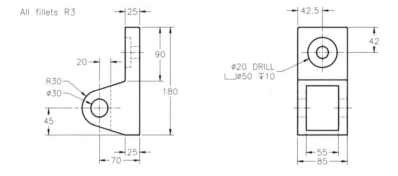

Figure 6-83 *Dimensions of the model for Exercise 1*

Exercise 2

Create the model shown in Figure 6-84. Its dimensions are given in the views shown in Figure 6-85. After creating the model, save it with the name given below:

\Solid Edge\c06\c06exr2.par **(Expected time: 30 min)**

Figure 6-84 *Model for Exercise 2*

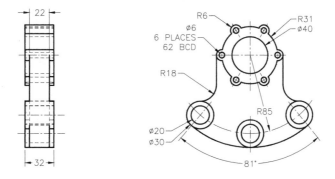

Figure 6-85 *Dimensions of the model for Exercise 2*

Exercise 3

Create the model shown in Figure 6-86. Its dimensions are given in the views shown in Figure 6-87. After creating the model, save it with the name given below:

   \Solid Edge\c06\c06exr3.par   **(Expected time: 30 min)**

Figure 6-86 *Model for Exercise 3*

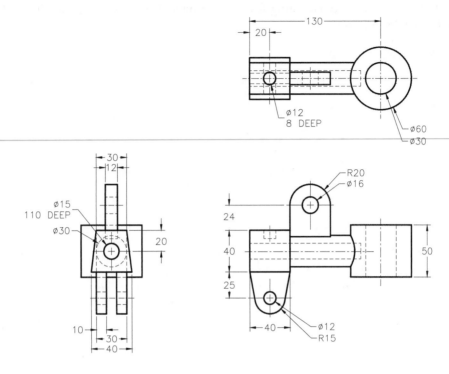

Figure 6-87 *Dimensions of the model for Exercise 3*

Answers to Self-Evaluation Test

1. T, **2.** T, **3.** T, **4.** T, **5. Pattern Along Curve**, **6. Smart**, **7.** Chamfering, **8. Round Options**, **9. Equal setbacks**, **10.** four

Chapter 7

Editing Features

Learning Objectives

After completing this chapter, you will be able to:
- *Edit features in a model.*
- *Edit the sketches of the sketched features.*
- *Redefine the sketching plane of a feature.*
- *Suppress features.*
- *Unsuppress features.*
- *Delete features.*
- *Copy and paste features.*
- *Assign a different color to a face or a feature.*

EDITING FEATURES IN A MODEL

Editing is one of the most important aspects of design process. Most designs require editing when they are being created or after their completion. As mentioned earlier, Solid Edge is a feature-based solid modeling tool. This is the reason any model created in Solid Edge is a combination of a number of features integrated together to complete the design. All these features are individual components and can be edited separately. For example, refer to Figure 7-1, which shows a plate with four counterbore holes.

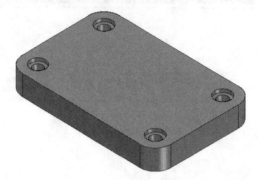

Figure 7-1 *Plate with four counterbore holes*

Next, if you want to change the counterbore holes to countersink holes and increase their number to six, you just need to perform two editing operations. The first editing operation is to invoke the **Holes** ribbon bar which can be used to modify the counterbore holes to countersink holes. You can specify various parameters for the countersink holes in the **Hole Options** dialog box that can be invoked using the ribbon bar. On exiting this dialog box, all four counterbore holes will be changed to countersink holes. The second editing operation is to invoke the **Pattern** ribbon bar that you can use to modify the number of occurrences in the pattern to six, as shown in Figure 7-2.

Similarly, you can also edit the sketches of the sketched features or edit the reference planes. The features created using the reference planes will be modified automatically when you edit the reference plane. For example, if you have created a feature on a reference plane that is at an angle of 45-degrees, the feature will be automatically repositioned on changing the angle value of the reference plane.

To edit features in Solid Edge, select the feature from the **EdgeBar** or from the drawing window. The ribbon bar displays three buttons, **Edit Definition**, **Edit Profile**, and **Dynamic Edit**. The use of all these buttons in editing the features is discussed next.

Edit Definition

You can invoke this editing tool by right-clicking on the feature in the **EdgeBar** or in the drawing window and choosing **Edit Definition** from the shortcut menu. When you select a feature and invoke this editing tool, the ribbon bar of the tool that was used to create that feature will be displayed with all the steps available in it. For example, if you select a protrusion feature and choose the **Edit Definition** button, the **Protrusion** ribbon

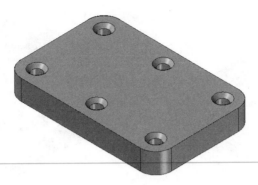

Figure 7-2 Plate with six countersink holes

bar will be displayed with the steps required for creating the protrusion feature. Also, the basic profile of the protrusion feature will be displayed in the model.

You can choose the button of the required step from the ribbon bar and modify the parameters as per your requirements. For example, if you want to change the plane on which the profile is drawn, choose the **Plane or Sketch Step** button and then select a reference plane or a planar face to place the profile; the **Part** dialog box will be displayed and you will be informed that the profile is placed on a new plane and some of the relationships may be lost. Choose **OK** from this dialog box to continue.

Edit Profile

You can invoke this editing tool by using the shortcut menu that is displayed when you right-click on the feature. This editing tool is used to directly invoke the sketching environment to edit the profile of a profile-based feature. Note that this button will not be available for a nonprofile-based feature such as a fillet or a chamfer. After editing the profile, exit the sketching environment; the ribbon bar of the tool that was used to create the profile-based feature will be displayed. Note that the changes made in the profile are reflected in the model. Exit this ribbon bar.

Dynamic Edit

When you choose this button, all dimensions of the selected feature will be displayed. You can select any of the dimensions and modify their values using the ribbon bar options. In case there are entities that have not been dimensioned, press and hold the left mouse button on such entities and then drag the cursor to dynamically edit the feature. Figure 7-3 shows a model being dynamically edited by dragging the entities and Figure 7-4 shows the same model after dynamically editing the sketch of the model.

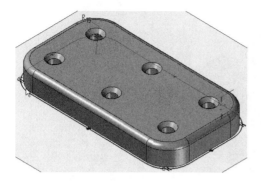

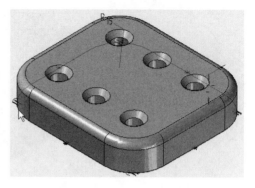

Figure 7-3 *Dynamically editing the model by dragging the sketch*

Figure 7-4 *The model after dynamically editing the profile*

Note

*If a feature of a model is not resolved after editing the selected feature, an arrow will be displayed on the left of the feature in the **EdgeBar**. You may also need to edit this feature to make sure that there is no error in it.*

Tip. *You are allowed to edit the profile of a profile-based feature dynamically by dragging because the option to do so is turned on in the **Options** dialog box. If you want to turn off the dynamic editing of profiles by dragging, choose **Tools > Options** from the menu bar to invoke the **Options** dialog box. Choose the **General** tab and clear the **Enable Dynamic Edit of profiles/sketches** check box in this tab.*

*If you select the **Recompute after edit** radio button, the model will be recomputed after the dragging is completed. By default, the model is recomputed as you drag the cursor to edit the profile.*

SUPPRESSING FEATURES

Sometimes, there may be a situation when you do not want some of the features to be displayed in the drawing views or in the printout of the model. In any of the nonfeature-based solid modeling tools, you need to either delete or create the feature after taking the printout. However, in Solid Edge, you can simply suppress the feature that you do not want at a particular stage. Once the feature is suppressed, it will not be displayed in the drawing window, drawing views of that model, or in the printout of the model. Remember that in such cases the features are not deleted, they are only temporarily turned off.

All the features that are dependent on the feature that you select to suppress are also suppressed. To suppress a feature, right-click on it in the **EdgeBar** and then choose **Suppress** from the shortcut menu, refer to Figure 7-5. All the features that are suppressed will have a red circle icon with an inclined line on their left in the **EdgeBar**. Alternatively, select the feature from the drawing area that you need to suppress and right-click on it; a shortcut menu will be displayed. Choose the **Suppress** option from this menu. The features dependent on the suppressed feature will have a red exclamatory mark in the **EdgeBar**.

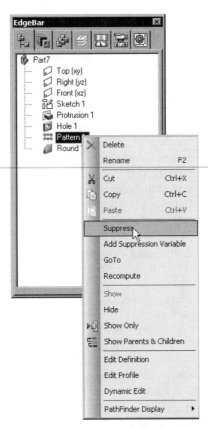

Figure 7-5 *Suppressing a feature using the* **EdgeBar**

UNSUPPRESSING THE SUPPRESSED FEATURES

The suppressed features can be resumed using the **EdgeBar**. To unsuppress a feature, right-click on the suppressed feature in the **EdgeBar** or in the drawing area and then choose **Unsuppress** from the shortcut menu; the selected feature will be displayed in the model again.

DELETING FEATURES

Select the feature to be deleted from the **EdgeBar** or from the model in the drawing window and press the DELETE key. The selected feature will be deleted. You can also right-click on a feature and choose **Delete** from the shortcut menu to delete it.

Tip. *If you generate the drawing views of the model that has some suppressed features, the suppressed features will not be displayed in the views. However, as soon as you unsuppress the features, they will be displayed in the drawing views.*

COPYING AND PASTING FEATURES

In Solid Edge, you can copy and paste a feature from the current file to any other file or at some other location in the same file. Note that if you select a nonprofile-based feature to copy, you must select the parent feature also. For example, you cannot select a fillet feature alone to copy. You also need to select the parent feature to which the fillet will be applied.

To copy a feature, right-click on the feature in the **EdgeBar** or in the drawing window and then choose **Copy** from the shortcut menu. You can also press the CTRL+C keys to copy the selected features. To paste the feature in another file, you need to open the file. Right-click in the drawing window to display the shortcut menu and then choose **Paste** from it; the ribbon bar will be displayed and the **Plane Step** will be activated. This is the reason you will be prompted to select a planar face or a reference plane. Select the reference plane or the planar face on which you want to paste the feature; the preview of the profile of the selected feature will be attached to the cursor. Also, you will be prompted to click on a point where the feature will be pasted. You can paste multiple copies of the feature by specifying the points.

Figure 7-6 shows the hole feature selected to be pasted on a different planar face and Figure 7-7 shows the model after placing three copies of the hole feature.

Figure 7-6 *Hole feature selected*   *Figure 7-7* *Three copies of the hole feature placed on the selected plane*

You can also copy and paste the feature within one file or from one file to the other by dragging. To copy and paste the feature from one file to the other, open the file from which you want to copy the feature and the file in which you want to paste it. After opening the files, choose **Window > Arrange** from the menu bar to display the **Arrange Windows** dialog box, as shown in Figure 7-8. Select the **Tiled**, **Horizontal**, or the **Vertical** option to arrange both windows. Activate the file from which you want to copy the feature by clicking on it. Press and hold the left mouse button on the feature that you want to copy and then drag the cursor to the other window. In the other window, release the left mouse button; the preview of the profile of the feature will be attached to the cursor. Also, the ribbon bar will be displayed and you will be prompted to click on a planar face or a reference plane. When you select the plane to paste the feature, the   copied feature will be placed on the sketched planar face. Figure 7-9 shows the countersink hole being copied from one file to the other.

*Figure 7-8 The **Arrange Windows** dialog box*

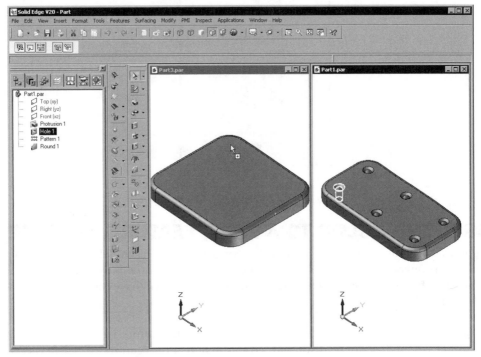

Figure 7-9 Copying a feature from one file to the other by dragging

ROLLING BACK THE MODEL TO A FEATURE

Solid Edge enables you to roll back the model to a particular feature in such a way that all features created after the selected feature are suppressed. Also, if you create a new feature in the rolled back state, it will be placed after the feature up to which the model is rolled back and before all the suppressed features. To roll back the model to a particular feature, select the feature in the **EdgeBar**. Right-click to display the shortcut menu and choose **GoTo**, as shown in Figure 7-10; the model will be rolled back to the selected feature. To retain the original state of the model, then you need to select the last feature and choose **GoTo** from the shortcut menu; all features of the model will be unsuppressed and the model will regain its original state.

Figure 7-10 *Rolling back the model to a particular feature*

ASSIGNING COLOR TO A PART, FEATURE, OR FACE

Sometimes, you may need to represent a face or a feature of a model differently from the others for the purpose of presentation. In Solid Edge, you can do this by assigning a different color to the selected face or feature. The remaining features will have the color of the model, but the selected face or feature can be assigned a different color.

To assign a different color to a face, choose **Format > Part Painter** from the menu bar; the **Part Painter** ribbon bar will be displayed. From the **Select** drop-down list, select the item to which you want to apply a different color. Now, from the **Style** drop-down list, select the color you want to assign to the selected item. Next, select the item in the model. The selected item will be assigned with the specified color.

PLAYING BACK THE CONSTRUCTION OF FEATURES

Using Solid Edge, you can view the animation of the sequence of the feature construction. This is done using the **Feature Playback** tab of the **EdgeBar**. Choose the **Feature Playback** button available at the top of the **Edgebar** toolbar; the **Feature Playback** tab, containing the list of features and animation features in the model will be invoked. Choose the **Play** button to view the animation of the feature construction of the model. All features in the model will be replayed in the sequence in which they were created. You can use other control buttons to control the playback of the features. You can also modify the time gap between playback of the features by entering the required value in the **seconds between features** edit box.

After playing back the features of the model, you can return to the tree view of the features by choosing the **Feature PathFinder** button from the toolbar available at the top of the **EdgeBar**. As soon as you switch to the tree view in the **Feature PathFinder** tab, all the features of the model will be restored.

CHECKING THE PHYSICAL PROPERTIES OF A MODEL

Checking the physical properties of a model and storing them for further use is an integral part of any designing tool. To check the physical properties of a model in Solid Edge, choose **Inspect > Physical Properties** from the menu bar; the **Physical Properties** dialog box will be displayed, as shown in Figure 7-11.

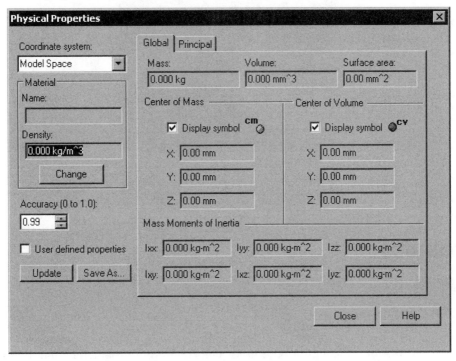

Figure 7-11 *The* *Physical Properties* *dialog box*

As is evident in this dialog box, the default density of the material is taken as 0. To specify the density of the required material, choose the **Change** button; the **Solid Edge Material Table** dialog box will be displayed. You can change the value of the required parameters in this dialog box. Choose the **Apply to Model** button and then the **Update** button; the physical properties of the model will be modified on the basis of the modified material properties from the **Solid Edge Material Table** dialog box and displayed in the **Global** and **Principal** tabs. You can also save the physical properties as text files by choosing the **Save As** button in Solid Edge.

MODIFYING THE DISPLAY OF CONSTRUCTION ENTITIES

 Solid Edge allows you to show or hide all the construction entities together using the **Construction Display** dialog box, as shown in Figure 7-12. To invoke this dialog box, choose the **Construction Display** button from the **Features** toolbar.

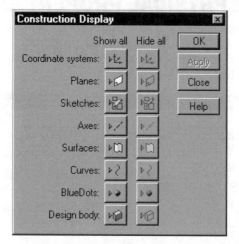

*Figure 7-12 The **Construction Display** dialog box*

You can choose the buttons in the **Show all** column or the **Hide all** column to modify the display of the construction entities.

TUTORIALS

Tutorial 1

In this tutorial, you will create the model shown in Figure 7-13. Its dimensions are given in the drawing views shown in Figure 7-14. After creating the model, modify the central hole in the cylindrical feature to a counterbore hole. The counterbore diameter should be 36 and the hole diameter should be 24. The counterbore depth should be 10.

Also, change the holes on the top planar face of the model to countersink holes with the countersink diameter 14 and hole diameter 8. The countersink angle should be 82-degrees. Increase the number of occurrences along the shorter side to 3. Save the model with the name given below:

  \Solid Edge\c07\c07tut1.par   **(Expected time: 30 min)**

The following steps are required to complete this tutorial:

a. Start Solid Edge in the **Part** environment and create the base feature on the front plane, refer to Figure 7-16.
b. Create a simple hole in the cylindrical feature of the model, refer to Figure 7-17.

Figure 7-13 Model for Tutorial 1

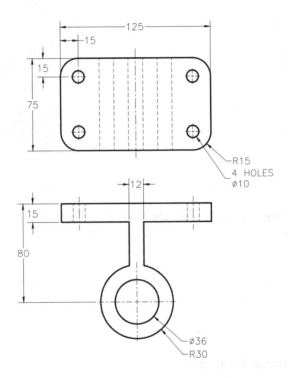

Figure 7-14 Dimensions of the model for Tutorial 1

c. Add a round to the vertical edges of the top of the base feature, refer to Figure 7-18.
d. Create a simple hole on the top face of the base feature, refer to Figure 7-19.
e. Create a rectangular pattern of the holes on the top face of the base feature, refer to Figure 7-20.
f. Modify the central hole and the hole on the top face of the base feature.
g. Modify the number of items in the rectangular pattern of holes.
h. Save the model and close the file.

Creating the Base Feature

As mentioned earlier, the base feature is a protrusion feature and its profile will be created on the front plane. The profile will be extruded symmetrically.

1. Start a new Solid Edge part document and then select the front plane as the sketching plane for the protrusion feature.

2. Draw the profile for the protrusion feature, as shown in Figure 7-15 and then add the required relationships and dimensions to the profile.

3. Exit the sketching environment and extrude the profile to 75 mm symmetrically to create the base feature, as shown in Figure 7-16.

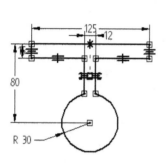

Figure 7-15 *Sketch of the base feature*   *Figure 7-16* *Base feature of the model*

Creating a Simple Hole in the Cylindrical Feature

1. Invoke the **Hole** tool and modify the diameter of the simple hole to 36 in the **Hole Options** dialog box.

2. Select the front planar face of the base feature as the sketching plane and place the profile of the hole concentric to the cylindrical feature.

3. Exit the sketching environment and create the hole, as shown in Figure 7-17.

Creating the Round Feature

1. Invoke the **Round** tool and select the vertical edges on the top planar portion of the base of the feature.

2. Specify the radius of the round and then exit the **Round** tool to complete the operation. The model, after creating the round, is shown in Figure 7-18.

Creating a Simple Hole on the Top Face

1. Invoke the **Hole** tool from the **Features** toolbar and modify the diameter of the simple hole to 10 in the **Hole Options** dialog box.

Figure 7-17 *Model after creating the central hole*   *Figure 7-18* *Model after creating the round*

2. Select the top planar face of the base feature as the sketching plane and place the profile of the hole concentric to the fillet on the lower left vertex.

3. Exit the sketching environment and create the hole, as shown in Figure 7-19.

Creating a Rectangular Pattern of the Hole

1. Invoke the **Pattern** tool from the **Features** toolbar. Select the hole on the top planar face as the feature to pattern and then select the top planar face as the sketching plane.

2. Use the center points of the fillets on the lower left corner and the upper right corner to draw the profile of the rectangular pattern. Accept the default value for the number of occurrences and exit the sketching environment.

3. Specify the side of the feature creation and then exit the tool. The model, after creating the pattern, is shown in Figure 7-20.

Figure 7-19 *Model after creating a simple hole on the top plane*   *Figure 7-20* *Model after patterning the hole*

Editing Holes

As mentioned in the tutorial statement, you need to modify the simple hole on the cylindrical feature to a counterbore hole, and the simple hole on the top face to a countersink hole. Therefore, you need to edit both these holes. The first hole was the central hole on the cylindrical feature and so it will be displayed as **Hole 1** in the **EdgeBar**.

1. Select **Hole 1** from the **EdgeBar** and then choose the **Edit Definition** button from the ribbon bar to display the **Hole** ribbon bar.

2. Choose the **Hole Options** button and then change the simple hole to a counterbore hole of the specified dimensions. The preview of the counterbore hole, along with its profile, is displayed on the model.

3. Choose the **Finish** button to complete the modification in the hole.

4. Now, select **Hole 2** from the **EdgeBar** and then choose the **Edit Definition** button from the ribbon bar to display the **Hole** ribbon bar.

5. Choose the **Hole Options** button and then change the simple hole to a countersink hole of specified dimensions. The preview of the countersink hole, along with its profile, is displayed on the model.

6. Again, choose the **Finish** button to complete the modification in the hole. The model, after making the changes in the holes, is shown in Figure 7-21.

Note that the remaining three holes are also modified to a countersink hole and an arrow is displayed on the left of **Pattern 1** in the **EdgeBar**. This arrow shows that the pattern feature is not recomputed properly and it needs to be edited.

Figure 7-21   *Model after editing the holes*

Editing the Pattern

Next, you will edit the pattern of the holes. To do so, you need to increase the number of occurrences along the short side of the top face to 3.

1. Click on **Pattern 1** in the **EdgeBar** and then choose the **Edit Profile** button from the ribbon bar to invoke the sketching environment.

    It is recommended that you delete the original profile and create the profile of the rectangular pattern again. This is because if you try to edit the existing profile, the arrow on the left of the pattern may still be displayed after you edit the pattern.

2. Delete the existing profile of the rectangular pattern and then draw the profile again.

3. Specify 3 occurrences of the pattern along the shorter edge of the face.

4. Exit the sketching environment and then choose **Finish** from the ribbon bar. The model, after editing the required features, is shown in Figure 7-22.

Figure 7-22 Final model after editing the pattern of holes

Saving the Model
1. Save the model in the location and the name given below and then close the file.

    \Solid Edge\c07\c07tut1.par

Tutorial 2

In this tutorial, you will create the model shown in Figure 7-23. Its dimensions are given in the drawing views shown in Figure 7-24. In this model, you will create one of the holes using the **Hole** tool and the remaining holes will be created by copying and pasting the first hole. Save the model in the location and with name given below:
    \Solid Edge\c07\c07tut2.par   **(Expected time: 30 min)**

The following steps are required to complete this tutorial:

a. Start a new part file and create the base feature on the top plane, refer to Figure 7-26.
b. Add the other protrusion features to the model, refer to Figure 7-27.
c. Create a simple hole on one of the faces of the model, refer to Figure 7-28.
d. Copy and paste the holes on the other faces, refer to Figure 7-30.

Figure 7-23 *Model for Tutorial 2*

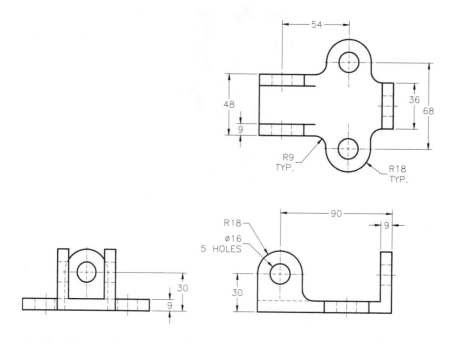

Figure 7-24 *Dimensions of the model for Tutorial 2*

e.   Edit the profiles of the copied holes and make them concentric to the arcs on the faces, refer to Figure 7-31.
f.   Save the model and close the file.

Creating the Base Feature

As mentioned earlier, the base feature is a protrusion feature and its profile will be created on the top plane.

1. Start a new part file and then select the top plane as the sketching plane for the protrusion feature.

2. Create the profile of the base feature, as shown in Figure 7-25 and then extrude it. The base feature of the model is shown in Figure 7-26.

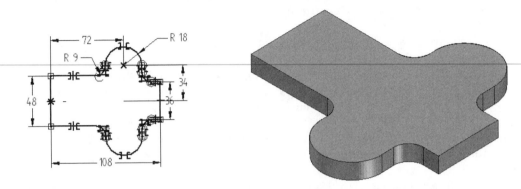

Figure 7-25 *Figure showing the ellipse*

Figure 7-26 *Base feature of the model*

Adding the Remaining Protrusion Features and Round Feature

1. Invoke the **Protrusion** and **Mirror Copy Feature** tools to add the remaining protrusion features to the model.

2. Add the required rounds to the model, as shown in Figure 7-27.

Creating a Simple Hole on a Face

1. Use the **Hole** tool to create a simple hole on one of the faces of the model, as shown in Figure 7-28. Make sure the hole is created using the **Through All** extents.

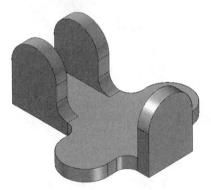

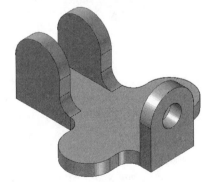

Figure 7-27 *Model after adding the other protrusion and round features*

Figure 7-28 *Model after adding the simple hole*

Copying and Pasting Holes on the Other Faces

Next, you need to copy and paste the holes on the other faces. Note that you need to edit the profiles of the holes after placing them to make sure the holes are concentric to the arc features on the faces on which they are placed.

1. Select the hole in the **EdgeBar** or in the drawing window and right-click to display the shortcut menu. Choose **Copy** from it.

2. Click anywhere in the drawing window to make sure the hole is no more selected.

3. Right-click in the drawing window and choose **Paste** from the shortcut menu; the ribbon bar is displayed and the **Plane** step is activated in the ribbon bar. This is the reason you are prompted to click on a planar face or a reference plane.

4. Select the front planar face of the vertical feature, as shown in Figure 7-29; the profile of the hole is attached to the cursor.

5. Move the cursor close to the center point of the arc on the face and place the hole feature. You will notice that the hole feature is also created on the protrusion feature on the other side of the base feature, as shown in Figure 7-30. This is because the original hole was created using the **Through All** extent.

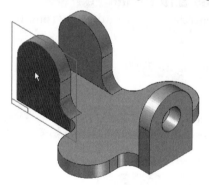

Figure 7-29 *Selecting the face to paste the hole feature*

Figure 7-30 *Model after pasting the hole on the selected face*

Next, you need to paste the holes on the top face of the base feature. Therefore, you need to invoke the **Plane** step again and select the top planar face of the base feature as the sketching plane.

Note

If you cannot find the center point of the arc, you can place the hole on the feature and can provide the concentric relationship to modify the sketch.

6. Choose the **Plane Step** button from the ribbon bar and select the top planar face of the base feature; the **Solid Edge** message box is displayed. Choose **OK** from this message dialog box.

7. Place two holes on the top planar face close to the two arcs on the base feature.

8. Choose **Finish** from the ribbon bar. You will notice that all the three holes are displayed as three separate hole features in the **EdgeBar**.

    Next, you need to edit the profiles of the three holes and add concentric relationships to them to properly locate the holes.

9. Right-click on **Hole 2** in the **EdgeBar** and choose **Edit Profile** from the shortcut menu; the sketching environment is invoked and the profile of the hole feature is displayed.

10. Add the concentric relationship to the hole profile and the arc in the feature. Exit the sketching environment and then choose **Finish** to terminate the tool.

11. Similarly, edit the profiles of the remaining two holes. The final model, after editing the profiles of all the holes, is shown in Figure 7-31.

Figure 7-31 Final model for Tutorial 2

Saving the Model

1. Save the model in the location and the name *Solid Edge\c07\c07tut2.par* and then close the file.

Tutorial 3

In this tutorial, you will create the model shown in Figure 7-32. Its dimensions are given in Figure 7-33. After completing the model, you will modify the dimension 100 of the base to 120 and modify the dimensions of the other corresponding features as well. Save the model in the location and the name and location given below:

　　　Solid Edge\c07\c07tut3.par.   **(Expected time: 30 min)**

The following steps are required to complete this tutorial:

a. Start a new part file and create the base feature on the front plane, refer to Figure 7-34.
b. Add the other protrusion features on the top face of the model, refer to Figure 7-35.

c. Add the features on the back face of the model, refer to Figure 7-36.
d. Create two hole features, refer to Figure 7-37.
e. Edit the extrusion depth of the base feature, refer to Figure 7-38.
f. Change the color of the model to copper.
g. Save the model and close the file.

Figure 7-32 *Model for Tutorial 3*

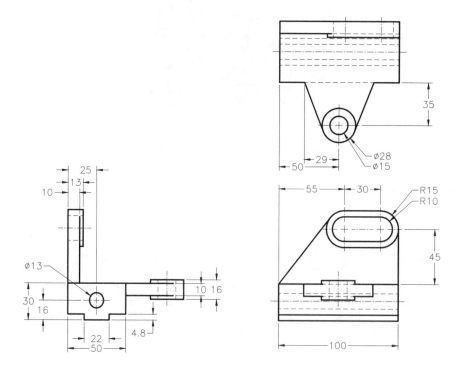

Figure 7-33 *Dimensions of the model for Tutorial 3*

Creating the Base Feature

1. Start a new part file and create the base feature of the model on the front plane, as shown in Figure 7-34. Make sure you create the feature by extruding the profile symmetrically.

Creating Protrusion Features on the Top Face of the Base Feature

1. Create two protrusion features on the top face of the base feature, as shown in Figure 7-35. It is recommended that you add the **Connect** relationship to the center of the arc in the second feature and the vertical plane. This ensures that even if the depth of extrusion of the base feature is modified, the second and third features will remain at the center of the base feature.

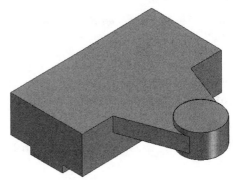

Figure 7-34 *Base feature of the model*

Figure 7-35 *Model after adding features on the top face of the base feature*

Creating Features on the Back Face of the Base Feature

1. Create two protrusion features and the cutout on the back face of the base feature, as shown in Figure 7-36. It is recommended that you include the horizontal edge of the base feature to create the protrusion feature. This is because when you edit the depth of the base feature, the protrusion feature is modified accordingly. Also, do not add the dimension 55. Instead, apply the **Vertical** relationship to the right edge. This helps in editing the base feature.

Creating Simple Holes

1. Create two simple holes in the model to complete it, as shown in Figure 7-37.

Editing the Base Feature

1. Double-click on **Protrusion 1** in the **EdgeBar**; all dimensions associated with the base feature are displayed in the drawing window.

2. Select the dimension that shows the depth of protrusion. The value of this dimension is 100.

    As soon as you select this dimension, the ribbon bar will display the **Dimension Value** edit box, in which you can modify this value.

3. Enter the value **120** in the **Dimension Value** edit box.

Figure 7-36 *Model after creating features on the back face*

Figure 7-37 *Model after creating holes*

All other features in the model are automatically modified. Note that if you add a dimension of 50 to the second feature from the left of the base feature, you will also need to modify this dimension.

4. Double-click anywhere in the drawing window to exit the editing operation. The model, after editing the feature, is shown in Figure 7-38.

Figure 7-38 *Final model after editing the base feature*

Changing the Color of the Model

Next, you need to change the color of the model to copper. This is done using the **Part Painter** tool.

1. Choose **Format > Part Painter** from the menu bar to display the **Part Painter** ribbon bar.

2. Select **Copper** from the **Style** drop-down list and **Body** from the **Select** drop-down list.

3. Select the model in the drawing window; the color of the model is automatically changed to copper. Close the ribbon bar.

Saving the Model

1. Save the model in the location and the name \Solid Edge\c07\c07tut3.par and then close the file.

Self-Evaluation Test

Answer the following questions and then compare them to those given at the end of this chapter:

1. The model created in Solid Edge is a combination of a number of features that are integrated together to complete the design. (T/F)

2. In Solid Edge, you can view the animation of the sequence of the feature construction. (T/F)

3. All the features that are suppressed will have a red square icon with an inclined line in the **EdgeBar**. (T/F)

4. In Solid Edge, the ribbon bar displays only two buttons, **Edit Definition** and **Dynamic Edit** to edit features. (T/F)

5. To check the physical properties of the model in Solid Edge, choose **Inspect > _____** from the menu bar.

6. To delete features, select them from the **EdgeBar** or from the drawing window and then press the _____ key.

7. When you suppress a feature that has some dependent features, the dependent features are also _____.

8. To suppress a feature, right-click on it and then choose _____ from the shortcut menu.

9. While calculating the physical properties of the model, the default density of the material is taken as _____.

10. To assign a different color to a face, choose **Format > _____** from the menu bar.

Review Questions

Answer the following questions:

1. If any feature of a model is not resolved after editing the selected feature, an arrow is displayed on the left of the feature in the **EdgeBar**. (T/F)

2. The **Edit Profile** button will not be available for editing a nonprofile-based feature such as a fillet. (T/F)

3.   In Solid Edge, you cannot copy and paste a feature within one file or from one file to the other by dragging. (T/F)

4.   Checking the physical properties of a model and storing it for further use is an integral part of any designing tool. (T/F)

5.   If you have created a feature on a reference plane that is at an angle of 45-degrees, the feature will not be automatically repositioned on changing the angle value of the reference plane. (T/F)

6.   In case some entities in the profile are not dimensioned, you can press and hold the left mouse button on them and then drag the cursor to dynamically edit the feature. (T/F)

7.   In Solid Edge, you can assign a different color to a selected face or feature. (T/F)

8.   Once the feature is _____, it still remains in the memory of the model but will not be displayed in the drawing window, drawing views, or in the printout of the model.

9.   If you select a nonprofile-based feature to copy, you must select the _____ feature also.

10. To copy a feature, right-click on it and choose _____ from the shortcut menu.

Exercises

Exercise 1

Open the model created in Exercise 1 of Chapter 6 and modify some of its dimensions. After modifying the dimensions, save it with the name given below so that the original file is not modified.

   \Solid Edge\c07\c07exr1.par   **(Expected time: 15 min)**

Exercise 2

Create the model shown in Figure 7-39. The dimensions of the model are given in the views shown in Figure 7-40. After creating the model, edit some of its dimensions. Save it with the name given below:

   \Solid Edge\c07\c07exr2.par   **(Expected time: 30 min)**

Figure 7-39 Model for Exercise 2

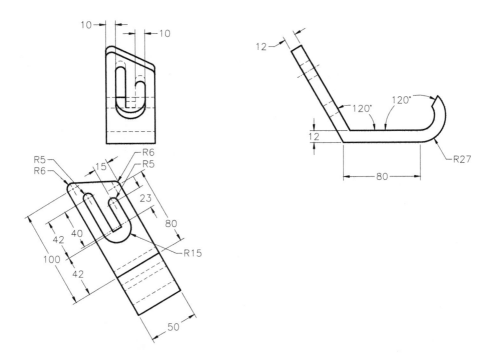

Figure 7-40 Dimensions of the model for Exercise 2

Answers to Self-Evaluation Test
1. T, **2.** T, **3.** F, **4.** F, **5. Physical Properties**, **6.** DELETE, **7.** suppressed, **8. Suppress**, **9.** 0,
10. Part Painter

Chapter 8

Advanced Modeling Tools-II

Learning Objectives

After completing this chapter, you will be able to:
- *Use the Thread tool for creating external and internal threads.*
- *Add drafts to models.*
- *Add lip features.*
- *Create thin wall features.*
- *Create thin region features.*
- *Create ribs.*
- *Create web networks.*
- *Create vent features.*
- *Create mounting bosses.*

ADVANCED MODELING TOOLS

In this chapter, you will learn about some advanced modeling tools. The remaining advanced modeling tools will be discussed in the later chapters.

CREATING INTERNAL OR EXTERNAL THREADS

Toolbar:	Features > Hole > Thread

In Solid Edge, you can create internal or external threads using the **Thread** tool. Internal threads are created in a hole or in circular cut features, and external threads are created on the external surface of a cylindrical feature. Note that you need to select only standard size holes or cylinders to create threads. These standard sizes are available in the **Diameter** edit box of the **Hole Options** dialog box. In Solid Edge, the faces that are threaded are shaded in green. To create threads, invoke the **Thread** tool; the **Thread Options** dialog box is displayed, as shown in Figure 8-1. The options available in this dialog box are discussed next.

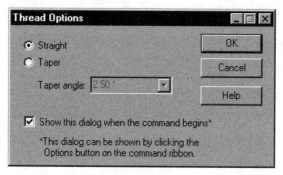

Figure 8-1 *The **Thread Options** dialog box*

Straight

This radio button is selected to create threads on a straight feature.

Taper

This radio button is selected to create threads on a tapered feature.

Taper angle

This edit box is available when you select the **Taper** radio button. You can enter the taper angle in this edit box or select the predefined taper angles from the **Taper angle** drop-down list.

After specifying the parameters in the **Thread Options** dialog box, this tool works in three steps that are discussed next.

Tip. *If you try to create threads on holes or cylinders with non-standard diameters, a warning box will be displayed, informing you that this diameter is not listed in the HOLES.txt file.*

Select Cylinder Step

This step is automatically invoked when you exit the **Thread Options** dialog box. It enables you to select the cylinder or hole to create threads.

Cylinder End Step

This step will be automatically invoked after you select a cylinder or a hole to create threads. In this step, you can select one of the ends of the selected cylinder or hole as the edge from where the threads will be offset.

Parameters Step

This step enables you to specify the parameters of the thread that you want to create. The options available in the ribbon bar of this step are discussed next.

Offset

This edit box is used to specify the distance between the start of the thread and the cylinder end selected in the second step.

Depth

This drop-down list is used to specify the depth up to which the thread will be created. The options available in this drop-down list are discussed next.

To cylinder extent

This is the default option and it creates threads through the entire length of the cylinder or hole.

Finite value

This option enables you to create threads up to a specified depth. When you select the **Finite value** option, the **Thread Depth** edit box is invoked on the right of this drop-down list. You can specify the depth value in this edit box.

Type

This drop-down list is used to specify the type of thread that you want to create. The options in this drop-down list are available depending on the size of the selected cylinder or hole. You can select any option from this drop-down list to create threads.

Note
If the hole or the cylinder feature that you selected does not have a standard diameter, then no option will be available in the **Type** *drop-down list and the threads will not be created.*

Thread unit

This drop-down list is used to specify the unit of threads.

ADDING DRAFTS TO THE MODEL

Toolbar:	Features > Add Draft

Adding a draft is the process of tapering the selected faces of a model for their easy removal from casting during manufacturing. You can add a draft using the **Add Draft** tool. In Solid Edge, you can add drafts using four options. You can select the required option to create a draft from the **Draft Options** dialog box, as shown in Figure 8-2. This dialog box will be displayed when you choose the **Draft Options** button from the **Add Draft** ribbon bar. In this chapter, you will learn to create a draft using the first two options. The remaining options will be discussed in the later chapters.

*Figure 8-2 The **Draft Options** dialog box*

Creating a Draft Using the From plane Option

This is the default option for creating a draft and is automatically selected in the **Draft Options** dialog box. You can create a draft from a plane in the following three steps:

Draft Plane Step

When you invoke the **Add Draft** tool or exit the **Draft Options** dialog box after selecting the option to create the draft, this step will be activated and you will be prompted to click on a planar face or a reference plane. You can also use the **Create-From Options** drop-down list from the **Add Draft** ribbon bar to create a new reference plane. The draft plane is a plane whose normal is used to define the draft angle. Figures 8-3 and 8-4 show the draft added to a model. In both figures, all parameters are the same, except the draft plane. In Figure 8-3, the top planar face is selected as the draft plane and in Figure 8-4, the bottom planar face is selected as the draft plane.

Select Face Step

This step will be automatically invoked as soon as you define the draft plane. This step enables you to select one or more faces on which the draft will be added. You can use the

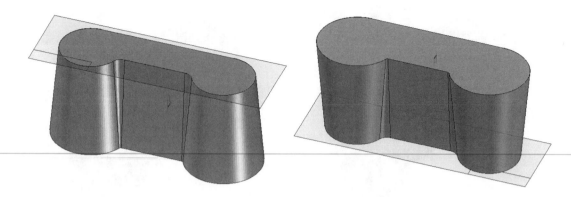

Figure 8-3 *Draft added with top face as the draft plane*

Figure 8-4 *Draft added with bottom face as the draft plane*

options in the **Select** drop-down list to select the faces to draft. Next, enter the draft angle in the **Draft Angle** edit box. Note that you cannot enter a negative draft angle value because you need to define the side of the draft in the next step.

After setting the parameters in the ribbon bar in the **Select Face Step**, right-click to accept the selection and then choose the **Next** button from the ribbon bar to proceed to the next step. You can also right-click again to proceed to the next step.

Draft Direction Step

This step enables you to define the direction of the draft. In this step, once the edge of the draft plane is selected, a two-sided arrow will be displayed on it. This arrow is used to define the direction of the draft. You can move the cursor in the drawing window and specify a point to define the direction of the draft. Figures 8-5 through 8-8 show the draft directions and the resulting drafts.

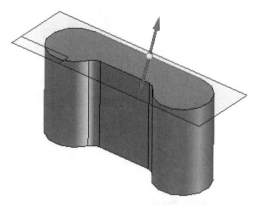

Figure 8-5 *Defining the draft direction using an inclined line on the upper horizontal edge*

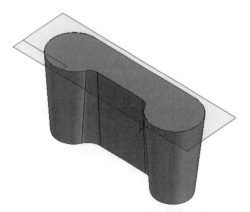

Figure 8-6 *Resulting draft*

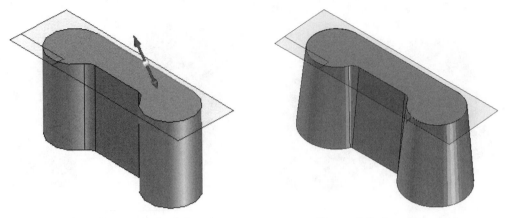

Figure 8-7 Defining the draft direction   *Figure 8-8 Resulting draft*

Creating a Draft Using the From edge Option

The method of creating a draft from an edge is similar to that of creating a draft from a plane. The only difference is that in the edge draft, you are allowed to select an edge from where the draft angle will be measured. This is done in the **Select Parting Geometry Step** that is invoked after the **Draft Plane** step. Note that out of all the selected faces, the draft will be added only to the face from which the selected edge will pass.

ADDING RIBS TO THE MODEL

Toolbar:	Features > Rib

Ribs are defined as thin wall-like structures which are used to bind the joints together so that they do not fail under an increased load. In Solid Edge, ribs are created using an open profile, see Figures 8-9 and 8-10.

Figure 8-9 Open profile to create a rib   *Figure 8-10 Resulting rib feature*

The process of creating ribs is completed in four steps, which are discussed next.

Plane or Sketch Step

This step enables you to select a sketching plane for drawing the profile of the rib feature. You can also select an existing profile using the **Select from Sketch** option from the **Create-From Options** drop-down list. It is recommended that the profile of the rib feature should be extruded symmetrically. Therefore, you need to select the sketching plane accordingly for drawing the profile.

Draw Profile Step

This step will be automatically invoked when you select the sketching plane for drawing the profile of the rib feature.

Direction Step

This step will be automatically invoked when you select the profile and accept it or draw the profile and exit the sketching environment. This step enables you to define the direction of the rib creation, and therefore, you are prompted to click to accept the displayed side or select the other side in the view. The feature can be created in a direction normal to the profile or parallel to it. If you move the cursor in the drawing window, a dynamic preview of the rib feature will be displayed in various directions. Note that the rib feature will be successfully created only if you define that side for the feature creation in which the profile meets the faces of the existing features. If the feature cannot be created, an error symbol will be displayed, as shown in Figure 8-11. Figure 8-12 shows the preview of the direction in which the rib feature will be successfully created.

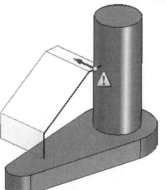

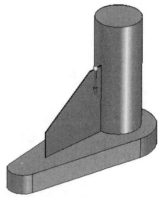

Figure 8-11 *Preview of the direction in which the rib will not be created and the error symbol*

Figure 8-12 *Preview of the direction in which the rib will be created*

Side Step

The **Side Step** button will be active in the ribbon bar. Choose this button to define the direction of the rib creation. In the **Side Step**, you are allowed to specify the side of the sketching plane on which the rib will be created. You can move the cursor on either side of the profile to define it. As mentioned earlier, it is recommended to create rib symmetrically on both sides of the sketching plane. To create a symmetric rib, move the cursor close to the profile; the preview of the symmetric rib will be displayed, as shown in Figure 8-13. Next, click to create the symmetric rib.

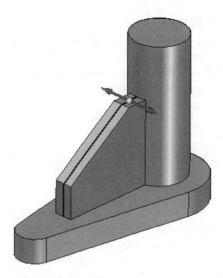

Figure 8-13 *Preview of the symmetric rib*

Note that in the **Direction** and **Side** steps, some additional options are available in the ribbon bar. These options are discussed next.

Extend Profile

This button is chosen by default and is used to extend the rib feature to the adjacent features, even if the profile does not extend to them. Figure 8-14 shows an open profile for creating the rib. As is evident in this figure, the open profile does not extend to the adjacent features. Figure 8-15 shows the rib feature created using the same profile with the **Extend Profile** button chosen. As is evident in this figure, the rib feature has been extended to the adjacent features.

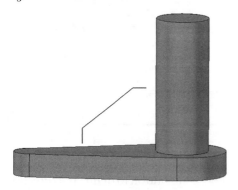

Figure 8-14 *Open profile not extended to the adjacent features for creating rib feature*

Figure 8-15 *Rib feature extended to the adjacent features*

No Extend

This button is chosen when you do not want to extend the rib to the adjacent faces. Figure 8-16 shows the profile and the resulting rib created by choosing the **Extend Profile** button and Figure 8-17 shows the rib feature created by choosing the **No Extend** button.

Figure 8-16 *Rib feature extended to the adjacent faces using the* ***Extend Profile*** *button*

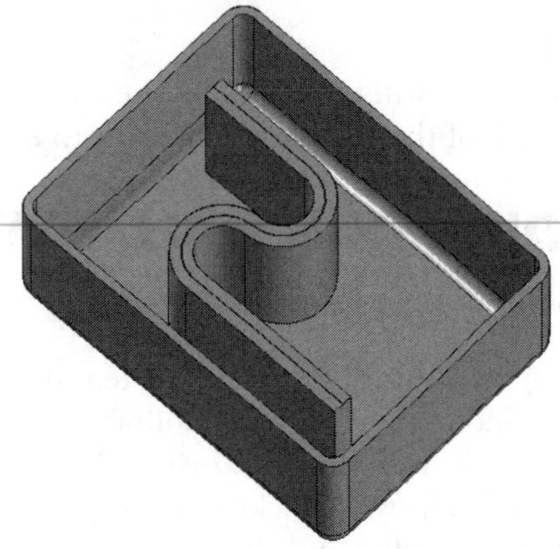

Figure 8-17 *Rib feature not extended to the adjacent faces using the* ***No Extend*** *button*

Extend to Next

This button is chosen when you want to extend the rib to the next features in the direction that you specified in the **Direction** step. Figure 8-18 shows the rib feature created using this option.

Finite Depth

This button is chosen when you want to extend the rib to a finite depth in the direction that you specified in the **Direction** step. The depth of the rib can be specified in the **Depth** edit box that will be displayed on the right of the **Thickness** edit box on choosing the **Finite Depth** button. Figure 8-19 shows the rib feature created using this option.

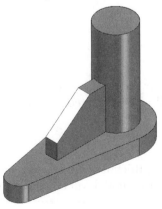

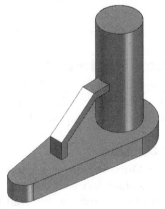

Figure 8-18 *Rib feature created by extending the profile to the next features*

Figure 8-19 *Rib feature created up to a finite depth*

Thickness

This edit box is used to specify the thickness of the rib feature. The default thickness is 0.25 and you can enter any desired thickness value for the rib in this edit box. You can also select the predefined thickness values using the **Thickness** edit box.

Depth

This edit box will be available when you choose the **Finite Depth** button. It is used to specify the depth of the rib when you want to extend it to a finite depth.

ADDING THIN WALL FEATURES

Toolbar:	Features > Thin Wall

By adding the thin wall feature, you will be able to scoop out the material from a model and make it hollow from inside. The resulting model will be a structure of walls with a cavity inside. You can also remove some of the faces of the model or apply different wall thicknesses to some of them. Figure 8-20 shows a model with the thin wall feature added and the front face removed.

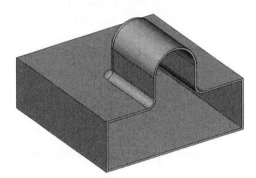

Figure 8-20 *Model with the thin wall feature added*

This tool works in the following three steps:

Common Thickness

This step enables you to specify the common thickness for the thin wall feature. You can also specify the side of the solid toward which the thin wall will be created. The options in the ribbon bar under this step are discussed next.

Offset Outside

The **Offset Outside** button is chosen to define the wall thickness outside the model with respect to its outer faces. In this case, the outer faces of the model will be considered as the inner walls of the resulting thin wall feature.

Offset Inside

The **Offset Inside** button is chosen by default and is used to define the wall thickness inside the model with respect to its outer faces. In this case, the outer faces of the model will be considered as the outer walls of the resulting thin wall feature.

Symmetrical

The **Symmetrical** button is chosen to calculate the wall thickness equally in both the directions of the outer faces of the model.

Common thickness

This edit box is used to specify the common thickness for the thin wall feature.

Open Faces

This step will be automatically invoked when you specify the common thickness and press ENTER. In this step, you can specify the face that you want to remove from the thin wall feature. You can use the **Select** drop-down list to define the selection method. After specifying the faces to be removed, choose the Accept button and then choose the **Preview** button to preview the thin wall feature. Figure 8-21 shows a thin wall model with the front and left side faces removed.

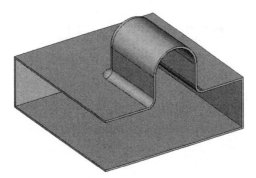

Figure 8-21 *Thin wall model with the front and left faces removed*

Unique Thickness

This step is not necessarily required to create the thin wall feature, and therefore, it will not be invoked automatically. You need to choose the button of this step to invoke it. You can use this step to select faces to which a different wall thickness will be applied. After selecting the face or faces, specify the unique thickness in the **Unique Thickness** edit box and press ENTER. Again, select another face or faces to which you want to add different wall thicknesses and specify the wall thickness in the edit box. Continue this process until you have selected all the faces to which you want to add different wall thicknesses. Figure 8-22 shows a thin wall model with a unique thickness added at the left and bottom faces.

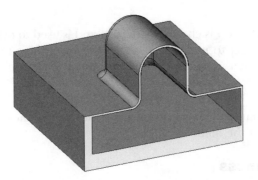

Figure 8-22 *Thin wall model with different wall thicknesses*

ADDING THIN WALL TO A PARTICULAR REGION

Toolbar:	Features > Thin Wall > Thin Region

 Sometimes, you may need to add the thin wall feature to a particular region instead of the complete model. For example, refer to the model shown in Figure 8-23. You can do this using the **Thin Region** tool.

The **Thin Region** tool works in the following four steps:

Faces To Thin Step

This is the first step and it is activated automatically when you invoke the **Thin Region** tool. In this step, you can select the faces of the region to add the thin wall feature and specify the common thickness. Note that while selecting the faces, you need to make sure that they result in a closed volume. For example, to create the thin wall region shown in Figure 8-23, you need to select the top curved face, side tangent faces, back face, and the front face of the region, as shown in Figure 8-24.

Open Faces Step

This step will be automatically invoked when you exit the previous step. In this step, you can select the faces that you want to remove from the thin wall region. For example, to create the model shown in Figure 8-23, you need to remove the front face.

 Note
*When you create the thin region feature, if the face that you selected to remove is still displayed, then you will need to edit the feature and select the face to be removed again in the **Open Faces** step.*

Capping Faces Step

Capping face can be considered as the face that defines the termination of the thin region. It is not necessary to select a capping surface. You can select any face of a model or an existing surface to define the capping faces. You can also define an offset value from the capping face

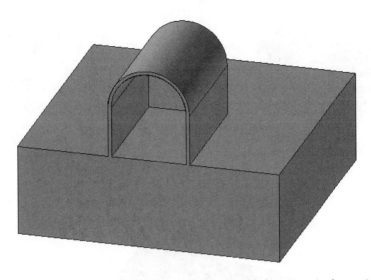

Figure 8-23 Model with the thin wall feature added to a particular region

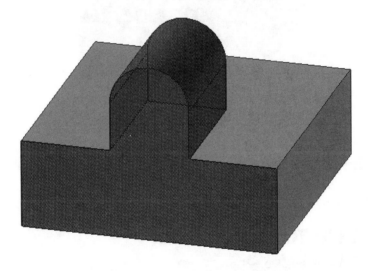

Figure 8-24 Selecting the faces of the model to create a thin wall region

using the **Offset** edit box that is displayed in the ribbon bar under this step. Figure 8-25 shows a surface used as the capping face and Figure 8-26 shows the same surface used as the capping face, but with an offset of 2. You will learn more about surfaces in the later chapters.

Figure 8-27 shows the preview of the model with the top planar face used as the capping face with an offset of 5.

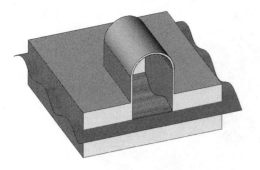 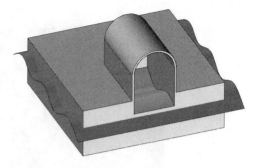

Figure 8-25 *Surface used as the capping face*   ***Figure 8-26*** *Surface used as the capping face with an offset of 2*

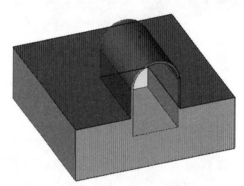

Figure 8-27 *Top face used as the capping face with an offset of 5*

Unique Thickness Step

This step is used to define different thicknesses to the selected faces and it works similar to the **Unique Thickness** step in the **Thin Wall** tool.

ADDING A LIP TO THE MODEL

Toolbar:	Features > Rib > Lip

 The **Lip** tool enables you to add a lip to the model by adding the material along the selected edges, or by adding a groove to the model by removing the material along the selected edges. The amount of material to be added or removed is defined by a rectangle whose width and height can be specified on invoking this tool.

The **Lip** tool works in the following two steps:

Select Edge Step

This step allows you to select the edge along which you want to add a lip or groove. You can use the options in the **Select** drop-down list to select an individual edge or a chain of edges.

Direction Step

This step enables you to specify the direction and size of the lip feature. When this step is invoked, the **Width** and **Height** edit boxes will be displayed. Specify the width and height of the rectangle, which defines the profile of the lip, in these edit boxes.

After specifying the width and height of the lip, move the cursor in the drawing window. You will notice that a red rectangle is displayed at the start of the edge. Move the cursor around the start of the edge to specify various locations of the lip. Note that if the rectangle is inside the feature, the resulting feature will be a groove and if the rectangle is outside the feature, the resulting feature will be a lip. Figures 8-28 through 8-31 show different positions of the rectangle and the resulting lip features.

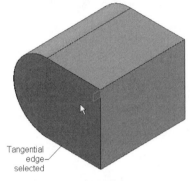

Figure 8-28 *Location of the rectangle*

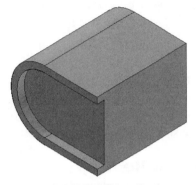

Figure 8-29 *Resulting lip feature*

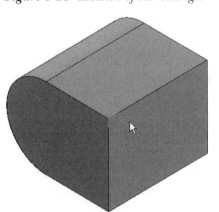

Figure 8-30 *Location of the rectangle*

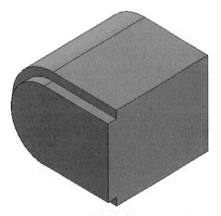

Figure 8-31 *Resulting lip feature*

CREATING WEB NETWORKS

Toolbar:	Features > Rib > Web Network

 The **Web Network** tool enables you to create a network of web using open entities, as shown in Figures 8-32 and 8-33.

Figure 8-32 *Thin wall model and a network of lines*

Figure 8-33 *Resulting web network*

This tool is similar to the **Rib** tool and works in the following four steps:

Plane or Sketch Step

This step enables you to select a sketching plane for drawing the profile of the web network. You can also select an existing profile using the **Select from Sketch** option from the **Create-From Options** drop-down list.

Draw Profile Step

This step will be automatically invoked when you select the sketching plane for drawing the profile of the web network.

Direction Step

This step will be automatically invoked when you select the profile and accept it or draw the profile and exit the sketching environment. This step enables you to define the direction in which the web network will be created. It is recommended to define the direction of the web network toward the bottom of the part.

You can specify the thickness of the webs in the web network in the **Thickness** edit box. The functions of the other buttons in the ribbon bar of this step are the same as those in the **Rib** tool. Figure 8-34 shows a web network in which the webs are not extended. Figure 8-35 shows a web network in which the webs are extended, but defined up to a finite depth.

Web Network Step

This step is used to add a draft to the webs in the web network. It works similar to the **Treatment Step** in the **Protrusion** tool.

Tip. *To select multiple individual entities, as shown in Figure 8-32, select the* **Single** *option from the* **Select** *drop-down list and then drag a box around the entities to select them.*

Figure 8-34 Web network with webs not extended

Figure 8-35 Webs defined up to a finite depth

CREATING VENTS

Toolbar: Features > Rib > Vent

The **Vent** tool enables you to create a vent in an existing model by defining the boundary of the vent, ribs and spars in the vent. This tool is available only after you have drawn the sketch for the vent. Figure 8-36 shows a model and a profile that defines the boundary. Note that in the vent, all the vertical lines are selected as ribs and all the horizontal lines are selected as spars. Figure 8-37 shows the resulting model with the vent.

To create the vent, invoke the **Vent** tool; the **Vent Options** dialog box will be displayed, as shown in Figure 8-38.

Vent Options Dialog Box Options

The options available in this dialog box are discussed next.

Saved settings

This drop-down list displays the list of settings that you have saved. By default, this drop-down list is blank. To save a setting, set the parameters in this dialog box, enter a name for the set parameter in the **Saved settings** edit box, and then choose the **Save** button. The saved settings will also be displayed on choosing the down arrow on the right of the **Vent Options** button in the ribbon bar. You can delete the unwanted settings by selecting them from this drop-down list and choosing the **Delete** button.

Thickness Ribs/Spars

These edit boxes are used to specify the thickness of the ribs and spars. Figure 8-39 shows a vent with the thickness of ribs and spars as 2. Figure 8-40 shows a vent with the thickness of ribs and spars as 5. You can have the same or different thickness values for the ribs and spars.

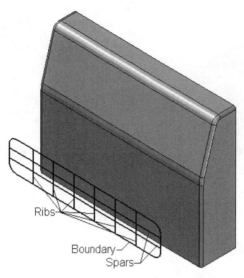

Figure 8-36 *Parameters related to the vent*

Figure 8-37 *Resulting model with the vent*

Extension Ribs/Spars

These edit boxes are used to specify the distance by which the ribs and spars will extend beyond the boundary of the vent. You can have the same or different extension values for the ribs and spars. Figure 8-41 shows the ribs and spars with no extension and Figure 8-42 shows the ribs and spars extended beyond the boundary.

Offset Ribs/Spars

These edit boxes are used to specify the distance by which the ribs and spars will be offset from the face on which the profile is projected. You can specify the same or different offset values for the ribs and spars. Figure 8-43 shows the ribs and spars starting at some offset from the face on which the profile is projected.

Note

If the offset value of the ribs and spars is more than the thickness of the face on which the profile of the vent is created, then the feature may not be created.

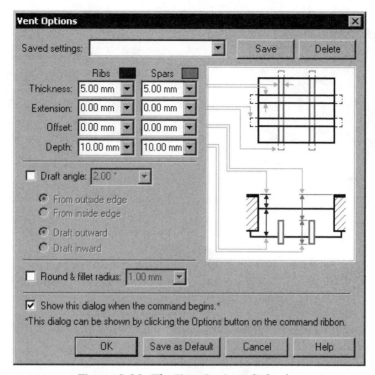

Figure 8-38 The Vent Options dialog box

Figure 8-39 Ribs and spars thickness as 2   Figure 8-40 Ribs and spars thickness as 5

Depth Ribs/Spars

These edit boxes are used to specify the depth of the ribs and spars. You can have the same or different depth values for each of them. Figures 8-44 and 8-45 show vent features with different depth values for the ribs and spars.

Draft angle

The **Draft angle** check box is selected to add a draft to the ribs and spars in the vent. The draft angle can be specified in the edit box available on the right of this check box. You can also specify whether the draft should be specified from the outside or the inside edge, and

Figure 8-41 *Ribs and spars not extended*

Figure 8-42 *Ribs and spars extended beyond the boundary*

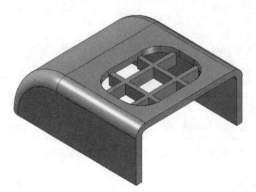

Figure 8-43 *Ribs and spars starting at an offset from the top face*

Figure 8-44 *Ribs and spars depth = 2*

Figure 8-45 *Ribs depth = 4, spars depth = 6*

whether the draft should be outward or inward. You can do so by selecting the required radio button below the **Draft angle** edit box.

Round & fillet radius

The **Round & fillet radius** check box is selected to add rounds and fillets to the vent. The radius of the round and fillet can be specified in the edit box available on the right of this check box. Figure 8-46 shows a vent with fillets and rounds.

Figure 8-46 Vent with fillets and rounds

After specifying the parameters in the **Vent Options** dialog box, this tool works in the following four steps:

Select Boundary Step

This step will be activated when you exit the **Vent Options** dialog box. In this step, you can select a chain of entities that will act as the boundary of the vent. You can also select the options in the **Select** drop-down list to select a chain of entities or an individual entity.

Select Ribs Step

This step will be automatically invoked when you accept the boundary in the **Select Boundary Step**. In this step, you can select closed or open entities to define the ribs in the vent. After selecting the entities, right-click to accept the selection.

Select Spars Step

This step will be automatically invoked when you accept the entities to define the ribs in the **Select Ribs Step**. In this step, you can select the entities that you want to use as spars in the vent. You can select closed or open entities to define the spars. After selecting the entities, right-click to accept the selection.

Extent Step

This step is used to specify the side and the extent of the vent. You can use the buttons in the ribbon bar of this step to define the extent.

CREATING MOUNTING BOSSES

Toolbar: Features > Rib > Mounting Boss

The **Mounting Boss** tool enables you to create mounting boss features, which are used in the plastic components to accommodate fasteners. Figure 8-47 shows a model with four mounting boss features.

Figure 8-47 *Model with four mounting bosses*

To create mounting boss features, invoke the **Mounting Boss** tool; the **Mounting Boss** ribbon bar will be displayed. It is recommended that before proceeding further, you should set the parameters of the mounting boss features in the **Mounting Boss Options** dialog box, as shown in Figure 8-48. This dialog box can be invoked on choosing the **Mounting Boss Options** button in the ribbon bar.

Mounting Boss Options Dialog Box

The options available in this dialog box are discussed next.

Saved settings

This drop-down list displays the list of settings that you have saved. By default, this drop-down list is blank. To save a setting, set the parameters in this dialog box, enter a name in the **Saved settings** edit box, and then choose the **Save** button. The saved settings will also be displayed on choosing the down arrow on the right of the **Mounting Boss Options** button in the ribbon bar. You can delete the unwanted settings by selecting them from this drop-down list and choosing the **Delete** button.

Settings Area

The options available in this area are used to set the parameters of the mounting boss feature. All these options have a gray arrow on the right that leads to a parameter in the preview window. The preview window explains the use of the options available in the **Settings** area. These options are discussed next.

Boss diameter

This edit box is used to specify the diameter of the mounting boss.

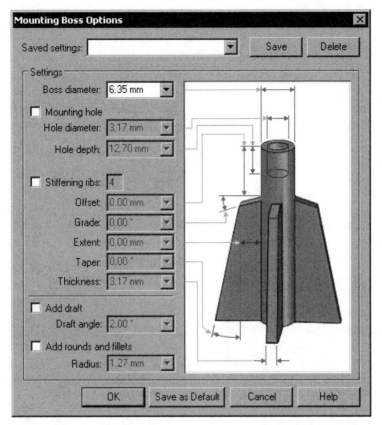

Figure 8-48 The **Mounting Boss Options** dialog box

Mounting hole

This check box is selected to create a hole on the top face of the mounting boss. On selecting this check box, the **Hole diameter** and the **Hole depth** edit boxes available below this check box will be activated and you can specify the diameter and the depth of the hole in these edit boxes.

Stiffening ribs

This check box is used to create a mounting box with ribs. If this check box is not selected, only a cylindrical feature will be created as the mounting boss. You can specify the number of stiffening ribs in the edit box available on the right of this check box.

Offset

This edit box will be available only when you select the **Stiffening ribs** check box and is used to specify the distance between the start of the rib and the top face of the mounting boss.

Grade

This edit box is used to specify the angle of the top face of the ribs with respect to the top face of the mounting boss.

Extent

This edit box is used to specify the extrusion depth of the top face of the ribs from the cylindrical surface of the mounting boss.

Taper

This edit box is used to specify the taper angle value of the rib. Note that you can enter only a positive taper angle value for the rib.

Thickness

This edit box is used to specify the thickness of the rib.

Add draft

This check box is selected to add a draft to the mounting boss. On selecting this check box, the **Draft angle** edit box will be activated and now you can enter the draft angle in this edit box. Figure 8-49 shows a model with mounting bosses without the draft and Figure 8-50 shows the mounting bosses with the draft.

Figure 8-49 Mounting bosses without draft   *Figure 8-50 Mounting bosses with draft*

All rounds and fillets

This check box is selected to add rounds and fillets to the mounting boss. On selecting this check box, the **Radius** edit box will be activated and now you can enter the radius value in this edit box.

After setting the options in the **Mounting Boss Options** dialog box, this tool works in the following three steps:

Plane Step

This step enables you to select a plane for placing the profiles of the mounting bosses. Note that the profiles of the mounting bosses are placed at a planar face or a reference plane parallel to the face on which you want to project them. The distance between the parallel plane and the face on which the mounting bosses are projected defines their depth. It is similar to extruding the profile from the parallel plane up to the face.

In this step, you need to place the profiles of the mounting bosses on a parallel plane and so the **Parallel Plane** option is selected in the **Create-From Options** drop-down list. If the face on which you want to project the profiles is curved, you can select the base reference plane that is parallel to the face.

Mounting Boss Step

This step will be automatically invoked when you select the parallel plane. In this step, you can place the profiles of the mounting boss on the selected plane. The sketching environment is invoked in this step and the **Mounting Boss Location** button is chosen in the **Features and Relationships** toolbar. Also, the profile of the mounting boss is attached to the cursor. You can click in the model to place the mounting boss.

You can also modify the mounting boss options by choosing the **Mounting Boss Options** button, which will be available in the ribbon bar when you choose the **Mounting Boss Location** button from the **Features and Relationships** toolbar. Figure 8-51 shows the profiles for four mounting bosses placed on a parallel plane.

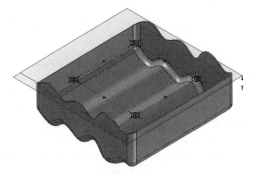

Figure 8-51 *Profiles for four mounting bosses*

Extent Step

This step will be automatically invoked when you choose the **Finish** button from the sketching environment in the **Mounting Boss** step. In this step, you can specify the side for creating the mounting boss. You can move the cursor on the side of the face where you want to project the profiles and click to accept the side. As soon as you specify the side, the preview of the mounting boss will be displayed. If the feature is correct, you can choose the **Finish** button to accept the feature, else choose the **Mounting Boss Options** button or the button of any other step to modify the options.

REORDERING FEATURES

While working on designs, you may sometime need to reorder the features. By reordering, you can change the sequence in which the features were created in the model. For example, in the model shown in Figure 8-52, the cavities were created first, followed by the thin wall feature. As a result, a thin wall is also created around the cavities, resulting in a protrusion feature. The original model required by you is the one shown in Figure 8-53.

To resolve this problem, Solid Edge allows you to change the order of the feature creation in the model. You can move a feature before or after another feature. However, note that the reordering is possible only between the features that are independent of each other. For example, if a part of any feature is dependent on another feature, then you cannot reorder the dependent feature above the parent feature.

Figure 8-52 *Thin wall created around cavities*   *Figure 8-53* *Original model required*

In Solid Edge, the features are reordered using the **EdgeBar**. Select the feature in the **EdgeBar** and drag it above or below the other features. If a feature cannot be dragged above a feature in the **EdgeBar**, then you cannot reorder the feature before it because the selected feature is dependent on the feature above which you want to drag it. However, if the feature is not dependent, a green arrow will be displayed on the left of the feature in the **EdgeBar** while you reorder it. Figure 8-54 shows the thin wall feature being dragged above the cutout feature to reorder it before the cutout feature. When you reorder the thin wall feature before the cutout, you will get the model, as shown in Figure 8-53.

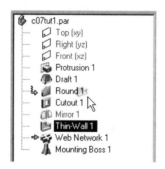

Figure 8-54 *Reordering features in the **EdgeBar***

TUTORIALS

Tutorial 1

In this tutorial, you will create the model shown in Figure 8-55. Its dimensions are given in the drawing views shown in Figure 8-56. Save the model with the name given below:

\Solid Edge\c08\c08tut1.par   **(Expected time: 30 min)**

Figure 8-55 *Model for Tutorial 1*

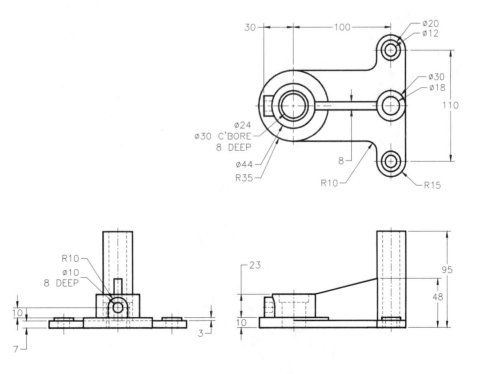

Figure 8-56 *Dimensions of the model for Tutorial 1*

The following steps are required to complete this tutorial:

a.   Start a new part file and create the base feature on the top plane, refer to Figure 8-57.
b.   Add the remaining protrusion features to the base feature, refer to Figure 8-58.
c.   Add holes to the model, refer to Figure 8-59.
d.   Create the rib feature, refer to Figure 8-62.
e.   Save the model and close the file.

Creating the Base Feature

1.   Start Solid Edge in the **Part** environment and then select the top plane as the sketching plane for the base feature, as shown in Figure 8-57.

Adding the Remaining Protrusion Features and Holes

1.   Add the remaining protrusion features to the model, as shown in Figure 8-58.

2.   Create holes in the model, as shown in Figure 8-59.

Creating the Rib Feature

Next, you need to create the rib feature. The profile for this rib is a single line. It is extruded symmetrically on both sides of the sketching plane.

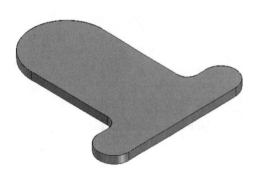

Figure 8-57 *Base feature of the model*

Figure 8-58   *Model after adding the remaining protrusion features*

Figure 8-59 *Model after adding holes*

1. Choose the **Rib** button from the **Features** toolbar; the **Plane or Sketch Step** is activated and you are prompted to click on a planar face or a reference plane.

2. Select or create a reference plane passing through the center of the circular features in the middle of the model.

3. Draw a single line for the rib feature and add the required relationships and dimensions to it, as shown in Figure 8-60.

4. Exit the sketching environment; the **Direction** step is activated and you are prompted to click to accept the displayed side or select the other side in the view.

5. Enter the value **8** in the **Thickness** edit box and specify the direction, as shown in Figure 8-61.

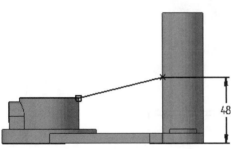

Figure 8-60 Profile for the rib feature

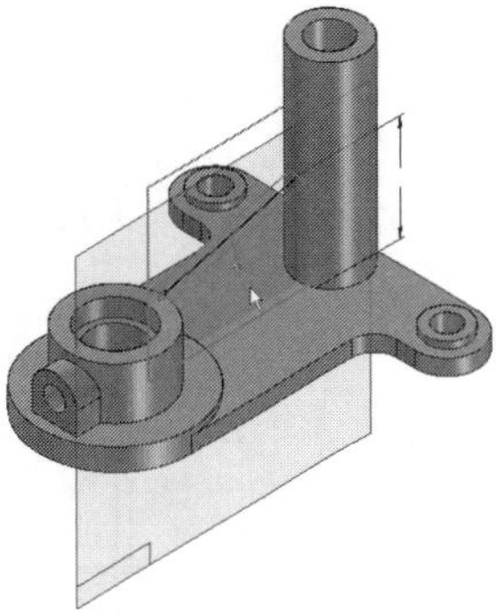

Figure 8-61 Specifying the direction of the rib

As soon as you specify the direction, the **Side** step is invoked and you are prompted to click to accept the displayed side or select the other side in the view.

6. Move the cursor close to the profile such that the preview of the rib feature is displayed symmetrically in both directions of the sketch. Click at this stage.

7. Choose **Finish** from the ribbon bar to create the rib feature. The final model, after creating the rib feature, is shown in Figure 8-62.

Saving the Model

1. Save the model with the name and location given below and then close the file.

\Solid Edge\c08\c08tut1.par

Figure 8-62 Model after creating the rib feature

Tutorial 2

In this tutorial, you will create the model of the ice tray shown in Figure 8-63. Its dimensions are given in the drawing views shown in Figure 8-64. Save the model with the name and the location given below:

   \Solid Edge\c08\c08tut2.par   **(Expected time: 30 min)**

Figure 8-63 Model for Tutorial 2

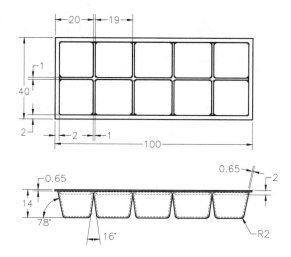

Figure 8-64 Dimensions of the model for Tutorial 2

The following steps are required to complete this tutorial:

a. Start a new part file and create the base feature on the top plane, refer to Figure 8-65.
b. Add a draft to the base feature, refer to Figure 8-66.
c. Add a thin wall feature to the model, refer to Figure 8-67.
d. Create a web network in the model, refer to Figures 8-68 and 69.
e. Add rounds to the sharp edges of the model, refer to Figure 8-70.
f. Add another thin wall feature, refer to Figure 8-71.
g. Save the model and close the file.

Creating the Base Feature

1. Start a new part file and then create the base feature of the model, which is a box of 100X40X14 size. The base feature of the model is shown in Figure 8-65.

Adding the Draft to the Base Feature

You need to add a draft to the outer faces of the base feature using the top planar face of the base feature as the draft plane.

1. Choose the **Add Draft** button from the **Features** toolbar; the **Add Draft** ribbon bar is displayed.

   When you invoke the **Add Draft** tool, the **Draft Plane Step** is activated and you are prompted to click on a planar face or reference plane.

2. Select the top planar face of the base feature as the draft plane; the **Select Faces Step** is invoked.

3. Select all the four side faces of the model to add the draft. Enter the value **12** in the **Draft Angle** edit box and press ENTER.

4. Choose **Next** from the ribbon bar to invoke the **Draft Direction** step. Move the cursor in the drawing window and click when the lower half of the line is inside the model.

5. Choose the **Finish** button to create the draft and then choose **Cancel** to exit this tool. The model, after adding the draft, is shown in Figure 8-66.

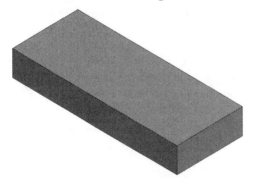 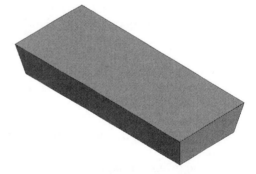

Figure 8-65 Base feature of the model   *Figure 8-66 Model after adding the draft*

Adding the Thin Wall Feature

Next, you need to scoop out the material from inside the model to create a thin wall model. This is done using the **Thin Wall** tool. You also need to remove the top face of the model while creating the thin wall.

1. Choose the **Thin Wall** button from the **Features** toolbar; the **Thin Wall** ribbon bar is displayed and the **Common Thickness** Step is activated. As a result, you are prompted to key in a common thickness value.

2.   Enter the value **2** in the **Common thickness** edit box and press ENTER; the **Open Faces** step is invoked and you are prompted to click on a face chain.

3.   Select the top planar face of the model as the face to be removed and then right-click to accept the selection.

4.   Choose the **Preview** button and then choose **Finish** to create the thin wall feature. The model, after creating the thin wall feature, is shown in Figure 8-67.

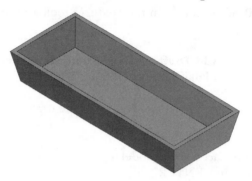

Figure 8-67 *Model after adding the thin wall feature*

Creating the Web Network

Next, you need to create the web network to accommodate the ice cubes. To create the web network, you need to use an open profile consisting of mutually perpendicular lines. Note that this profile needs to be created on a reference plane located at an offset distance of 2 from the top planar face of the thin wall model.

1.   Choose the **Web Network** button from the **Rib** flyout in the **Features** toolbar; the **Web Network** ribbon bar is displayed and the **Plane or Sketch** Step is activated. As a result, you are prompted to click on a planar face or a reference plane.

2.   Define a plane parallel to the top planar face of the thin wall feature. The plane should be offset 2 units in the downward direction.

3.   Draw the profile of the web network, as shown in Figure 8-68.

4.   Exit the sketching environment; the **Direction Step** is invoked and you are prompted to click to accept the displayed side or select the other side in the view.

     You will notice that in the preview, only one line is selected. But it is just for display. While creating the web network, all lines will be used.

5.   Enter **1** in the **Thickness** edit box and move the cursor to the lower side of the model to create the web network in the downward direction.

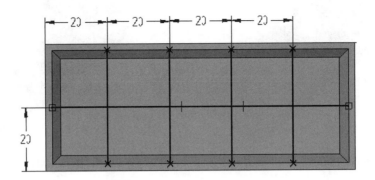

Figure 8-68 *Sketch for the web network*

To add a draft of 8-degrees to the web network, you need to invoke the **Web Network** step manually.

6. Choose the **Web Network** button from the ribbon bar to invoke the **Web Network** step.

7. Choose the **Draft** button and then enter **8** in the **Angle** edit box. Choose the **Flip**
    1 button to make sure that the draft is applied in the outward direction.

8. Choose the **Preview** button and then choose the **Finish** button from the ribbon bar to complete the web network, see Figure 8-69.

Creating Rounds

1. Add a round of radius 1 to the inner edges of the cavities created by the web network.

2. Next, add a round of radius 0.5 to the top face of the web network. The model, after adding the rounds, is shown in Figure 8-70.

Adding the Thin Wall Feature

Next, you need to add a thin wall feature such that all side faces and the bottom face of the model are removed.

1. Choose the **Thin Wall** button from the **Features** toolbar; the **Thin Wall** ribbon
    bar is displayed and the **Common Thickness** step is activated. Hence, you are prompted to key in a common thickness value.

2. Enter the value **0.65** in the **Common thickness** edit box and press ENTER; the **Open Faces** step is invoked and you are prompted to click on a face chain.

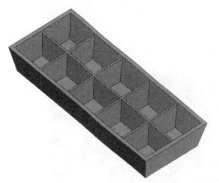

Figure 8-69 Model after creating the web network   *Figure 8-70 Model after adding the rounds*

3. Select the four side faces and the bottom face of the model as the faces to be removed and then right-click to accept the selection.

4. Choose **Preview** and then the **Finish** button to create the thin wall feature. The final model of the ice tray, after creating the thin wall feature, is shown in Figure 8-71.

Figure 8-71 Final model of the ice tray

Saving the Model

1. Save the model with the name and location given below and then close the file.

    \Solid Edge\c08\c08tut2.par

Tutorial 3

In this tutorial, you will create the model of the cover shown in Figure 8-72. Its dimensions are given in Figure 8-73. The outer fillet in Figure 8-73 is removed for the purpose of dimensioning. The radius of this fillet is 8. A draft of 1-degree needs to be added to the base feature of the model. The parameters of the mounting bosses are given next.

Boss diameter = 4, hole diameter = 2, hole depth = 5, rib offset = 3, rib grade = 10degrees, rib extent = 1, rib taper = 10-degrees, rib thickness = 1.

Save the model with the name and the location given below:
\Solid Edge\c08\c08tut3.par   **(Expected time: 45min)**

Figure 8-72 Model for Tutorial 3

The following steps are required to complete this tutorial:

a. Start Solid Edge in the **Part** environment. Create the base feature on the front plane, refer to Figure 8-74.
b. Add a draft to the base feature.
c. Add rounds to the sharp edges of the model, refer to Figure 8-75.
d. Add a thin wall feature to the model, refer to Figure 8-76.
e. Create two cutouts in the model, refer to Figure 8-77.
f. Create a web network in the model, refer to Figure 8-79.
g. Add mounting bosses to the model, refer to Figure 8-81.
h. Save the model and close the file.

Creating the Base Feature

1. Start Solid Edge in the **Part** environment and then select the front plane as the sketching plane for the protrusion feature.

2. Create the profile of the base feature and extrude it symmetrically. The base feature of the model is shown in Figure 8-74.

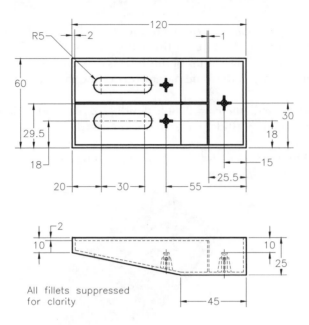

Figure 8-73 Dimensions of the model for Tutorial 3 with the fillets removed for clarity

Adding Draft to the Base Feature

As mentioned earlier, the drafts are added for the easy removal of the component from the casting. Therefore, you need to add the draft to the side walls of this model before you proceed further. To add the draft to the side walls, you need to use the top face as the draft plane.

1. Choose the **Add Draft** button from the **Features** toolbar; the **Add Draft** ribbon bar is displayed.

   You need to add the draft with the top face of the base feature as the draft plane. By default, the **From plane** option is selected to create the draft. Therefore, you do not need to invoke the **Draft Options** dialog box.

   When you invoke the **Add Draft** tool, the **Draft Plane** step is activated and you are prompted to click on a planar face or a reference plane.

2. Select the top planar face of the base feature as the draft plane; the **Select Face** step is invoked.

3. Select all four side faces of the model to add the draft. Enter the value **1** in the **Draft Angle** edit box and press ENTER.

4. Choose **Next** from the ribbon bar to invoke the **Draft Direction** step. Move the cursor in the drawing window and click when the lower half of the line is inside the model.

5. Choose the **Finish** button to create the draft and then choose **Cancel** to exit this tool.

6. Add a round of radius **8** to the sharp edges of the model, as shown in Figure 8-75.

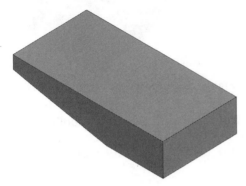

Figure 8-74 Base feature of the model

Figure 8-75 Viewing the model from the bottom after adding the draft and round

Adding the Thin Wall Feature

Next, you need to scoop out the material from inside the model to create a thin wall model. This is done using the **Thin Wall** tool. You also need to remove the top face of the model while creating a thin wall.

1. Choose the **Thin Wall** button from the **Features** toolbar; the **Thin Wall** ribbon bar is displayed and the **Common Thickness** step is activated. Therefore, you are prompted to key in a common thickness value.

2. Enter the value **2** in the **Common thickness** edit box and press ENTER; the **Open Faces** step is invoked and you are prompted to click on a face chain.

3. Select the top planar face of the model as the face to be removed and then right-click to accept the selection.

4. Choose the **Preview** button and then choose **Finish** to create a thin wall feature. The model, after creating the thin wall feature, is shown in Figure 8-76.

Creating Cutouts

1. Create two cutouts in the model, as shown in Figure 8-77.

Creating the Web Network

Next, you need to create a web network by using an open profile consisting of two mutually perpendicular lines. Note that this profile needs to be created on a reference plane located at an offset distance of 2 below the top planar face of the thin wall model.

Figure 8-76 *Model after creating the thin wall feature*

Figure 8-77 *Model after creating the cutouts*

1. Choose the **Web Network** button from the **Rib** flyout in the **Features** toolbar. The **Web Network** ribbon bar is displayed and the **Plane or Sketch Step** is activated. As a result, you are prompted to click on a planar face or reference plane.

2. Define a plane parallel to the top planar face of the thin wall feature. The plane should be offset 2 units inside the model.

3. Draw the profile of the web network, as shown in Figure 8-78.

4. Exit the sketching environment; the **Direction Step** is invoked and you are prompted to click to accept the displayed side or select the other side in the view.

    You will notice that in the preview, only one line is selected. But this is just for display. While creating the web network, both lines will be used.

5. Enter **1** in the **Thickness** edit box and move the cursor to the bottom of the model to create the web network in the downward direction.

6. Choose the **Finish** button from the ribbon bar to complete the web network, see Figure 8-79.

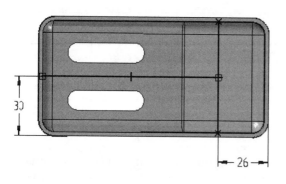

Figure 8-78 *Profile for the web network*

Figure 8-79 *Model after creating the web network*

Creating the Mounting Bosses

Next, you need to create the mounting bosses. The profiles of the mounting bosses need to be placed on a reference plane located at an offset distance of 10 from the top planar face of the thin wall model.

1. Choose the **Mounting Boss** button from the **Web Network** flyout in the **Features** toolbar.

    The **Mounting Boss** ribbon bar is displayed and the **Plane Step** is activated. Therefore, you are prompted to click on a planar face or a reference plane. Note that you need to define a reference plane parallel to the top planar face of the thin wall feature.

2. Define a plane parallel to the top planar face of the thin wall feature. The plane should be offset 10 units inside the model.

    As soon as you define the parallel plane, the **Mounting Boss Step** is activated and the sketching environment is invoked. Also, the **Mounting Boss Location** button is chosen in the **Features** and Relationship toolbar of the sketching environment. Before you start placing the mounting boss profile, you need to modify the parameters of the mounting boss.

3. Make sure that the **Mounting Boss Location** button is chosen in the **Features** toolbar. Next, choose the **Mounting Boss Options** button from the ribbon bar.

4. Set the parameters in the **Mounting Boss Options** dialog box based on the values given in the tutorial statement.

5. Place three instances of the mounting boss profiles and then add the required dimensions, as shown in Figure 8-80. It is recommended that you select the edge of the model as the first entity and the mounting boss profile as the second entity to add the dimension.

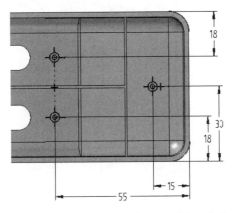

Figure 8-80 *Partial view of the model with the profiles for mounting bosses*

6. Exit the sketching environment and specify the direction of the feature creation downward. Choose the **Finish** button to complete the tool. The final model of the cover, after creating the mounting bosses, is shown in Figure 8-81.

*Figure 8-81 Final model after creating
the mounting bosses*

Saving the Model

1. Save the model with the name and the location given below and then close the file.

\Solid Edge\c08\c08tut3.par

Self-Evaluation Test

Answer the following questions and then compare them to those given at the end of this chapter:

1. By adding the thin wall feature, you are allowed to scoop out the material from a model and make it hollow from inside. (T/F)

2. The **Vent** tool enables you to create a vent in an existing model by defining only its boundary. (T/F)

3. Internal threads are created in a hole or circular cut features and external threads are created on the external surface of a cylindrical feature. (T/F)

4. Ribs are defined as thin wall-like structures used to bind the joints together so that they do not fail under an increased load. (T/F)

5. The _____ features are used in the plastic components to accommodate fasteners.

6. In Solid Edge, the features are reordered using the _____.

7. _____ is a process of tapering the selected faces of a model for its easy removal from casting while manufacturing.

8. After setting the options in the **Mounting Boss Options** dialog box, the **Mounting Boss** tool works in _____ steps.

9. You can add a thin wall feature to a particular region of the model using the _____ tool.

10. In the **Lip** tool, the amount of material to be added or removed is defined by a _____ whose width and height you specified by invoking this tool.

Review Questions

Answer the following questions:

1. Which of the following tools enables you to create a network of web using open entities?

    (a) **Lip**   (b) **Rib**
    (c) **Web Network**   (d) **Web**

2. Which of the following tools enables you to add a taper to the selected faces of a model?

    (a) **Add Draft**   (b) **Taper**
    (c) **Rib**   (d) None

3. Which of the following tools enables you to create a vent in an existing model by defining its boundary, ribs, and spars?

    (a) **Add Draft**   (b) **Taper**
    (c) **Rib**   (d) **Vent**

4. Which of the following tools can be used to add a thin wall to the entire model?

    (a) **Add Draft**   (b) **Thin Region**
    (c) **Rib**   (d) **Thin Wall**

5. In which of the following steps, you can place the profiles of the mounting boss on the selected plane?

    (a) **Mounting Boss Step**   (b) **Sketch Step**
    (c) **Profile Step**   (d) None

6. Which of the following buttons is chosen to extend the rib feature to the adjacent features, even if the profile does not extend to them?

    (a) **Extend Profile**   (b) **Extend**
    (c) Both   (d) None

7. The **Lip** tool enables you to add a lip to the model by adding the material or by adding a groove to the model by removing the material. (T/F)

8. In Solid Edge, the faces that are threaded are shaded in blue color. (T/F)

9. In Solid Edge, you can add drafts using five options. (T/F)

10. In the **Thin Wall** tool, you can also remove some of the faces of the model or apply different wall thicknesses to some of them. (T/F)

Exercises

Exercise 1

Create the model shown in Figure 8-82. Its dimensions and drawing views are shown in Figure 8-83. After creating the model, save it with the name and location given below:

\Solid Edge\c08\c08exr1.par   **(Expected time: 30 min)**

Figure 8-82   *Model for Exercise 1*

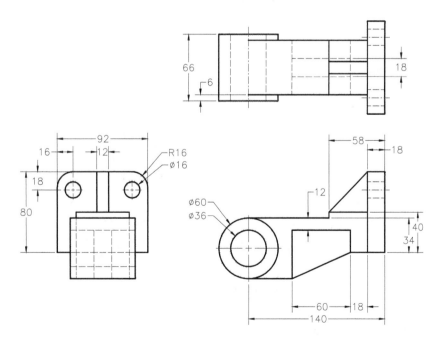

Figure 8-83   *Dimensions of the model*

Exercise 2

Create the model shown in Figure 8-84. Its dimensions are given in Figure 8-85. Save it with the name and the location given below:

\Solid Edge\c08\c08exr2.par   **(Expected time: 30 min)**

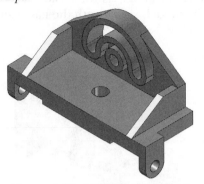

Figure 8-84 Model for Exercise 2

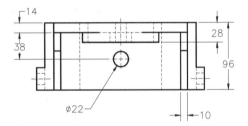

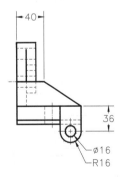
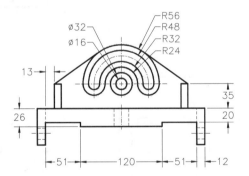

Figure 8-85 Dimensions of the model

Answers to Self Evaluation Test
1. T, **2. F**, **3. T**, **4. T**, **5.** mounting boss, **6. EdgeBar**, **7.** Adding draft, **8.** three, **9. Thin Region**, **10.** rectangle

Chapter 9

Advanced Modeling Tools-III

- *Create swept protrusions.*
- *Create swept cutouts.*
- *Create lofted protrusions.*
- *Create lofted cutouts.*
- *Create helical protrusions.*
- *Create normal protrusions.*
- *Create normal cutouts.*

ADVANCED MODELING TOOLS

In earlier chapters, you learned about some of the advanced modeling tools. In this chapter, you will learn about the remaining ones.

Advanced Tools to Create Protrusions

In the earlier chapters, you learned about the basic protrusion tools such as **Extrude** and **Revolve** that are used to create base features. As mentioned earlier, these tools add material to the sketch. In this chapter, you will learn about some advanced tools that, apart from adding material, also have the capability of creating base features. You will also learn how to remove the material using these advanced tools. The following are the tools that are discussed in this chapter:

- **Swept Protrusion and Cutout**
- **Lofted Protrusion and Cutout**
- **Helical Protrusion and Cutout**
- **Normal Protrusion and Cutout**

CREATING SWEPT PROTRUSIONS

Toolbar:	Features > Revolved Protrusion > Swept Protrusion

The **Swept Protrusion** tool sweeps a section along an open or a closed path. The order of operation is to first create or select a path and then create or select a section. This tool is similar to the **Protrusion** tool, with the only difference being that in this case, the section is swept along a specified path.

Using the **Swept Protrusion** tool, you can sweep a single section along a single path or use multiple paths with multiple sections. On choosing the **Swept Protrusion** tool from the **Revolved Protrusion** flyout in the **Features** toolbar, the **Sweep Options** dialog box will be displayed, as shown in Figure 9-1.

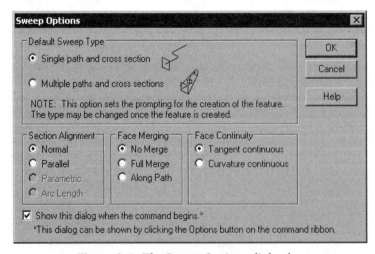

*Figure 9-1 The **Sweep Options** dialog box*

Single path and cross section Option

This option for creating a swept feature is selected by default, and is used to sweep a section along an open or a closed path, as shown in Figures 9-2 and 9-3.

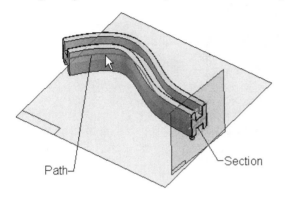

Figure 9-2 *Path and the cross-section used to create the swept protrusion*

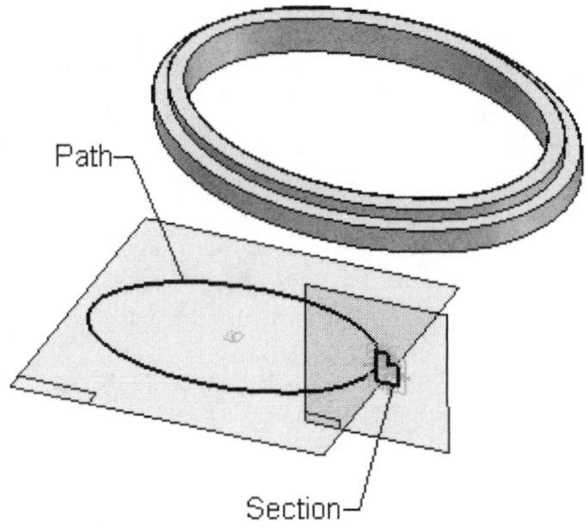

Figure 9-3 *Closed path and closed cross-section used to create the swept protrusion*

The following steps explain the procedure for creating a swept protrusion using this option:

1. Select the **Single path and cross-section** radio button from the **Sweep Options** dialog box and exit it; the **Swept Protrusion** ribbon bar is displayed and the **Path Step** button is chosen. Also, you are prompted to select a reference plane or a face to be used to draw the sketch of the path. If you need to select the edge of an existing feature as the path, select the **Select from Sketch/Part Edges** option from the **Create-From Options** drop-down list.

2. Select a reference plane and draw the sketch of the path that will be used to create a swept protrusion. Exit the sketching environment.

3. Next, choose the **Finish** button from the ribbon bar; the **Cross Section Step** button is chosen in the ribbon bar.

4. Select the **Plane Normal to Curve** option from the **Create-From Options** drop-down list, if it is not already selected. Move the cursor close to one of the endpoints on the path to draw the section for the swept protrusion. Click when the desired endpoint is highlighted in red. The reference plane is displayed at the selected point, as shown in Figure 9-4. You can move the cursor along the path. Notice that the reference plane also moves with it. Click to specify the location of the reference plane where the cross-section needs to be drawn. The reference plane is oriented parallel to the screen.

5. Draw the sketch for the cross-section and exit the sketching environment.

6. Next, you need to select a start point on the cross-section if it has vertices. If the cross-section is a circle, the start point is not required.

7. Choose the **Finish** button from the ribbon bar; the swept protrusion is created.

8. Choose **Finish** and then **Cancel** to exit the tool.

After learning the procedure of creating a swept protrusion, you will learn the steps available in the **Smart Step** ribbon bar. These steps guide the user to create swept protrusions.

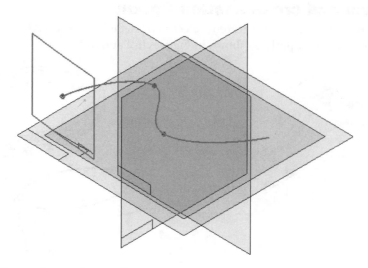

Figure 9-4 Reference plane created at the point of selection on the path

Path Step

 After selecting the type of protrusion from the **Sweep Options** dialog box, the **Path Step** button will be chosen automatically. This step enables you to define a path along which the section will be swept.

Cross Section Step

 After sketching or selecting the path for the sweep, the **Cross Section Step** button will be chosen automatically. In the **Create-From Options** drop-down list, the **Plane Normal To Curve** option is selected by default. You are prompted to click on a curve or an edge for the normal plane. As you move the cursor on the path, the possible points where the reference plane can be placed are highlighted in red. As soon as you select a point on the path, the reference plane is displayed. Move the cursor along the path and you will notice that the reference plane also moves with it. Click to specify the location of the reference plane where the cross-section needs to be drawn. The reference plane is oriented parallel to the screen, thus allowing you to draw the sketch of the cross-section.

Note

*To specify a plane to draw a cross-section, you can also create a reference plane by choosing the other options available in the **Create-From Options** drop-down list.*

Multiple paths and cross sections Option

The **Multiple paths and cross sections** option uses multiple cross-sections and multiple paths to create the swept protrusion. Note that you can at the most select three cross-sections. Generally, this option is used when you want to vary the cross-sections and the variation is controlled by the paths and the geometry of the cross-sections. Figure 9-5 shows the three paths and a cross-section that is used to create the swept protrusion shown in Figure 9-6. Remember that while sketching the cross-section, it should be aligned to the endpoints of all the paths. Else, the feature will be created without following that path.

The following steps explain the procedure for creating the swept protrusion shown in Figure 9-6:

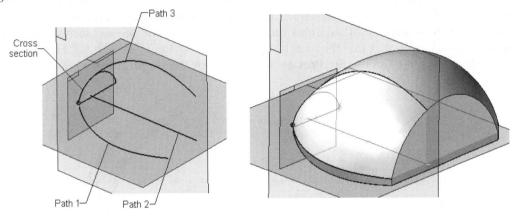

Figure 9-5 *Three paths and a cross-section* *Figure 9-6* *Swept protrusion*

1. Select the **Multiple paths and cross sections** radio button and exit the **Sweep Options** dialog box. The **Swept Protrusion** ribbon bar is displayed and you are prompted to select a reference plane or a face. You need to specify the method of creating the swept feature. These methods are to draw a sketch, or to select a sketch or edge. Notice that in the ribbon bar, the **Path Step** button is chosen.

2. Select **Coincident Plane** from the **Create-From Options** drop-down list, if it is not selected by default.

3. Select a reference plane and draw the sketch of the first path that will be used to create the swept protrusion.

4. After drawing the sketch, exit the sketching environment and choose **Finish** from the ribbon bar.

5. Next, you need to draw the second path. Select the reference plane to draw the sketch of the second path.

6. Repeat step 4.

7. Finally, you need to draw the third path. Select the reference plane to draw the sketch of the third path. Exit the sketching environment after creating it.

8. Next, choose the **Finish** button from the ribbon bar. Notice that in the ribbon bar, the **Cross Section Step** button is chosen automatically.

9. Move the cursor to the point on the path where you will draw the section for the swept

protrusion. Click on the point. The reference plane is displayed at the selected point and is oriented parallel to the screen.

10. Draw the sketch for the cross-section and make sure that the cross-section is aligned to all the three endpoints of the three paths. Then, exit the sketching environment.
11. Next, select the start point on the cross-section.
12. Choose the **Finish** button from the ribbon bar to create the swept protrusion and then exit the tool.

Figure 9-7 shows a single path and two cross-sections that are used to create the swept protrusion feature shown in Figure 9-8. After drawing the path on the reference plane, you need to choose the **Next** button from the ribbon bar to invoke the **Cross Section Step**. Select a point on the path where the reference plane will be placed for drawing the first cross-section. Draw the cross-section and exit the sketching environment. Choose the **Finish** button from the ribbon bar. Now select another point on the path to draw the second section. Draw the second cross-section and exit the sketching environment. Again, choose the **Finish** button from the ribbon bar. Choose the **Preview** button to view the swept protrusion.

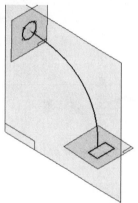

Figure 9-7 Two cross-sections and a path to create a multiple section swept protrusion

Figure 9-8 Swept protrusion

Sweep Options Dialog Box Options

The options available in the **Sweep Options** dialog box are discussed next.

Section Alignment Area

The options available in this area are used to specify the alignment of the sections along the path curve. These options are discussed next.

Normal

This option ensures that the cross-section will remain oriented relative to the path used for creating a sweep. Figure 9-9 shows the swept protrusion created using this option.

Parallel

This option is used when you want the cross-section to remain oriented parallel to the sketch plane while sweeping. Figure 9-10 shows the swept protrusion created using this option.

Figure 9-9 *Swept protrusion created using the normal section alignment*

Figure 9-10 *Swept protrusion created using the parallel section alignment*

Parametric

This option is available only when you are using multiple paths. It ensures that the orientation of the cross-section varies on the basis of the parameter distance of the path curve. Note that the paths that you select in this option should be created from a single entity. Figure 9-11 shows the multiple path swept protrusion created using the **Normal** option and Figure 9-12 shows the multiple path swept protrusion created using the **Parametric** option. These figures also show the cross-section and the paths used for creating them.

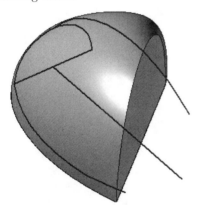

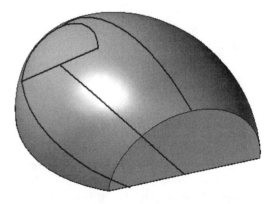

Figure 9-11 *Swept protrusion created using the normal section alignment*

Figure 9-12 *Swept protrusion created using the parametric section alignment*

Arc Length

This option is also available only when you are using multiple paths. This option is similar to the **Parametric** option, with the only difference being that in this case the cross-section varies on the basis of the arc length distance of the path curve. Also, the paths that you select for this option can consist of multiple entities.

Face Merging Area

The options available in this area are used to specify the methods for merging the faces of the sweep feature. These options are discussed next.

No Merge

This option ensures that the faces of the sweep feature are not merged. Figure 9-13 shows the swept protrusion with the faces that are not merged. The black lines in the model show different faces of the model.

Full Merge

This option ensures that the faces of the sweep feature are fully merged. Figure 9-14 shows the swept protrusion with faces fully merged.

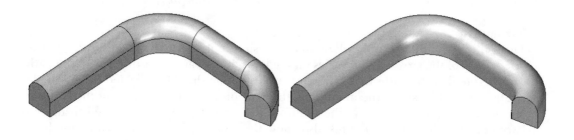

Figure 9-13   *Swept protrusion with faces not merged*

Figure 9-14   *Swept protrusion with a full merger of the faces*

Along Path

This option ensures that the faces along the direction of the path of the sweep feature are merged. Figure 9-15 shows the swept protrusion with the faces that are merged along the path of the sweep feature. The black lines in the model show the different faces of the model.

Face Continuity Area

The options available in this area are used to specify the methods of face continuity. You can select the option of face continuity and curvature continuity.

Figure 9-15   *Swept protrusion with faces along the path curve merged*

CREATING SWEPT CUTOUTS

Toolbar:	Features > Revolved Cutout > Swept Cutout

The **Swept Cutout** tool is in the flyout that is displayed when you press the down arrow on the right side of the **Revolved Cutout** button. The tool is available only when a base feature is already created in the drawing window. The procedure used to create the swept cutout is the same as the one that was used to create a swept protrusion. Figure 9-16 shows the swept cutout created on a base feature.

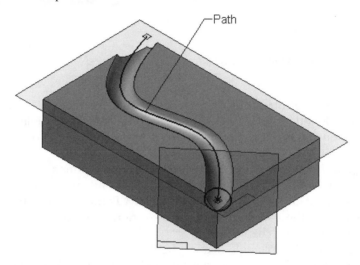

Figure 9-16 Swept cutout created using the cross-section and the path

CREATING LOFTED PROTRUSIONS

Toolbar:	Features > Revolved Protrusion > Lofted Protrusion

The **Lofted Protrusion** tool is in the flyout that is displayed when you press the down arrow on the right side of the **Revolved Protrusion** button. Lofted features are created by blending more than one similar or dissimilar cross-sections together. These cross-sections may or may not be parallel to each other. However, all cross-sections must be closed profiles.

You can create a lofted protrusion by drawing or selecting the existing sketches or edges. When you choose the **Lofted Protrusion** button, and if the sketches of the cross-sections are already drawn, you will be prompted to select an edge, a sketch, or a curve chain. Select the existing sketches that are shown in Figure 9-17 and choose the **Preview** button. The lofted protrusion will be created, as shown in Figure 9-18. On the other hand, to draw the sketches of the cross-sections, you need to select a reference plane to draw them one by one.

The steps given next explain the procedure for creating a lofted protrusion:

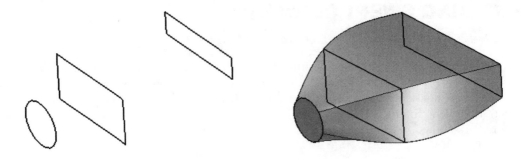

Figure 9-17 *Three cross-sections to create a lofted*
protrusion

Figure 9-18 *Resulting lofted protrusion*

1. Invoke the **Lofted Protrusion** tool. Select the front reference plane and draw the first cross-section. Exit the sketching environment. If the sketch is a circle, you do not need to specify the start point. Else, specify the start point and then choose the **Finish** button from the ribbon bar.
2. Select the **Parallel Plane** option from the **Create-From Options** drop-down list and create a plane parallel to the previous plane. Draw the second cross-section on this plane.
3. Exit the sketching environment. The **Define Start Point** button is chosen by default and you need to select the start point of the cross-section. The need for selecting a start point is discussed later in the chapter.
4. Select a vertex on the rectangle that will be the start point and then choose **Finish**.
5. Similarly, draw the third cross-section on the third plane. After exiting the sketching environment, specify the start point on the third cross-section, if required.
6. Choose the **Preview** button and then choose **Finish** to create the lofted protrusion.
7. Choose **Cancel** to exit the tool.

After learning the procedure of creating a lofted protrusion, you will learn about the options available under various steps required for creating a lofted protrusion.

Cross Section Order Option

The **Cross Section Order** button is used to reorder the sequence of sections that blend with each other. This button will be available only when you choose the **Edit** button on the ribbon bar after selecting the sections. This means that the sections can be reordered only while editing.

When you choose the **Cross Section Order** button, the **Cross Section Order** dialog box will be displayed, as shown in Figure 9-19. This dialog box is used to reorder the sections. As is evident from the figure, Section 1 blends with Section 2 and then Section 2 blends with Section 3. You can use the **Up** and **Down** buttons available in the dialog box to reorder the sections. Note that the section you select in this dialog box will be highlighted in yellow on the screen. You can reorder only newly created sketches created while editing the already existing feature.

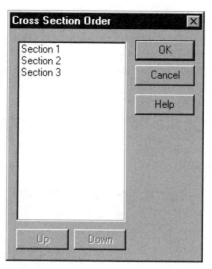

*Figure 9-19 The **Cross Section Order** dialog box*

Define Start Point

The **Define Start Point** button is used to define the start points of the new sections or redefine the start points of existing sections of the lofted feature. For new sections, this button will be available after creating them. In case of existing sections, this button will be available after choosing the **Edit** button.

When you select the section to blend, a point will be highlighted. This point will be selected as the start point of the section. After selecting the sections, choose the **Edit** button. Now using the **Define Start Point** button, you can redefine the start points on the sections. Figure 9-20 shows the start points of the sections and Figure 9-21 shows the resulting lofted protrusion. Depending on the start points specified, the lofted feature changes its profile.

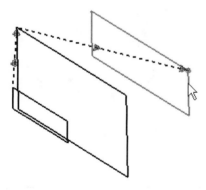

Figure 9-20 Three sections and their start points joined by a dotted line

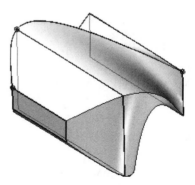

Figure 9-21 Lofted protrusion

Vertex Mapping Option

 On selecting at least two sections for the lofted protrusion, you will notice that the **Guide Curve Step** and **Extent Step** buttons are available in the ribbon bar. When you choose the **Extent Step** button, the **Vertex Mapping** button will be available on the ribbon bar along with the other buttons.

This button is used when you want to control the blending of the sections using their vertices. By default, the start points of the sections are used as mapping points to create the loft. If you want to modify the mapping of the points, choose the **Vertex Mapping** button in the **Extent Step**. The **Vertex Mapping** dialog box will be displayed, as shown in Figure 9-22.

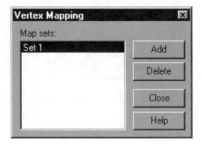

*Figure 9-22 The **Vertex Mapping** dialog box*

This dialog box shows a set of mapping points, which is the default mapping shown by the blue lines in the preview. To modify the default mapping, select any other point on the sections. The new mapping is shown by continuous lines, see Figure 9-23. Figure 9-24 shows the resulting lofted protrusion.

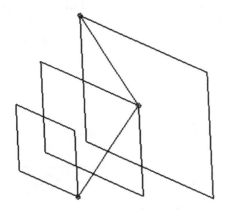

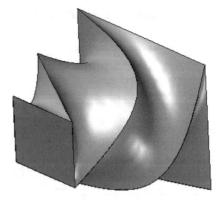

Figure 9-23 Sections selected to create a loft   *Figure 9-24 Resulting loft*

You can add additional mapping sets by choosing the **Add** button. A new set with the name **Set 2** will be added. One by one, select the vertices of the cross-sections to add the additional vertex mapping.

To control the blending points on a circle, sketch the points on the circle while drawing it, see Figure 9-25. This means that the points and the circle are in one sketch feature. Next, select a circle and then a pentagon. Choose the **Preview** button; the lofted protrusion is created as shown in Figure 9-26. While creating the lofted protrusion, choose the **Extent Step** button from the ribbon bar. Choose the **Vertex Mapping** button from the ribbon bar to display the **Vertex Mapping** dialog box.

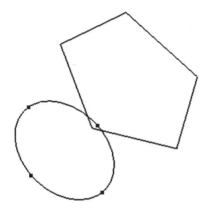

Figure 9-25 *Points added on the circle*

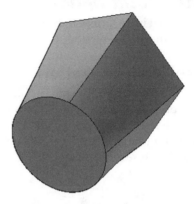

Figure 9-26 *Lofted protrusion created between a circle and a pentagon*

Select the set of points marked 1 and then choose the **Add** button, refer to Figure 9-27. Select a set of points 2 and then choose the **Add** button. Again, select point 2 that lies on the pentagon and point 2 that lies on the circle. Similarly, add the other sets of points. After adding the sets, choose the **Preview** button from the ribbon bar to create the lofted protrusion, as shown in Figure 9-28. Notice the difference between the resulting loft features shown in Figures 9-26 and 9-28.

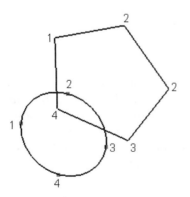

Figure 9-27 *Points numbered on two sections*

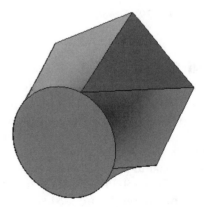

Figure 9-28 *Loft created*

Tip: *In order to create a smooth loft between a circle and a polygon, it is a good practice to place the required number of points on the circle. The number of points should be equal to the number of sides of the polygon. While creating the loft feature, you can use vertex mapping to add the sets of points in both the sections. This results in a smoother loft protrusion.*

Finite Extent Option

 The **Finite Extent** button is chosen by default. It enables you to blend the first section with the last section.

Closed Extent Option

The **Closed Extent** button blends the last section with the first section and closes the loft protrusion. Figure 9-29 shows the four sections to be lofted. Figure 9-30 shows the resulting closed extent loft. If the **Finite Extent** button is chosen, then the blend will start from the first section and end at the fourth section. But in Figure 9-30, it is evident that the fourth section closes the loft feature by blending it with the first section.

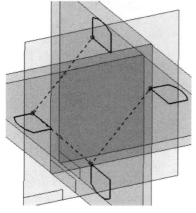
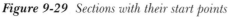

Figure 9-29 *Sections with their start points*

Figure 9-30 *Loft created using the* ***Closed Extent*** *button*

End 1 and End 2

These drop-down lists are available under the **Extent Step** and provide the **Natural** and **Normal to section** options. These options determine the start and end of the blending from the cross-sections. The **Natural** option, which is selected by default, does not constrain the blending at the start and end. Figure 9-31 shows three sections and their start points. Figure 9-32 shows the lofted protrusion whose end conditions are set to the **Natural** option. The **Normal to section** option constrains the end conditions of the loft to be normal to the sections. Figure 9-33 shows the loft feature created with the end conditions set to the **Normal to section** option. Figure 9-34 shows the difference between the two end conditions. In this figure, the left section is set to the **Normal to section** option, while the right section is set to the **Natural** option.

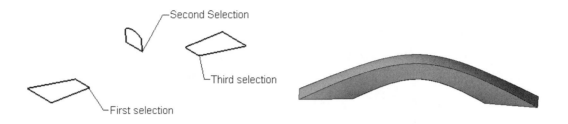

Figure 9-31 *Sections, selection points, and sequence of selection*

Figure 9-32 *Loft feature created with the **Natural** option*

Figure 9-33 *Loft feature created with the **Normal to section** option*

Figure 9-34 *Difference between the two end conditions*

Adding Guide Curves to a Loft

Guide curves can also be defined between the sections of the loft feature to control its transition. The sketches drawn for the guide curve must have a **Connect** relationship with the sketches that define the loft section.

The **Guide Curve Step** button on the ribbon bar is used to select or sketch the guide curve. To draw the sketch of the guide curve, you need to select or create a reference plane on which the guide curve will be drawn. Figure 9-35 shows the sections and the guide curve used to create the lofted protrusion, shown in Figure 9-36. Notice the variation in the section caused by the guide curve.

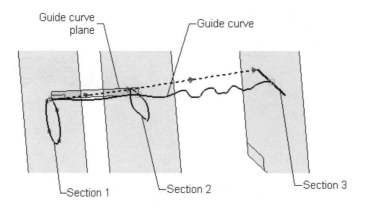

Figure 9-35 *Sections and guide curve*

Figure 9-36 *Lofted protrusion created using the guide curve*

CREATING LOFTED CUTOUTS

Toolbar:	Features > Revolved Cutout > Lofted Cutout

The **Lofted Cutout** tool is available on the **Revolved Cutout** flyout. This tool is used to remove material and works in the same way as the **Lofted Protrusion** tool. Figure 9-37 shows a lofted cut.

CREATING HELICAL PROTRUSIONS

Toolbar:	Features > Revolved Protrusion > Helical Protrusion

The **Helical Protrusion** tool is used to create springs, threads, and so on. To create a helical protrusion, choose the **Helical Protrusion** button from the flyout which will be displayed when you press and hold the **Revolved Protrusion** button. On invoking this tool, the **Helical Protrusion** ribbon bar will be displayed. The buttons available in this ribbon bar are discussed next.

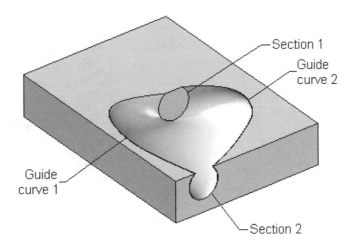

Figure 9-37 Lofted curve

Helix Options

When you choose the **Helix Options** button, the **Helix Options** dialog box will be displayed, as shown in Figure 9-38.

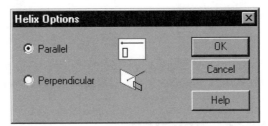

*Figure 9-38 The **Helix Options** dialog box*

The **Parallel** option enables you to create a helical protrusion in which the cross-section remains parallel to the axis, while revolving around it. Figures 9-39 and 9-40 show the sketch and the helix protrusion created using the **Parallel** option.

The **Perpendicular** option enables you to draw the cross-section of the helical protrusion perpendicular to the axis of revolution. Figure 9-41 shows the sketch of the cross-section and Figure 9-42 shows the helical protrusion created using this option.

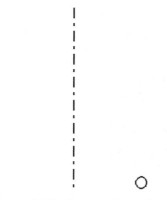

Figure 9-39 *Cross-section and axis*   *Figure 9-40* *Parallel helical protrusion*

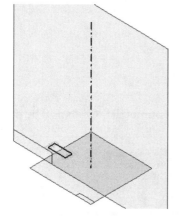

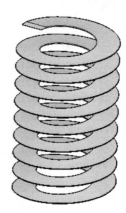

Figure 9-41 *Cross-section and axis*   *Figure 9-42* *Perpendicular helical protrusion*

Axis and Cross Section Step

 On invoking the **Helical Protrusion** tool, the **Axis and Cross Section Step** button will be chosen by default, and you will be prompted to select a planar face or a reference plane. This is the plane on which you will draw the axis and the cross-section, in case of the **Parallel** option.

If the **Perpendicular** option is selected from the **Helix Options** dialog box, then the **Axis Plane or Sketch Step** button will be chosen and you will be prompted to select a planar face or a reference plane. This is the plane on which you will draw the axis. After drawing the helix axis, exit the sketching environment; the **Cross Section Plane** or **Sketch Step** button will be chosen. You are required to draw the cross-section on a plane normal to the axis. As a result, the **Plane Normal to Curve** option is selected from the **Create-From Options** drop-down list. This option enables you to create a plane normal to the axis.

Start End Button

The **Start End** button will be available only when you select the **Parallel** option from the **Helix Options** dialog box. This button is chosen automatically when you exit the sketching environment and it is used to specify the start end of the helix axis. Figure 9-43 shows that when the start end is selected at the bottom, the spring is created in the upward direction. Figure 9-44 shows that when the start end is selected at the top, the spring is created in the downward direction. Note that there is no change in other parameters of the spring apart from the direction of creation.

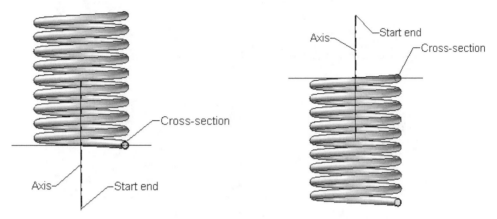

Figure 9-43 *Spring created when the start end is selected at the bottom*

Figure 9-44 *Spring created when the start end is selected to be at the top*

Parameters Step

After you specify the start end of the helix axis, the **Parameter** step will be invoked automatically and you will be prompted to enter the helix parameters. The **Helix Method** drop-down list is available in the ribbon bar. There are three options available in this drop-down list which are discussed next.

Axis length & Pitch

The pitch of a helix is the distance measured parallel to the axis and between the corresponding points on the adjacent turns. This option allows you to specify the pitch of the helix and it assumes the length of the axis as the height of the helical protrusion.

Axis length & Turns

This option enables you to specify the number of turns in the helix and assumes the length of the axis as the height of the helical protrusion.

Pitch & Turns

This option enables you to specify the pitch of the helix and the number of turns. The number of turns and the value of the pitch determine the height of the helical protrusion.

In the **Parameters** step, the **More** button will be available in the ribbon bar. When you choose this button, the **Helix Parameters** dialog box will be displayed, as shown in Figure 9-45. The options in this dialog box that are used to specify the helix parameters are discussed next.

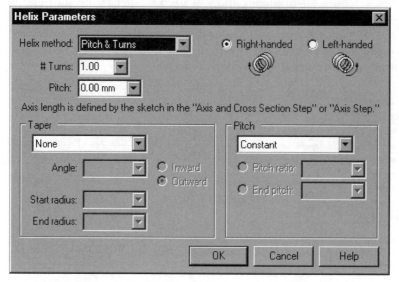

*Figure 9-45 The **Helix Parameters** dialog box*

Helix method

In this drop-down list, the three above-mentioned methods of creating a helical protrusion are available.

Turns

The number of turns of the helical protrusion can be specified in this edit box.

Pitch

The pitch of the helix can be specified in this edit box.

Right-handed

This radio button is selected by default. The right-handed helical protrusion creates the spring whose direction matches the direction of the curled fingers of the right hand, when the thumb of the right hand points from the start point to the end point of the axis. Figure 9-46 shows the right-handed helical protrusion.

Left-handed

The left-handed helical protrusion creates the spring whose direction matches the direction of the curled fingers of the left hand, when the thumb of the left hand points from the start point to the end point of the axis. Figure 9-47 shows the left-handed helical protrusion.

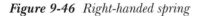

Figure 9-46 *Right-handed spring*   ***Figure 9-47*** *Left-handed spring*

Taper Area

The options in this area of the dialog box are used to specify the parameters related to the taper of the helix. The options in this area are discussed next.

Drop-down List

The drop-down list is used to specify the taper methods. There are two methods available in this drop-down list: **By Angle** and **By Radius**. The **By Angle** option enables you to specify the taper angle. This taper angle can be inward or outward. When you select the **By Angle** option from the drop-down list, the **Inward** and **Outward** radio buttons are activated. The **Inward** radio button enables you to create a helical protrusion that tapers inside, that is, toward the axis, see Figure 9-48. The **Outward** option creates a helical protrusion that tapers outside, that is, away from the axis, see Figure 9-49.

The **By Radius** option enables you to specify the end and start radii of the helical protrusion. This radius is from the axis of the helical protrusion. When you select the **By Radius** option from the drop-down list, the **Start radius** and **End radius** edit boxes will be activated. The start radius value is applied at the start end of the helical protrusion and the end radius value is applied at the end of it. Figure 9-50 shows the spring created with the taper specified in terms of the start and end radii.

Pitch Area

The options in this area of the dialog box are used to specify the parameters related to the pitch of the helix. These options are discussed next.

Drop-down List

The drop-down list is used to specify the pitch methods. There are two methods available in this drop-down list, **Constant** and **Variable**. The **Constant** option enables you to maintain a constant pitch throughout the helical protrusion.

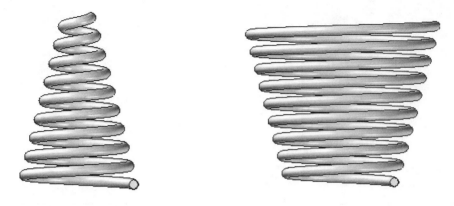

Figure 9-48 *Inward tapered spring*   **Figure 9-49** *Outward tapered spring*

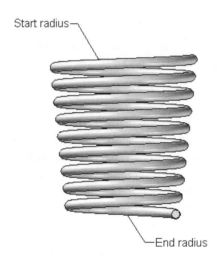

Figure 9-50 *Taper specified by the start and end radii*

When you select the **Variable** option from the drop-down list, the **Pitch ratio** and the **End pitch** radio buttons are activated. The **Pitch ratio** specifies the variable pitch ratio for a variable pitch helix. The **End pitch** specifies the ending pitch length for the helix. Note that if you use the **End Pitch** option to create a variable spring, then the actual start pitch and end pitch values will not be equal to the specified values.

In Solid Edge, the variable pitch helical protrusion is created by increasing the pitch value from the start to the end by using a formula. According to this formula, the increase in pitch value is equal to the half of the difference between the start and end pitch values divided by the number of turns. In mathematical notations, this can be written as $I=1/2(P_s-P_e)/N$, where I is the increase in pitch, P_s is the pitch at start, P_e is the pitch at end, and N is the number of turns. For example if P_s is 20, P_e is 44, and N is 12 then according to the formula $I=1$ refer to Figure 9-51. In this figure, the actual start pitch

(Ps) is 20+1 and similarly the next turn is calculated by adding 1 to the previous turn's value.

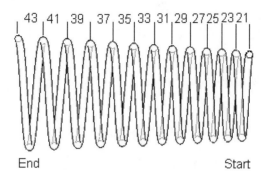

Figure 9-51 Taper specified by the start and end pitch values

CREATING NORMAL PROTRUSIONS

Toolbar: Features > Revolved Protrusion > Normal Protrusion

The **Normal Protrusion** button is the flyout that is displayed when you press and hold the **Revolved Protrusion** button. This tool is used to create a normal protrusion by selecting a closed curve. This curve can lie on any surface, planar or cylindrical. Note that it is not possible to draw a sketch on a non-planar surface. Therefore, you need to create a plane at an offset from the cylindrical surface and then draw the sketch on it. Next, using the **Project Curve** tool available in the **Surfacing** toolbar, project the sketch on the nonplanar surface. Note that to project text profiles, each alphabet will be projected separately. Next, invoke the **Normal Protrusion** tool and select the sketch to be projected. After selecting the sketch, right-click to accept the selection; you are prompted to specify the projection direction. Depending on the projection direction you specify, the material is added to the sketch or to outside of the sketch. Adding material outside the sketch implies that the material is added to the entire surface on which the curve lies, except the area covered by the sketched curve.

Figure 9-52 shows the material added to the curves that lie on a nonplanar surface. Figure 9-53 shows the material added outside the sketch. Note that in this case, the diameter of the cylinder has increased.

Figure 9-52 Material added to the curves   *Figure 9-53* Material added outside the curves

CREATING NORMAL CUTOUTS

Toolbar: Features > Revolved Cutout > Normal Cutout

The **Normal Cutout** tool is available on the flyout that is displayed when you press and hold the **Revolved Cutout** button. This tool functions in the same way as the **Normal Protrusion** tool with the only difference this tool is used to remove the material.

TUTORIALS

Tutorial 1

In this tutorial, you will create the model of the Upper Housing of a Motor Blower assembly. The model is shown in Figure 9-54. Figure 9-55 shows the left-side view of the top view, front view, and the sectioned left-side view of the model. All dimensions are in inches. After creating it, save it with the name given below.

\Solid Edge\c09\c09tut1.par   **(Expected time: 45 min)**

Figure 9-54 *Isometric view of the Upper Housing*

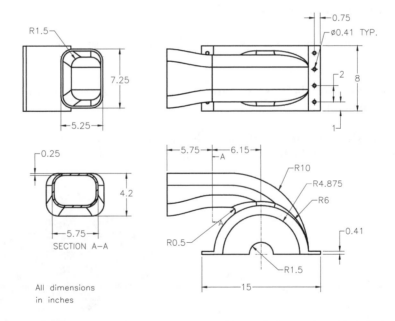

Figure 9-55 *Views and dimensions of the Upper Housing*

The following steps are required to complete this tutorial:

a. Create the base feature on the front plane, refer to Figure 9-57. This feature is extruded symmetrically on both sides of the front plane.
b. Create the swept protrusion feature on the front plane, refer to Figure 9-68.

c. Create round of radius 0.5 on the swept protrusion feature, refer to Figure 9-7.
d. Create the thin wall feature on the model, refer to Figure 9-71.
e. Create the cut features on the base feature, refer to Figures 9-73 and 9-75.
f. Create a protrusion feature on the base feature, refer to Figure 9-77.
g. Mirror the previous protrusion feature to the left side of the model, refer to Figure 9-78.
h. Create a hole feature on the previous feature, refer to Figure 9-79.
i. Create a pattern of the hole feature, refer to Figure 9-80.

Starting a New File

The dimensions of this model are in inches. Therefore, you need to select a template that has units in inches.

1. Choose the **New** button from the **Main** toolbar to display the **New** dialog box.

2. Choose the **More** tab from the dialog box and double-click on the **Normeng.Par** option to open a new part file with the unit of length as inches.

Creating the Base Feature

The file that you have opened has units set to inches and so, the model that you create will have dimensions in inches.

1. Invoke the **Protrusion** tool and select the front plane to draw the profile of the base feature.

2. Draw the profile of the base feature, as shown in Figure 9-56 and then exit the sketching environment.

3. Extrude the sketch symmetrically on both sides of the profile plane to the depth of 8. The isometric view of the base feature is shown in Figure 9-57.

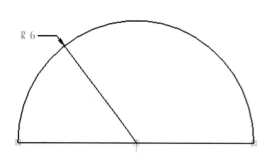

Figure 9-56 *Sketch of the base feature*

Figure 9-57 *Base feature*

Creating the Swept Protrusion

The second feature is the swept protrusion. The sketches of the path and the cross-sections to be used in the swept protrusion will be drawn using this tool.

1. Choose the **Swept Protrusion** button to display the **Sweep Options** dialog box.

2. Select the **Multiple paths and cross sections** radio button and make sure the **No Merge** option is selected in the **Face Merging** area. Choose **OK** to close the dialog box.

    Next, you need to draw the sketch for the path of the swept protrusion.

3. From the **Create-From Options** drop-down list, select the **Coincident Plane** option, if it is not selected.

4. Select the front plane to draw the sketch.

5. Draw the sketch of the path, as shown in Figure 9-58, and then exit the sketching environment.

6. Choose the **Finish** button from the ribbon bar and then choose the **Next** button; the **Cross Section Step** button is activated on the ribbon bar. You are now ready to select the plane to draw the cross-section.

7. Select the **Plane Normal To Curve** option from the **Create-From Options** drop-down list, if it is not selected.

8. Select the arc close to its lower endpoint; the profile plane is displayed, as shown in Figure 9-59.

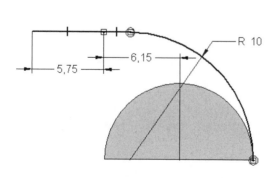

Figure 9-58 Sketch of the path

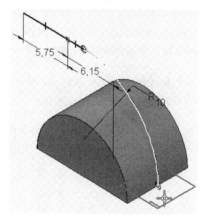

Figure 9-59 Profile plane at the end of the path

You will notice that on moving the cursor along the path curve, the profile plane also moves.

9. Click when the plane is at the lower endpoint of the path. The plane is oriented parallel to the screen and you can draw the cross-section of the swept protrusion.

10. Draw the sketch of the cross-section, as shown in Figure 9-60, and exit the sketching environment.

    Next, you need to select the start point of the cross-section. As mentioned earlier, the swept protrusion is created by joining the start points on various cross-sections.

11. Select the point on the cross-section, as shown in Figure 9-61.

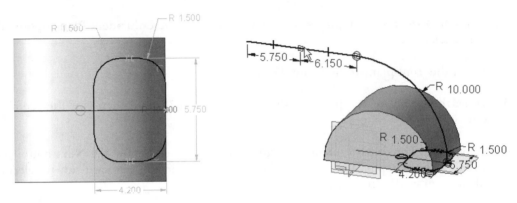

Figure 9-60 The first cross-section of the swept protrusion

Figure 9-61 Arrow showing the start point on the cross-section

12. Choose the **Finish** button on the ribbon bar. Next, you need to select another point on the path to draw the second cross-section.

    It is evident from the drawing views of the model that the second cross-section should be drawn at the location on the path where the section A-A is given.

13. Select the point where the line of length 5.75 starts, as shown in Figure 9-62, to place the profile plane.

14. Draw the sketch of the cross-section, as shown in Figure 9-63. While drawing the sketch, constrain the midpoint of the upper horizontal line to the point you selected on the curve path.

15. Exit the sketching environment. You need to select the start point of this cross-section.

16. Select the upper left point on the cross-section, as shown in Figure 9-64.

17. Choose the **Finish** button on the ribbon bar. Next, you need to select another point on the path to draw the last cross-section.

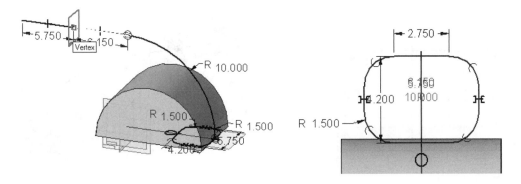

Figure 9-62 *Location for the profile plane*   Figure 9-63 *The second cross-section of the swept protrusion*

18. Select the point shown in Figure 9-65 to place the profile plane.

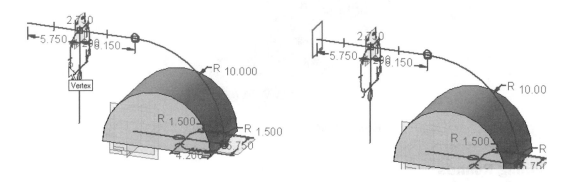

Figure 9-64 *Arrow showing the start point on the second cross-section*   Figure 9-65 *Location for the last profile plane*

19. Draw the sketch of the cross-section, as shown in Figure 9-66, and exit the sketching environment.

   Next, you need to select the start point of this cross-section.

20. Select the point on the cross-section, as shown in Figure 9-67.

21. Choose the **Finish** button from the ribbon bar and then choose the **Preview** button.

22. Choose **Finish** and then the **Cancel** button to exit the **Swept Protrusion** tool. The swept protrusion feature is created and displayed, as shown in Figure 9-68.

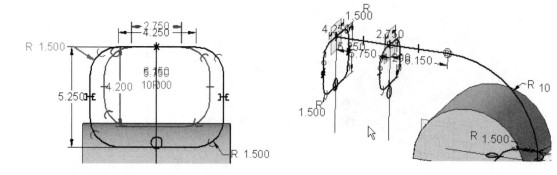

Figure 9-66 *The third cross-section of the swept protrusion*

Figure 9-67 *Arrow showing the start point on the third cross-section*

Figure 9-68 *Swept protrusion feature*

Adding Rounds

Before creating a thin wall feature, you need to add a round to the model. This is because while creating the thin wall feature, the round is also included along with the other faces of the model.

1. Choose the **Round** button from the **Features** toolbar.

2. Select the edge where the base feature and the swept feature join, as shown in Figure 9-71.

3. Enter the value **0.5** in the **Radius** edit box and choose the **Accept** button.

4. Choose the **Preview** button; the rounds are created on the selected edges, as shown in Figure 9-69.

5. Choose **Finish** to create the round.

6. Exit the round tool. The round is created, as shown in Figure 9-70.

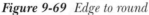

Figure 9-69 *Edge to round*

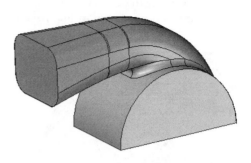

Figure 9-70 *Edge after creating the round*

Adding a Thin Wall Feature

A thin wall feature of thickness 0.25 will be created on the model so that it has a uniform wall thickness.

1. Choose the **Thin Wall** button from the **Features** toolbar; you are prompted to specify the thickness value. By default, a value of 0.25 is specified in the **Common thickness** edit box.

2. Press ENTER; you are prompted to select a face chain.

3. Select the front face of the swept protrusion feature and the bottom face of the base feature. Right-click to accept the selection.

4. Choose the **Preview** button and then exit the tool. The thin wall feature is created, as shown in Figure 9-71.

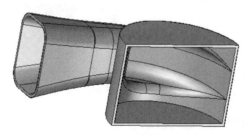

Figure 9-71 *Thin wall feature created*

Creating Cutout Features

1. Create an extrude cutout feature on the front face of the base feature. The sketch of the cutout feature is shown in Figure 9-72.

2. To specify the depth of extrusion, choose the **Thru Next** button from the ribbon bar. The cutout is created, as shown in Figure 9-73.

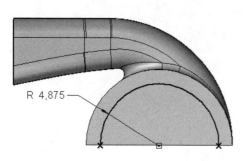
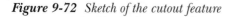

Figure 9-72 *Sketch of the cutout feature*

Figure 9-73 *Model after creating the cutout feature*

3. Create the next cutout whose sketch is shown in Figure 9-74.

4. Specify the depth of the cutout using the **Thru All** option. The model, after creating this cutout feature, is shown in Figure 9-75.

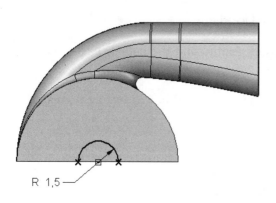

Figure 9-74 *Sketch of the cut feature*

Figure 9-75 *Model after creating the cut feature*

Creating a Protrusion Feature

1. Create a protrusion feature nn the front face of the base feature. Its sketch is shown in Figure 9-76. Note that to draw this sketch, you need to project the curved edge of the base feature and then corner trim the top horizontal line with this edge.

    The model, after creating the protrusion feature, is shown in Figure 9-77.

Creating a Mirror Copy

1. Choose the **Mirror Copy Feature** button. You are prompted to select the features to be included in the mirror copy operation.

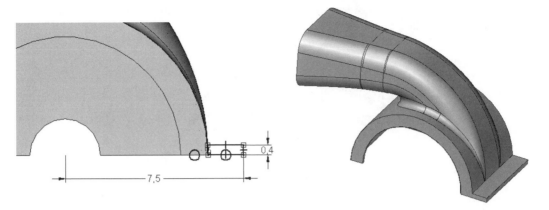

Figure 9-76 *Sketch of the protrusion feature*

Figure 9-77 *Model after creating the protrusion feature*

2. Select the protrusion feature created in the previous step and mirror it about the right plane. Use the **Smart** option to create the mirror. The feature is mirrored, as shown in Figure 9-78.

Creating a Hole Feature

1. Choose the **Hole** button; you are prompted to select a face on which the hole will be created.

2. Select the top face of the protrusion feature on the right. Specify the hole parameters and create the hole, see Figure 9-79.

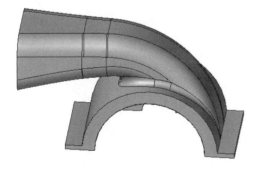

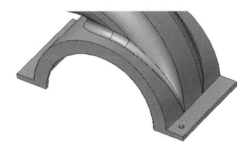

Figure 9-78 *Model after mirroring the protrusion feature*

Figure 9-79 *Hole on the protrusion feature*

Creating a Pattern of the Hole Feature

1. Choose the **Pattern** button; you are prompted to select the feature that needs to be patterned.

2. Select the hole feature from the **EdgeBar**.

3.　Create the pattern of the hole, as shown in Figure 9-80. You may need to use the **Smart** option to create the pattern.

Figure 9-80　*Final model for Tutorial 1*

Saving the File

1.　Save the model with the name given below and then close the file.

\Solid Edge\c09\c09tut1.par

Tutorial 2

In this tutorial, you will create the model shown in Figure 9-81. Figure 9-82 shows the section views of the loft feature. Use these sections to create the loft feature. After creating the model, save it with the name and location given below.

\Solid Edge\c09\c09tut2.par   **(Expected time: 45 min)**

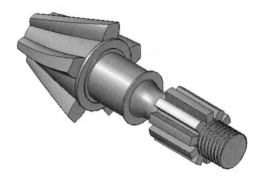

Figure 9-81 *Isometric view of the model for Tutorial 2*

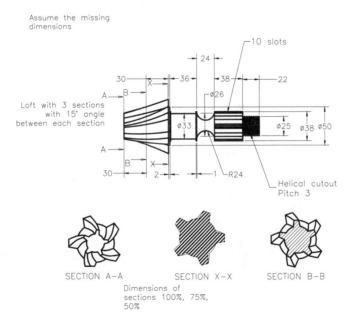

Figure 9-82 *Front and section views of the model*

The following steps are required to complete this tutorial:

a. Create a base feature on the right plane, refer to Figure 9-83.
b. Create a helical cutout on the base feature, refer to Figure 9-86.
c. Create a protrusion feature on the end face of the base feature, refer to Figure 9-87.
d. Create the cutout to create a slot on the cylindrical feature and then create a pattern of the slot, see Figures 9-89 and 9-90.
e. Create a revolved protrusion, refer to Figure 9-92.
f. Create a protrusion feature on the end face of the previous feature, refer to Figure 9-94.
g. Create the next feature, which is also a protrusion feature, refer to Figure 9-95.
h. The last feature of the model is the loft protrusion. Three sections will be used to create this feature, refer to Figures 9-98, 9-100, 9-104, and 9-106.

Creating the Base Feature

1. Create a cylindrical feature on the right plane, as shown in Figure 9-83.

Creating the Helical Cutout

Next, you will create a helical cutout on the cylindrical feature. The cross-section of the helical cutout will be triangular.

1. Choose the **Helical Cutout** button from the **Revolved Cutout** flyout. The **Axis and Cross Section Step** button is chosen by default and you are prompted to select a reference plane to draw the sketch of the axis and the cross-section.

2. Choose the front plane and draw the center line and the profile of the section, as shown in Figure 9-84. The sketch of the section is shown in Figure 9-85.

Figure 9-83 *Base feature*

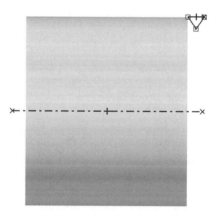

Figure 9-84 *Sketch and the center line*

3. Exit the sketching environment; you are prompted to select the start end of the helix axis.

4. Select the right end of the axis; you are prompted to specify the helix parameters.

5. Specify the value of pitch as **3** in the **Pitch** edit box and choose the **Next** button.

6. Choose the **Preview** button to view the helical cutout. The helical cutout is created, as shown in Figure 9-86. Choose **Finish** and then **Cancel** to exit the tool.

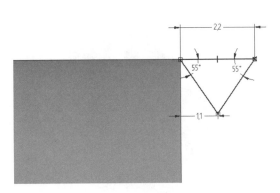

Figure 9-85 Sketch of the section with dimensions

Figure 9-86 Helical cutout

Creating the Third Feature

The third feature is a cylindrical feature that will be created on the end face of the previous feature.

1. Create a protrusion feature on the end face of the previous feature, as shown in Figure 9-87.

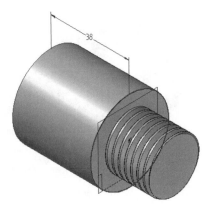

Figure 9-87 The model after creating the third feature

Creating the Fourth Feature

The fourth feature is a cutout that will be created on the previous feature. After creating the cutout, you will create its pattern.

1. Create a cutout on the cylindrical feature by drawing the sketch shown in Figure 9-88. The cutout feature is shown in Figure 9-89.

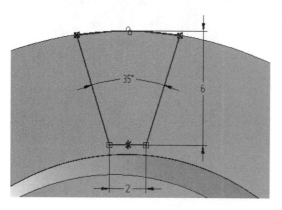

Figure 9-88 *Sketch of the section with dimensions*

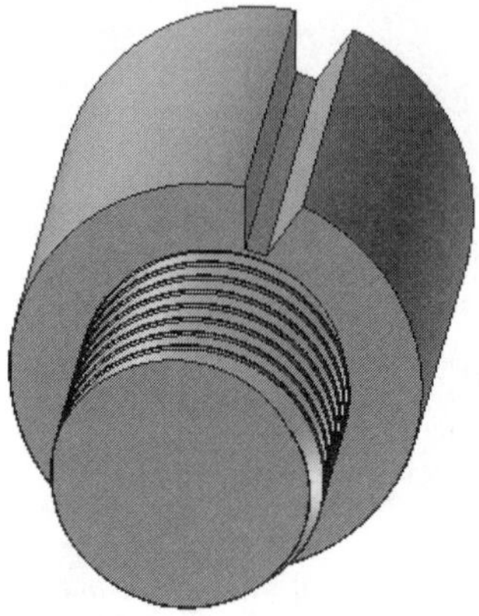

Figure 9-89 *After creating the cutout*

2. Choose the **Pattern** button from the **Features** toolbar. Create the rotational pattern of the cutout feature. The total number of instances in the pattern is 10.

The pattern is created, as shown in Figure 9-90.

Figure 9-90 *Model after creating the pattern*

Creating Revolved Protrusions

The next two features are the revolved protrusions.

1. Choose the **Revolved Protrusion** button from the **Features** toolbar and select the front plane. Draw the sketch shown in Figure 9-91 to revolve.

The revolved feature is created, as shown in Figure 9-92.

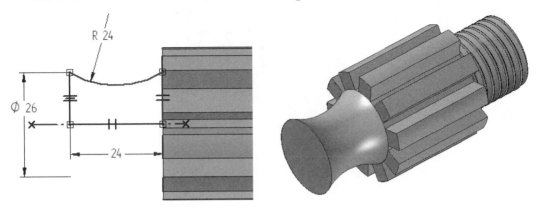

Figure 9-91 *Sketch to revolve*

Figure 9-92 *Model after creating the revolved protrusion*

2. Create another revolved protrusion on the front plane by drawing the sketch, as shown in Figure 9-93.

The revolved feature is created, as shown in Figure 9-94.

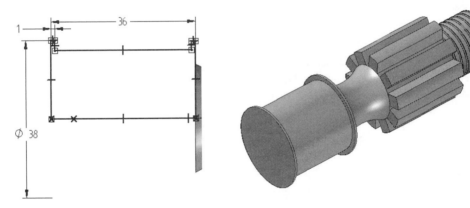

Figure 9-93 *Sketch to revolve*

Figure 9-94 *Model after creating the revolved protrusion*

Creating the Protrusion Feature

1. Create the protrusion feature, as shown in Figure 9-95. The diameter of this protrusion is 50 and the depth of extrusion is 2.

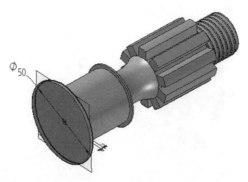

Figure 9-95 *Protrusion feature with dimensions*

 Note
The last three features could have been created as a single revolved feature. By creating them as separate features, you can make the model more flexible. This is because in separate you can modify any dimension of the individual features very easily. But to modify the dimensions of the sketch that involves all the three features would be difficult.

Creating the Lofted Protrusion Feature

The lofted protrusion that you are going to create uses three cross-sections. The sizes of the second and third cross-sections will be 75% and 50% of the first cross-section.

1. Choose the **Lofted Protrusion** button from the flyout.

2. Select the **Coincident Plane** option from the **Create-From Options** drop-down list in the ribbon bar and select the end face of the previous feature. The first cross-section will be drawn on this face.

3. Draw the sketch, as shown in Figure 9-96. After drawing it, you need to create four more instances of the same sketch.

4. Choose the **Rotate** button in the sketching environment. Create four instances of the sketch using the **Copy** option, see Figure 9-97.

5. After creating the instances, use the **Include** tool to use the circular edge. Then trim the arcs that are not required. Remember that the sketch should be a closed loop. Figure 9-98 shows the final sketch of the first cross-section.

6. After drawing the first section, exit the sketching environment. You need to select the start point of the cross-section. This point is used to determine the vertices on the cross-sections that will be joined while creating the loft.

7. Select the point, as shown in Figure 9-99, and choose the **Finish** button from the ribbon bar.

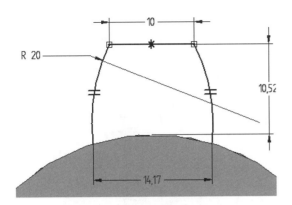

Figure 9-96 *Sketch with dimensions*

Figure 9-97 *Creating copies of the sketch*

8. Create a reference plane that is parallel to the previous plane and at an offset distance of 30. This plane will be used to draw the sketch of the second cross-section.

Now, you need to draw the same sketch profile but with some scale factor.

9. Choose the **Include** button from the toolbar to display the **Include Options** dialog box. Clear all check boxes in this dialog box except the last one and then exit the dialog box by choosing **OK**.

10. Select the **Wireframe Chain** option from the **Select** drop-down list. Select the sketch profile.

You will scale this profile with some scale factor.

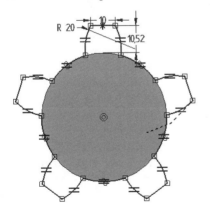

Figure 9-98 *Final sketch of first section*

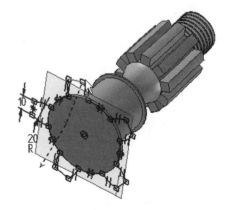

Figure 9-99 *Start point on the section*

11. Choose the **Scale** button and enter a scale factor of **0.75** in the **Scale Factor** edit box.

12. Scale the existing sketch, as shown in Figure 9-100.

13. Rotate the sketch in the clockwise direction by 15-degrees using the **Rotate** tool. Make sure the **Copy** option available on the ribbon bar is not active. The sketch, after rotating, is shown in Figure 9-101.

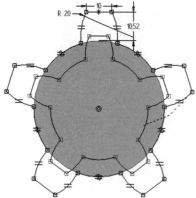

Figure 9-100 *Sketch after scaling*   **Figure 9-101** *Sketch after revolving*

14. After drawing the second section, exit the sketching environment. You are prompted to select the start point of the cross-section.

15. Select the point, as shown in Figure 9-102, and choose the **Finish** button from the ribbon bar.

16. Create a reference plane parallel to the previous plane at a distance of 30. This plane will be used to draw the sketch of the third cross-section.

17. Follow steps 9 to 13 to draw the third cross-section. Remember to use the scale factor of **0.5** in the **Scale Factor** edit box, while scaling.

    Figure 9-103 shows the sketch after scaling and Figure 9-104 shows the sketch after rotating.

18. Exit the sketching environment and select the start point, as shown in Figure 9-105. Choose the **Finish** button.

19. Choose the **Preview** button. Next, choose **Finish** and then **Cancel** to exit the tool. The final model is created, as shown in Figure 9-106.

Saving the File

1. Save the model with the name and location given below and then close the file.

    \Solid Edge\c09\c09tut2.par

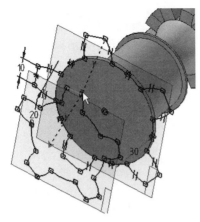

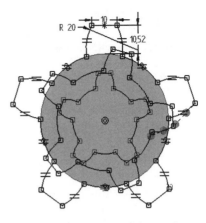

Figure 9-102 Start point on the section

Figure 9-103 Sketch after scaling

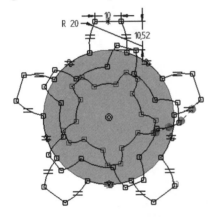

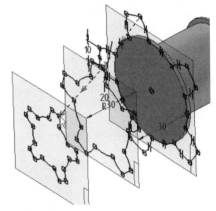

Figure 9-104 Sketch after rotating

Figure 9-105 Start point on the section

Figure 9-106 Model after creating all features

Tutorial 3

In this tutorial, you will create the model shown in Figure 9-107. Figure 9-108 shows the drawing views of the model. Use these dimensions to create it. After creating the model, save it with the name given below.

  \Solid Edge\c09\c09tut3.par   **(Expected time: 45 min)**
  The following steps are required to complete this tutorial:

a. Create the base feature on the top plane, refer to Figure 9-109.
b. Create a swept cutout on the base feature, refer to Figure 9-113.
c. Create a lofted cutout on the bottom face of the base feature, refer to Figure 9-116.
d. Create a mirror copy of the lofted cutout, refer to Figure 9-117.
e. Create a round, refer to Figure 9-119.
f. Create a thin wall feature, refer to Figure 9-120.
g. Create the next feature, which is a mounting boss created on the bottom face of the base feature, refer to Figure 9-122. Similarly, the other mounting boss is created on the bottom face of the base feature, refer to Figure 9-124.
h. Create a round on the two mounting bosses, refer to Figures 9-126 and 9-127.
i. Select the first mounting boss created on the bottom face and the round feature created on it and create their mirror copy, refer to Figure 9-128.

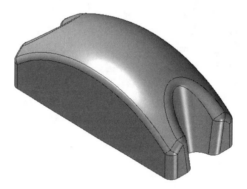

Figure 9-107 *Isometric view of the Carburetor cover*

Creating the Base Feature

1. Create a rectangular block on the top plane, as shown in Figure 9-109. The dimensions of this block are 125X50X50.

.

Creating the Swept Cutout

1. Choose the **Swept Cutout** button from the flyout; the **Sweep Options** dialog box is displayed.

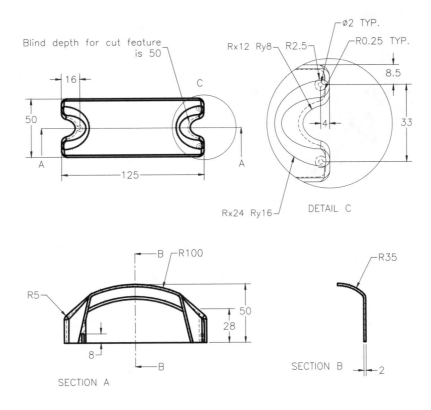

Figure 9-108 *Views and dimensions of the Carburetor Cover*

2. Select the **Single path and cross section** radio button, if it is not selected, and choose **OK** to exit the dialog box.

3. From the **Create-From Options** drop-down list, select the **Coincident Plane** option.

4. Select the front plane to draw the sketch.

5. Draw the sketch of the path, as shown in Figure 9-110. Notice that two points are placed close to each end of the arc. These points are constrained to lie on each vertical edge of the base feature. The connect relationship and dimension 28 are used to constrain the points. After drawing the sketch, exit the sketching environment.

6. Choose the **Finish** button from the ribbon bar, the **Cross Section Step** button is activated on the ribbon bar. This indicates that you are now ready to select the plane to draw the cross-section.

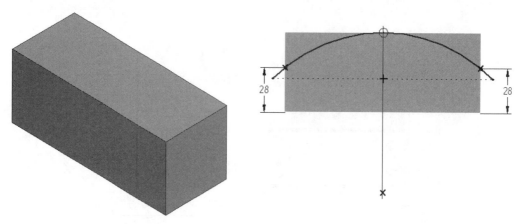

Figure 9-109 Rectangular block   *Figure 9-110* Sketch of the path

7. Select the **Plane Normal To Curve** option from the **Create-From Options** drop-down list, if it is not selected. This option is selected because you need to draw the cross-section on the datum plane normal to the endpoint of the path.

8. Select the arc. As soon as you click on the arc, the profile plane is displayed, as shown in Figure 9-111. On moving the cursor along the path curve, you will notice that the profile plane also moves itself.

9. Click when the plane is at the endpoint of the path. The plane is oriented parallel to the screen and you can draw the cross-section of the swept protrusion.

10. Draw the sketch of the cross-section, as shown in Figure 9-112, and exit the sketching environment.

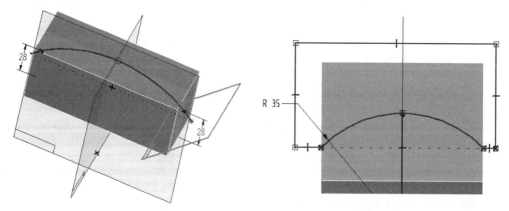

Figure 9-111 Profile plane for cross-section   *Figure 9-112* Sketch with constraints and dimensions

You need to select the start point of the cross-section.

11. Select the point that was selected to create the profile plane.

12. Choose the **Finish** button on the ribbon bar. The cutout is created, as shown in Figure 9-113.

Creating the Lofted Cutout

The next feature that you are going to create is a lofted cutout. Two ellipses drawn on two different planes will be used to create this cutout.

1. Choose the **Lofted Cutout** button from the toolbar and select the **Coincident Plane** option from the **Create-From Options** drop-down list. You are prompted to select a reference plane or a face.

2. Select the bottom face of the base feature to enter the sketching environment.

3. Draw the sketch of the first cross-section of the cut feature. The orthographic drawing views of this model show that the lofted cutout is elliptical in shape. So, draw the ellipse and dimension it, as shown in Figure 9-114.

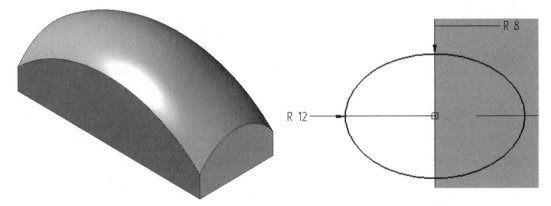

Figure 9-113 Swept cutout

Figure 9-114 Sketch with constraints and dimensions of the first cross-section

4. After drawing the first cross-section, exit the sketching environment. Now, choose **Finish** from the ribbon bar to proceed to draw the second cross-section. You are prompted to select a reference plane or a face.

5. Create a reference plane parallel to the bottom face of the base feature at a distance of 50.

6. Draw the sketch of the second cross-section of the cut feature and dimension it, as shown in Figure 9-115.

7. After drawing the sketch, exit the sketching environment. Now, choose **Finish** from the ribbon bar.

8. Choose the **Preview** button. The lofted cutout is created, as shown in Figure 9-116.

9. Exit the **Lofted Cutout** tool by choosing the **Finish** button.

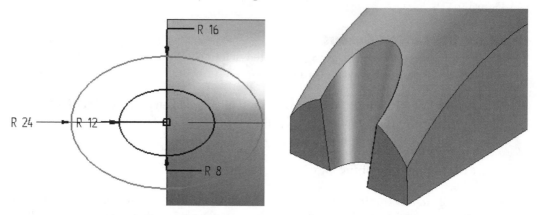

Figure 9-115 Sketch with constraints and dimensions of the second cross-section

Figure 9-116 Lofted cutout

Creating a Mirror Copy of the Lofted Cutout

1. Choose the **Mirror Copy Feature** button from the **Features** toolbar and mirror the lofted cutout to the right side of the model, as shown in Figure 9-117. You can use the right reference plane for creating the mirror copy.

Creating the Round

1. Choose the **Round** button and create a round of radius 5 on the edges highlighted in Figure 9-118. The model, after creating the round, is shown in Figure 9-119.

Figure 9-117 Model after mirroring the feature

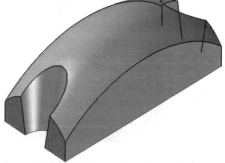

Figure 9-118 Edges selected to add the round feature

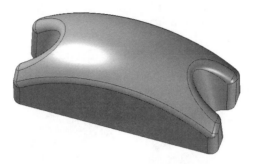

Figure 9-119 *Model after creating the round*

Creating the Thin Wall Feature

1. Create a thin wall feature by selecting the bottom face of the base feature to remove. The thickness of this thin wall feature is 2, see Figure 9-120.

Creating the Mounting Boss

Next, you need to create two mounting bosses. Both of them will be created on the bottom face of the base feature.

1. Choose the **Mounting Boss** button from the **Rib** flyout available in the **Features** toolbar.

2. Select the bottom face of the base feature. Set the parameters of the mounting boss and then place the profile of the mounting boss, as shown in Figure 9-121.

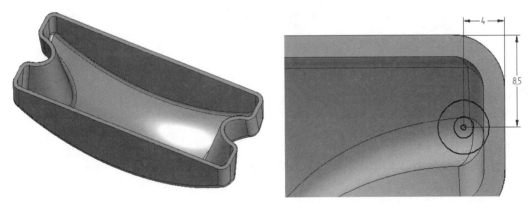

Figure 9-120 *Profile with dimensions*   *Figure 9-121* *Profile with dimensions*

3. Choose the **Finish** button to exit the tool; the mounting boss is created, as shown in Figure 9-122.

4. Similarly, create another mounting boss feature whose profile, along with the placement dimensions, is shown in Figure 9-123. The second mounting boss feature is created, as shown in Figure 9-124.

Figure 9-122 *Mounting boss*

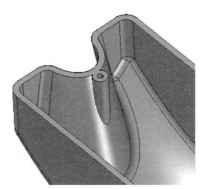

Figure 9-123 *Sketch with dimensions*

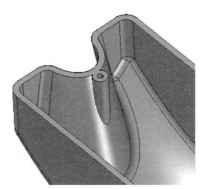

Figure 9-124 *Second mounting boss*

Creating Rounds

1. Create two separate rounds of radii 0.25, as shown in Figures 9-125 and 9-126.

Creating the Mirror Copy

1. Choose the **Mirror Copy Feature** button from the **Features** toolbar and mirror the first mounting boss feature and its round. Use the front plane to mirror the feature. The feature is mirrored, as shown in Figure 9-127.

The model is completed and is shown in Figure 9-128.

Saving the File

1. Save the model with the name and the location given below and then close the file.

\Solid Edge\c09\c09tut3.par

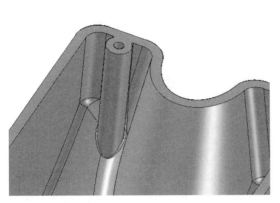

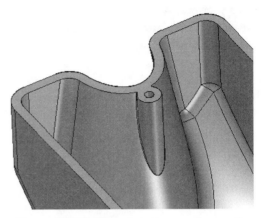

Figure 9-125 *Round on the first mounting boss*   **Figure 9-126** *Round on the second mounting*

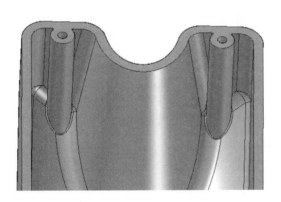

Figure 9-127 *Mirrored mounting boss feature*   **Figure 9-128** *Completed model*

Self-Evaluation Test

Answer the following questions and then compare your answers with those given at the end of this chapter:

1. The **Swept Protrusion** tool extrudes a section along a specified path. The order of operation is to first create or select a path, and then create or select a section. (T/F)

2. Using the **Swept Protrusion** tool, you can create a swept feature only along a single path with a single section. (T/F)

3. In Solid Edge, while using the **Swept Protrusion** tool, the maximum number of paths that you can draw is three. (T/F)

4. You can create a lofted protrusion by selecting the existing sketches, edges, or by drawing the sketches. (T/F)

5. The **Parallel** option enables you to create a helical protrusion, in which the cross-section remains parallel to the axis, while revolving around it. (T/F)

6. In Solid Edge, the variable pitch helical protrusion is created by increasing the pitch value from start to end by using a formula according to which, the increase in pitch value is equal to the half the difference in start and end pitch values divided by the number of turns. (T/F)

7. You can also select an edge or an existing curve that acts as a path for creating the swept protrusion. To select a path, choose the _____ option from the **Create-From Options** drop-down list.

8. The **Lofted Protrusion** tool is available in the _____, which is displayed when you press and hold the **Revolved Protrusion** button.

9. The _____ button is used to redefine the start points of the sections that take part in blending.

10. The _____ option enables you to specify the end and start radii of the helical protrusion.

Review Questions

Answer the following questions:

1. Which tool is used to create embossing on a cylindrical face?

   (a) **Lofted Protrusion**   (b) **Normal Protrusion**
   (c) **Swept Protrusion**   (d) None of the above

2. Which of the following buttons is selected automatically after sketching or selecting the path for sweep?

   (a) **Cross Section Step**   (b) **Relative Orientation**
   (c) **Path Step**   (d) None of the above

3. Which button available in the **Surfacing** toolbar is used to project a sketch on a face?

   (a) **Contour Curve**   (b) **Project Curve**
   (c) **Intersection Curve**   (d) None of the above

4. Which button in the **Lofted Protrusion** ribbon bar is used for vertex mapping?

   (a) **Vertex Mapping**   (b) **Closed Extent**
   (c) **Finite Extent**   (d) None of the above

5. To specify a plane to draw a cross-section, you can also create a reference plane by choosing the options available in the **Create-From Options** drop-down list. (T/F)

6. While creating a swept protrusion using more than one guide curve, the cross-section should be aligned to the endpoints of all guide curves. (T/F)

7. The **Vertex Mapping** dialog box is used to add sets of points. (T/F)

8. Guide curves can also be defined between the sections of the loft feature to control the transition of the loft feature. (T/F)

9. The **Helical Protrusion** tool is used to create springs, threads, and so on. (T/F)

10. In the **Lofted Protrusion** tool, the **Normal to section** option constrains the end conditions of the loft to be normal to the sections. (T/F)

Exercises

Exercise 1

Create the model shown in Figure 9-129. The dimensions of the model are shown in Figure 9-130. After creating the model, save it with the name given below.

\Solid Edge\c09\c09exr1.par   **(Expected time: 30 min)**

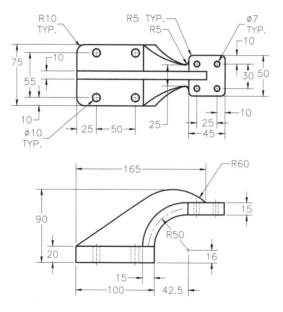

Figure 9-129 *Model for Exercise 1*

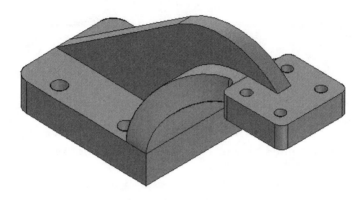

Figure 9-130 *Drawing views of the model*

Exercise 2

Create the model shown in Figure 9-131. Its dimensions are shown in Figure 9-132. After creating the model, save it with the name given below.

\Solid Edge\c09\c09exr2.par **(Expected time: 30 min)**

Figure 9-131 Model for Exercise 2

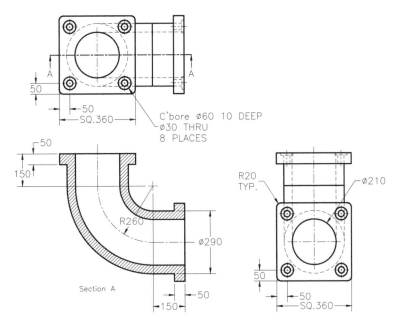

Figure 9-132 Drawing views of the model

Answers to Self-Evaluation Test

1. T, 2. F, 3. T, 4. T, 5. T, 6. T, 7. Select from Sketch/Part Edges, 8. flyout, 9. Define Start Point, 10. By Radius

Chapter 10

Assembly Modeling-I

Learning Objectives

After completing this chapter, you will be able to:

- *Understand the Assembly environment.*
- *Set the Assembly environment to work easily.*
- *Learn the types of assembly design approaches.*
- *Create assemblies using the bottom-up approach.*
- *Understand assembly relationships.*
- *Create an assembly using the top-down approach.*
- *Create a pattern of parts in an assembly.*
- *Create a multipart cutout.*
- *Move parts in an assembly.*

THE ASSEMBLY ENVIRONMENT

An assembly is a design consisting of two or more components assembled together at their respective work positions using the assembly relationships. These relationships enable you to constrain the degrees of freedom of the components at their respective work positions. To start the **Assembly** environment, choose **Assembly** from the **Create** area of the welcome screen.

If the Solid Edge session is already running on your computer, choose the **New** button from the **Main** toolbar to display the **New** dialog box. In this dialog box, the **Normal.asm** template is selected by default in the **General** tab. Choose the **OK** button to exit the dialog box and invoke the **Assembly** environment.

Setting up the Assembly Environment

Before assembling the parts, you need to configure some settings to ensure that while working on the assembly, its handling becomes easy. The following steps explain the settings that you need to check and set:

1. Choose **File > File Properties** from the menu bar to display the **Properties** dialog box. Use the **Units** tab for setting the units to the desired system of units. In the same dialog box, you can specify the title of the assembly and the related information.

2. While creating an assembly, you must make sure that the **EdgeBar** is displayed on the left of the screen. This will be used extensively while assembling the parts. If it is not displayed, choose **Tools > EdgeBar** from the menu bar to display the **EdgeBar**.

The default screen appearance of the **Assembly** environment is shown in Figure 10-1.

Types of Assembly Design Approaches

In Solid Edge, the assemblies are created using two types of design approaches, the bottom-up approach and the top-down approach. Both these design approaches are discussed next.

Bottom-up Approach of the Assembly Design

The bottom-up assembly design approach is the traditional and the most widely preferred approach of an assembly design. In this approach, all components are created as separate part documents and then placed and referenced in the assembly document. The components are created in the **Part** environment as *.par* files. Next, you need to open an assembly document and assemble the components one by one at their respective work positions using the assembly relationships. This approach is preferred while handling large assemblies.

Top-down Approach of the Assembly Design

In the top-down approach of an assembly design, the components are created in the same assembly document. Therefore, this approach is entirely different from the bottom-up approach. You will start your work in the assembly document and then create the components one-by-one. The geometry of one part helps you define the geometry of the other part.

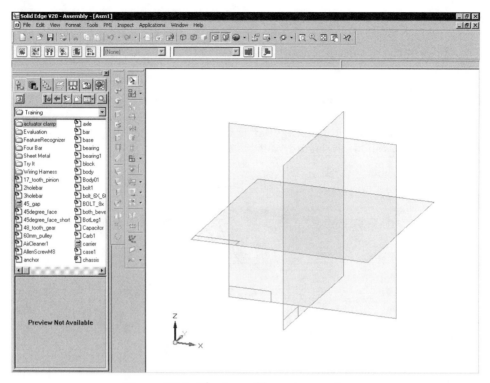

Figure 10-1 *The **Assembly** environment screen*

Note
Most of the assemblies use a combination of both assembly design approaches.

CREATING THE BOTTOM-UP ASSEMBLY

As mentioned earlier, bottom-up assemblies are those in which the components are created as separate part files in the **Part** environment. After creating the components, they are inserted in the assembly and then assembled using the assembly relationships. For starting an assembly design with this approach, you first need to insert the components in the assembly. It is recommended that the first component should be placed at the origin of the assembly document. By doing this, the base reference planes of the assembly and the part will coincide and the component will be in the same orientation as it was in the **Part** environment. When you place the first component in the assembly, the component is fixed at its placement position. The technique used to place the part files in the assembly file is discussed next.

Assembling the First Component in an Assembly

As mentioned earlier, there is an extensive use of the **EdgeBar** in the **Assembly** environment. This is because the parts are inserted in the assembly using the **EdgeBar**.

The first part that is placed in the assembly is called the base component. The base component is generally the component that does not have any motion relative to the other components in the assembly. This component acts as a foundation of the whole assembly. The following steps explain the procedure of inserting the first component in the assembly file:

1. If the **EdgeBar** is not displayed on the screen, choose the **Tools > EdgeBar** from the menu bar.

2. Choose the **Parts Library** button from the **EdgeBar**, refer to Figure 10-2.

3. From the drop-down list in the **EdgeBar**, browse to the folder where the assembly part files are stored, as shown in Figure 10-2.

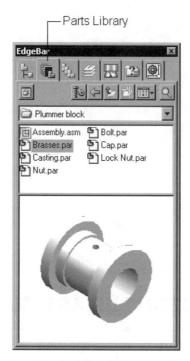

*Figure 10-2 Invoking the **Parts Library** using the **EdgeBar***

4. Select and drag the base component from the **EdgeBar** into the assembly window and then release the mouse button. The first component you place in the assembly will be automatically assigned the **Ground** relationship. You do not need to apply any other assembly relationship to this component.

Assembling the Second Component in an Assembly

Next, you will insert the second component in the assembly. But to fully position this component in the assembly, you need to use the assembly relationships. The following steps explain the procedure of inserting the second component in the assembly file:

1. Before placing the second component, you need to configure the option of displaying the new component in a separate file. To do so, choose **Tools > Options** from the menu

Tip. *Right-click in the assembly window to invoke the shortcut menu, in order to hide the reference planes after placing the base component. Choose **Hide All > Reference Planes** from the shortcut menu. To redisplay the reference planes, right-click on the **Reference Planes** in the **Assembly PathFinder**. Choose the **Show** option from the shortcut menu.*

bar; the **Options** dialog box will be displayed. Choose the **Assembly** tab and clear the **Do not create new window during Place Part** check box, if it is selected. Next, bring the assembly window to the restored state, if it is maximized. If it is in the maximized state, the placement part window will fully overlap the target assembly window and you may not be able to view both parts at the same time. On the other hand, if the assembly window is set to **Restore**, then a subwindow will be displayed at the top right corner of the main window. This method can be used to view both the parts and to apply the assembly relationships easily.

2. Double-click or drag the second component in the **Assembly PathFinder** to insert it in the assembly window. The component will be displayed in a separate window on the top right corner of the screen. Next, you need to apply assembly relationships to assemble the component.

3. As soon as you drag and drop the second component into the assembly window, the **Relationship** ribbon bar is displayed. Choose the **Options** button in this ribbon bar to display the **Options** dialog box. Select the **Use FlashFit as the default placement method** and the **Use Reduced Steps when placing parts** check boxes. This will ensure that you do not have to select the target part first to add the relationships.

Note
To insert parts that have some other file format such as .prt, .sldprt, and so on, you first need to convert them into the .par file format.

Adding Assembly Relationships

After the base component is placed in the assembly, you can insert the second component. To assemble the second component, you need to constrain its degrees of freedom. As mentioned earlier, the components are assembled using the assembly relationships. These relationships help you place and position a component precisely with respect to the other components or the surroundings in the assembly. There are two methods of adding relationships to the components in the assembly. The first method is to use the twelve assembly relationship buttons available in the **Relationship Types** flyout. The second method is to use a single button from the **Relationship Types** flyout to apply a relationship. This button is named **FlashFit**. These two methods are discussed next.

Note
The part that is placed in the assembly is called the placement part. The part that is in the assembly with respect to which the placement part is to be positioned is called the target part.

Using Assembly Relationships to Assemble the Components

There are twelve types of assembly relationships available in the **Relationship Types** flyout, as shown in Figure 10-3. This flyout is available in the ribbon bar, which is displayed after you insert the placement part in the assembly. These relationships are discussed next.

Mate

The **Mate** relationship enables you to make two selected faces or reference planes parallel and reorient them to face each other. Figure 10-4 shows the two faces that are selected to apply the **Mate** relationship. After applying the **Mate** relationship, the two components are placed, as shown in Figure 10-5.

Figure 10-3 The Relationship Types flyout

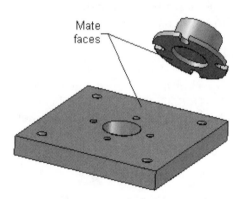

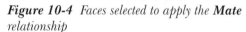

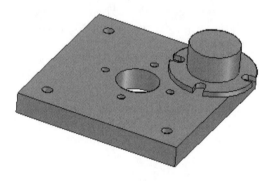

*Figure 10-4 Faces selected to apply the **Mate** relationship*

*Figure 10-5 The two faces after applying the **Mate** relationship*

While applying the **Mate** relationship, you can also choose between the two options of floating and fixed offsets. These two buttons are available in the ribbon bar, and are used to specify the type of offset that will be present between the two mating faces.

The **Floating Offset** button is chosen when the mating faces have only to be made parallel and are not required to be placed at a specified offset distance from each other. This way the distance between the two mating faces remains floating, that is, not fixed. It will be modified depending on the other relationships that are applied to the placement part.

The **Fixed Offset** button is used when the mating faces are to be placed at some specified offset distance from each other. The offset value can be entered in the edit box available on the right of this button. By applying the **Mate** relationship with the **Fixed Offset** button chosen, you can restrict the two degrees of freedom of the placement part. These are: movement normal to the mating faces and the rotatory movement around the axes normal to the other two faces.

 Note
The number of relationships required to make a part fully constrained depends on the degrees of freedom by which the part is free to move. A single relationship can restrict the movement of the part in more than one degree of freedom, depending on the type of relationship applied.

Planar Align

The **Planar Align** relationship aligns the face or the reference plane of the placement part with the face or the reference plane of the target part. The aligned faces become parallel to each other and face in the same direction. The **Planar Align** relationship is also used with the fixed or floating offset options.

As mentioned earlier, if you use the **Floating Offset** button, you can apply an additional relationship to further constrain the placement part to the target part. The **Fixed Offset** button enables you to enter an offset value. Figure 10-6 shows the faces selected on the two parts to apply the **Planar Align** relationship. Figure 10-7 shows the fixed offset, after applying the **Planar Align** relationship. In this figure, you will notice that an offset distance is applied to the faces that were selected to be aligned using the **Fixed Offset option**.

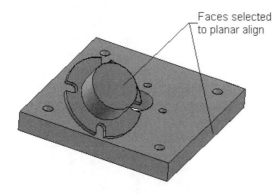

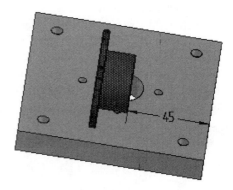

Figure 10-6 Faces to be selected

*Figure 10-7 The two parts after applying the **Planar Align** relationship with the fixed offset*

Axial Align

The **Axial Align** relationship enables you to align the axis of a cylindrical feature on the placement part with the axis of the cylindrical feature on the target part. To apply this relationship, you need to select the cylindrical surfaces of the two parts, see Figure 10-8. The axis of the bolt is aligned with the axis of the hole. The bolt is assembled with the plate, as shown in Figure 10-9.

You can apply the **Axial Align** relationship with a locked rotation or with an unlocked rotation. If you select the **Unlock Rotation** option, the rotational degrees of freedom of the part will remain free. You can apply an additional relationship to constrain the

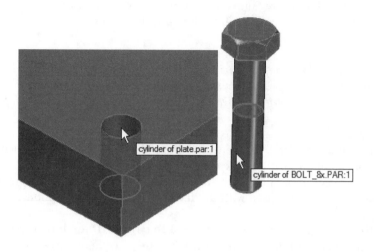

Figure 10-8 *Cylindrical surfaces selected to align the axes*

rotational movement. If you select the **Lock Rotation** option, the rotational movement will be locked.

Figure 10-10 shows the face of the bolt made parallel to the face of the plate. This is made possible by applying three relationships. Firstly, the axes of the bolt and the hole in the plate are aligned using the **Axial Align** relationship with the **Unlock Rotation** option selected. This option enables you to keep the rotational movement of the bolt free. Then, the bottom face of the bolt head and the top face of the plate are mated using the **Mate** relationship. Finally, the **Planar Align** relationship with the floating offset is applied to make the two faces parallel.

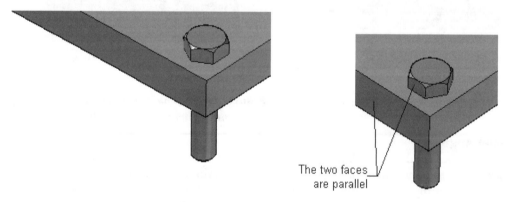

Figure 10-9 *Bolt assembled with the plate*

Figure 10-10 *The two faces made parallel by applying the **Planar Align** relationship with the **Floating Offset** option*

Note

*The dimension box in the ribbon bar is not available when you apply the **Axial Align** relationship.*

Insert

The **Insert** relationship combines the functions of both **Mate** and **Axial Align** relationships. This means that you can make the cylindrical faces of the placement and target parts concentric, as well as mate their planar faces using a single relationship. For example, the **Insert** relationship can be applied between a bolt and a hole feature. On choosing this button in the **Relationship Types** flyout, you will be prompted to click on the face to mate or on the axis to align. You can select the cylindrical surfaces of the bolt and the hole to align their axes. Then, you can set the two faces to mate. Remember that if you have applied the **Insert** relationship, the rotational degrees of freedom are constrained automatically.

However, you can rotate the placement part by some angle by editing the relationships. You need to modify the **Axial Align** relationship from locked to unlocked. After doing this, you can apply the **Angle** relationship to rotate the placement part.

Parallel

The **Parallel** relationship is used to force two edges, axes, or an edge and an axis parallel to each other. You can apply this relationship with a fixed offset or a floating offset. Figure 10-11 shows the edges selected to apply the **Parallel** relationship. Figure 10-12 shows the assembly after applying this relationship.

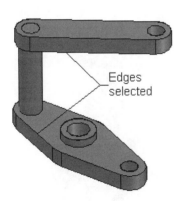

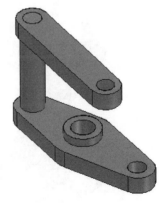

*Figure 10-11 Edges selected for applying the **Parallel** relationship*

*Figure 10-12 The assembly after applying the **Parallel** relationship*

Connect

The **Connect** relationship is used to connect two parts by positioning a keypoint with another keypoint. A keypoint can also be positioned to a face or an edge. In Figure 10-13, the corner of the block is connected to the center of the hole.

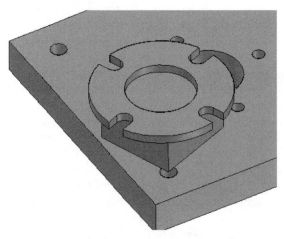

Figure 10-13 The corner of the block is connected to the center of the hole

Angle

The **Angle** relationship is used to specify the angular position between the selected faces, reference planes, or edges of two parts. For example, in Figure 10-14, the two faces are at an angle. But the two faces should be at an angle of 60-degrees to each other. Here, you can force the two faces to be at a particular angle to each other by applying the **Angle** relationship and by specifying the angular value of 60-degrees, see Figure 10-15.

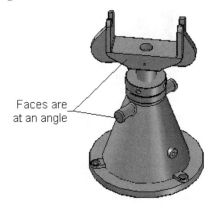

Faces are at an angle

Figure 10-14 Faces at an angle   *Figure 10-15 After applying the **Angle** relationship*

On choosing the **Angle** button from the **Relationship Types** flyout, you will be prompted to select a linear element to measure to. After selecting the element to measure to, as shown in Figure 10-16, you will be prompted to select the element to measure from. From the target part, select the plane or element to measure from, refer to Figure 10-16.

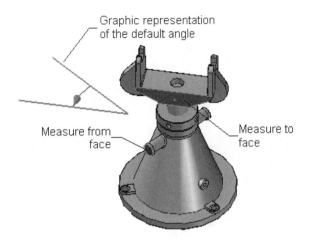

*Figure 10-16 Various parameters to be specified for applying the **Angle** relationship*

After applying the **Angle** relationship, you can modify the angle format. To do so, choose the **Assembly PathFinder** tab of the **EdgeBar** and then select the component to which the relationship will be applied. From the lower portion of the **EdgeBar**, select the relationship that shows the symbol of the **Angle** relationship. From the ribbon bar, choose the down arrow on the right of the **Angle Format** button and select the format of the angle. Before selecting the format, you can move the cursor over the format to preview it in the drawing window.

Tangent

 The **Tangent** relationship is used to apply a tangency between two surfaces. On choosing this button from the **Relationship Types** flyout, you will be prompted to select the face that you need to make tangent. Next, you will be prompted to select the tangent face on the target part. Figure 10-17 shows the two faces that are made tangent.

Cam

 The **Cam** relationship is applied between a face of the follower and the tangential faces of the cam. The face of the follower that is selected to apply the relationship can be a

*Figure 10-17 The **Tangent** relationship*

cylindrical, spherical, or a planar surface. The faces selected on the cam must form a closed loop of tangential surfaces.

Figure 10-18 shows the selected faces and Figure 10-19 shows the cam and the follower assembly.

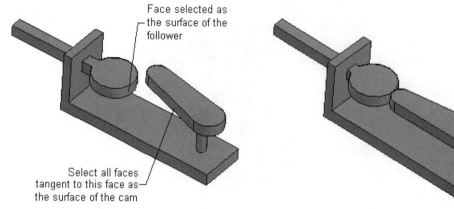

Face selected as
the surface of the
follower

Select all faces
tangent to this face as
the surface of the cam

Figure 10-18 *Faces to be selected for the* ***Cam*** *relationship*

Figure 10-19 *Cam and follower assembly*

Note

It is preferred to make the front faces of the cam and the follower coplanar so that the ***Cam*** *relationship executes properly.*

Gear

The **Gear** relationship allows you to add rotation- rotation, rotation-linear, or a linear-linear relation between two components. The components that can be used are gears, pulleys, and pneumatic or hydraulic actuators. On choosing this button from the **Relationship** flyout, you will be prompted to select the cylindrical faces, linear edges, or axes of the rotational components. To select the type of movement between the components, choose the down arrow on the right of the **Gear Type** button in the **Ribbon bar**; a flyout will be displayed. The options in the flyout are **Rotation-Rotation**, **Rotation-Linear**, and **Linear-Linear**. Figure 10-20 shows the selected faces of gear parts with the **Rotation-Rotation** type of movement. Rack and pinion is an example of the **Rotation-Linear** type of movement. Rack undergoes translation motion and pinion undergoes rotational motion. Select the **Ratio** or the **Teeth** option from the **Gear Value Type** drop-down list. Set the values of the two mating components in the **Value 1** and **Value 2** edit boxes. This option allows you to set the movement of one component relative to the other.

Note

Before applying the ***Gear*** *relationship on the components, you need to apply other assembly relationships such as* ***Mate***, ***Axial Align***, *and so on to assemble the components.*

Match Coordinate Systems

The **Match Coordinate Systems** relationship uses the coordinate systems of two components to assemble them. You need to create

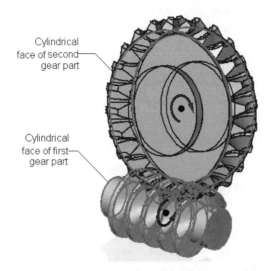

Cylindrical face of second gear part

Cylindrical face of first gear part

*Figure 10-20 Faces to be selected for the **Gear** relationship*

the coordinate systems of placement and target parts in the part environment of each component by using the **Coordinate System** tool. To view the coordinate system in the **Assembly** environment, right-click in the drawing window and choose **Show All > Coordinate Systems**.

FlashFit

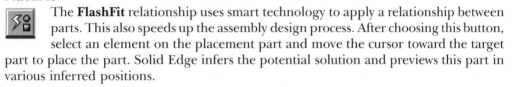

The **FlashFit** relationship uses smart technology to apply a relationship between parts. This also speeds up the assembly design process. After choosing this button, select an element on the placement part and move the cursor toward the target part to place the part. Solid Edge infers the potential solution and previews this part in various inferred positions.

Relationships such as **Mate**, **Insert**, **Planar Align**, and **Axial Align** can be easily applied using the **FlashFit** relationship.

Points to be Remembered while Assembling the Components

The following points should be remembered to work efficiently on the assembly design in Solid Edge:

1. The first assembly relationship you apply to the two parts in the assembly restricts certain degrees of freedom of both the components. As you continue to apply additional relationships, the parts become fully constrained or fully positioned and cannot be moved in the assembly. Moving the partially constrained parts in the assembly is discussed later in this chapter.

    Figure 10-21 shows the symbols in the **EdgeBar** that help you identify whether a part is fully constrained or partially constrained. It is recommended that the part should be fully constrained in the assembly before you proceed to assemble the next part.

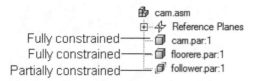

Figure 10-21 Symbols in the EdgeBar

2. It is recommended for beginners that the assembly window should not be maximized. Otherwise, the placement part window will fully overlap the target assembly window. It is not recommended to assemble the parts using this method because in this case, you will not be able to see both parts at the same time.

    If the assembly window is set to **Restore**, a subwindow will be displayed at the top right corner of the main window. This method can be used to view both the parts and also to apply the assembly relationships simultaneously.

3. Choose the **Options** button in the **Relationship** ribbon bar to display the **Options** dialog box, as shown in Figure 10-22.

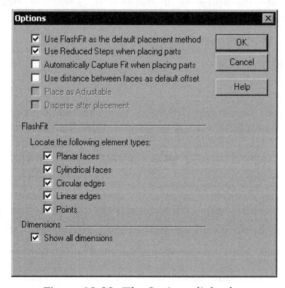

*Figure 10-22 The **Options** dialog box*

When you select the **Use FlashFit as the default placement method** check box, the **FlashFit** option in the **Relationship Types** flyout will be displayed as the default option. If you clear this check box, the **Mate** relationship will be displayed as the default option.

The **Use Reduced Steps when placing parts** check box is used to reduce the number of steps to assemble a part with the assembly. For example, if this check box is cleared, you first need to select the target part and then an element on it. If the check box is selected, you can directly select the element on the target part. Selecting this check box reduces the steps of the assembly design by 60 percent.

When you double-click on a placement part to bring it to the assembly for assembling, it will appear in the subwindow. At this stage, if you feel that the part you have brought in the **Assembly** environment is not the correct part, press the ESC key to close the part.

4. Choose the **Placement Part-Element** button from the ribbon bar, if you have selected an incorrect element on the placement or the target part while applying the assembly relationships. Next, invoke the window of the placement part and select the element again.

5. If after applying one relationship, you apply the second relationship and press the ESC key, the placement part will be assembled with the target part but without being fully constrained.

6. To apply relationships to a part that is not fully positioned, select it from the **Assembly PathFinder** tab in the **EdgeBar**; the bottom pane of the **EdgeBar** will display the relationships that are already applied to the selected part. If you want to delete a relationship, select it from the bottom pane and press the DELETE key. To apply a relationship, choose the **Edit Definition** button from the ribbon bar. Now, you can add relationships to the part you selected from the **EdgeBar**.

CREATING THE TOP-DOWN ASSEMBLY

As discussed earlier, top-down assemblies are those in which the components are created inside the assembly file. However, to create the components, you require an environment in which you can draw the sketches and then convert them into features. In other words, to create the components in the assembly file, you need the sketcher tools as well as the **Part** environment in the assembly file itself. In Solid Edge, you can invoke the **Part** environment from the **Assembly** environment. The basic procedure of creating the components in the assembly or the procedure of creating the top-down assembly is discussed next.

Creating a Component in the Top-down Assembly

You first need to save the assembly file before creating the first component in the top-down assembly. After starting a new assembly file, choose the **Save** button from the **Main** toolbar to save the assembly file. It is recommended that you create a new folder and save the assembly file and the other referenced files in the same folder.

Make sure the current assembly file is saved. Now, choose the **Parts Library** button from the bottom of the **EdgeBar** and then choose the **Create In-Place** button from the top left corner of the **EdgeBar**; the **Create New Part In-Place** dialog box will be displayed, as shown in Figure 10-23. In this dialog box, enter the name of the component, file location, and the template for creating the new part.

There are three placement options for placing the new component and these are discussed next.

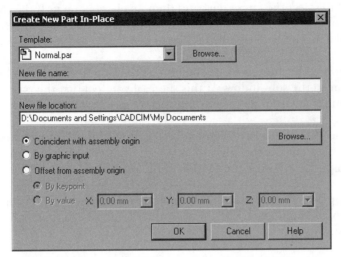

*Figure 10-23 The **Create New Part In-Place** dialog box*

Coincident with assembly origin

When you select this radio button, the origin of the new part becomes coincident with the assembly origin. Also, the reference planes of the new part are coplanar with the respective reference planes of the assembly. You will use these new reference planes to create the new part. You can also create additional reference planes for creating the new part.

By graphic input

This radio button enables you to select a face or edge, or an existing part to place the reference planes of the new part.

Offset from assembly origin

This radio button is used to create the reference planes of the part at an offset distance from the assembly origin. The offset distance can be specified by entering the x, y, and z distance values or by specifying a keypoint.

After selecting the placement options, exit the dialog box. Now, you have entered the **Part** environment to create a new part. After creating the part, save it and choose **File > Close and Return** from the menu bar. The same procedure can be used to create the remaining components of the assembly.

Note
*It is recommended that you save the part file before you exit the **Part** environment. To do so, choose the **Save** button in the **Part** environment.*

By default, a component created in a top-down assembly is fixed using the **Ground** relationship. You can delete this relationship using the **EdgeBar**. After deleting this relationship, you can assign another relationship to make the assembly fully constrained. The assembly shown in Figure 10-24 is created using the top-down assembly approach.

Figure 10-24 Assembly created using the top-down approach

CREATING THE PATTERN OF COMPONENTS IN AN ASSEMBLY

While working in the **Assembly** environment of Solid Edge, you may need to assemble more than one instance of the component about a specified arrangement. Consider the case of a flange coupling, where you have to assemble four instances of the bolt to fasten the coupling. You will need to assemble all the four bolts manually. Therefore, to reduce the time of the assembly design cycle, Solid Edge has provided a tool to create the patterns of the components. This tool is discussed next.

Creating a Reference Pattern

Toolbar:	Assembly Commands > Pattern Parts

The reference pattern is used to pattern the instances of the components using an existing pattern feature. This means that the pattern on the existing part should be created using the **Pattern** tool. To create a reference pattern, choose the **Pattern Parts** button from the **Assembly** toolbar; you will be prompted to select the parts that will be included in the pattern. Select the instance of the part that is already assembled and then accept the selection. Next, you will be prompted to select the part that contains the pattern. After selecting the part, you will be prompted to select the pattern. Select any one hole; you will be prompted to select the reference feature in the pattern. Select the instance of the hole that is the source. Choose the **Finish** button from the ribbon bar; the pattern will be created. Figure 10-25 shows the component to be patterned and the pattern source of the feature. Figure 10-26 shows the resulting pattern.

If you need to skip some of the instances of the pattern, then after creating the component pattern, click on the plus sign (+) located on the left of the pattern feature in the **EdgeBar**;

the list of the pattern instances will be displayed in the **EdgeBar**. Select the instance that needs to be skipped and right-click on it; a shortcut menu is displayed. Choose the **Suppress** option from it.

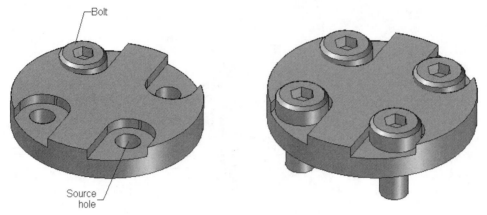

Figure 10-25 Assembly before creating a pattern   *Figure 10-26* Assembly after creating a pattern

Note

All instances of the pattern are associated with each other. For example, if you give an offset distance to the bottom face of the bolt from the top face of the base plate, all bolts will be positioned at that offset distance.

CREATING THE MATERIAL REMOVAL FEATURES IN AN ASSEMBLY

Sometimes, an assembly design is such that after the components of an assembly are assembled, you need to cut a portion of the assembly. These cuts are generally created for cutting lubrication grooves, keeping the holes concentric, design purposes, and so on. These cutouts can be assembly features or assembly-driven part features. These features are discussed next.

Assembly Features

In Solid Edge, assembly features are the features that are created in the **Assembly** environment. These features are saved in the assembly file only, and not in the parts on which they are created. In other words, the assembly features are for display purpose only and are not associative with the parts on which they are created.

Assembly-driven Part Features

In Solid Edge, assembly-driven part features are the features that are created in the **Assembly** environment and are associatively linked with the parts that are affected by this feature. In other words, they are associatively linked with the modified parts. This means that if you open the part, the assembly cutout or an assembly-driven feature will be displayed.

Solid Edge allows you to create various types of material removal features using tools such as **Cutout**, **Revolved Cut**, **Hole**, and so on.

To create a material removal feature such as a cutout, choose the **Cutout** button from the **Assembly Features** toolbar; the **Feature Options** dialog box will be displayed, as shown in Figure 10-27. The options in this dialog box have been discussed earlier. Select any one of the radio buttons and choose **OK** to exit the dialog box; you will be prompted to select a reference plane or a face to draw the sketch. After drawing the sketch, specify the depth of the cut. Next, select the parts that will be included in the multipart cutout. Choose the **Finish** button from the ribbon bar to create the cut.

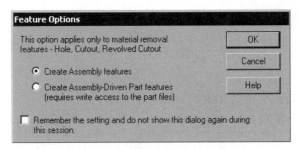

*Figure 10-27 The **Feature Options** dialog box*

The material removal tools are used for creating cutouts simultaneously in the assembled components. These tools enable you to select the parts on which the cutout will be created. Figure 10-28 shows the three parts that need to be assembled together with the help of a nut and bolt. To assemble the bolt in the assembly, all the three parts must have a hole cut on them. For the bolt to assemble properly with all the parts, it is necessary that the hole on one part should be concentric to the hole on the other part. For this purpose, a multipart hole is created on the assembly of the three components in the **Assembly** environment. Figure 10-29 shows the assembly, after creating the hole.

In the **Assembly** environment, the assembly features are listed under the **Assembly Features** heading in the **Assembly PathFinder**. Remember that because the cutout that you create can be an assembly feature or an assembly-driven part feature, you need to save the existing assembly before creating the cutout.

MOVING INDIVIDUAL COMPONENTS

Toolbar:	Assembly Commands > Move Part

In Solid Edge, you can move the individual unconstrained or partially constrained components in the assembly without affecting the position and location of the other components. The partially constrained components are the components of the assembly whose at least one degree of freedom is free. You can translate or rotate the selected partially positioned components.

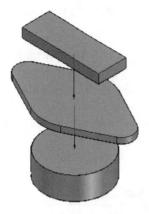

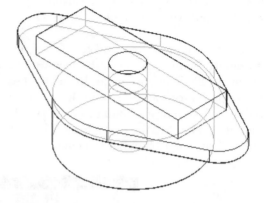

Figure 10-28 *Three parts to be assembled*

Figure 10-29 *Parts after assembling and creating a multipart cutout*

Procedure of Moving the Components

Choose the **Move Part** button from the **Assembly Commands** toolbar; the **Analysis Options** dialog box will be displayed. Choose the **OK** button; the **Move Part** ribbon bar will be displayed and you will be prompted to select the component that need to be moved. When you select the component, the three axes will be displayed. You can select any of the three axes and drag the component, as shown in Figure 10-30. Remember that if any assembly relationship exists with the selected component such that its movement is restricted in that direction, the component will not move in that direction.

 If you want to rotate the component, choose the **Rotate** button from the ribbon bar and select the axis about which the component's rotatory movement is free, as shown in Figure 10-31.

 The **Freeform Move** button is used to move the selected component in any direction that is free.

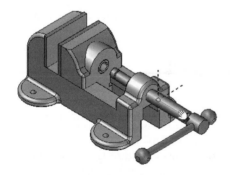

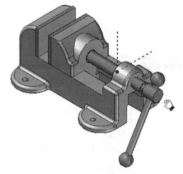

Figure 10-30 *Moving the component along the selected axis*

Figure 10-31 *Rotating the component using the axes*

TUTORIALS

Tutorial 1

In this tutorial, you will create all the components of the Stock Bracket assembly and then assemble them. The Bracket assembly is shown in Figure 10-32. The dimensions of various components are given in Figures 10-33 through 10-39. Note that all dimensions are in inches. After completing the tutorial, save the file with the name given below:

Solid Edge\c10\Stock Bracket\Stock Bracket.asm   **(Expected time: 3 hrs)**

The following steps are required to complete this tutorial:

a. Create all components in individual part files and save them. Note that all dimensions of the parts are in inches. So you need to change the system of units of the new part file that will be created. Save the files in the *\Solid Edge\c10\Stock Bracket* folder.
b. Start a new file in the **Assembly** environment.
c. Select the base component, which is the Stock Support Base, and drag it into the assembly window. This component will automatically assemble with the assembly reference planes, using the **Ground** relationship.
d. Drag the Thrust Bearing into the assembly window. Apply the required relationships, refer to Figure 10-43.
e. Next assemble the Adjusting Screw Nut with the Thrust Bearing using the assembly relationships, refer to Figure 10-46.
f. Assemble the Support Adjusting Screw with the assembly, refer to Figure 10-49.
g. Assemble the Support Roller Bracket with the assembly, refer to Figure 10-53.
h. Next, assemble the Stock Support Roller with the Support Roller Bracket, refer to Figure 10-57.
i. Assemble one instance of the Adjusting Nut Handle and pattern it to create the other instances, refer to Figures 10-59 and 10-60.
j. Then assemble the Adjusting Screw Guide with the Stock Support Base, refer to Figure 10-63.
k. Save the assembly file.

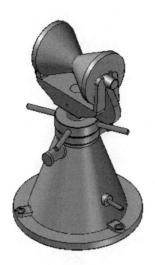

Figure 10-32 *Assembly of the Stock Bracket*

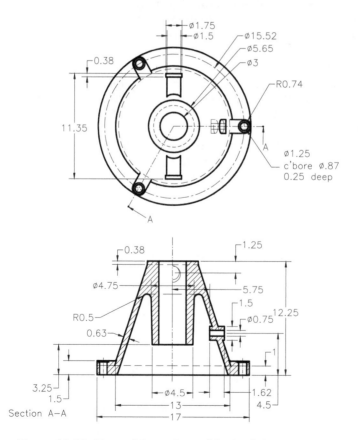

Figure 10-33 *Top and front views of the Stock Support Base*

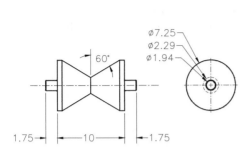
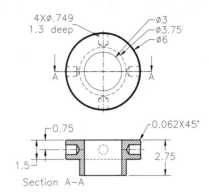

Figure 10-34 *Front and right side views of the Stock Support Roller*

Figure 10-35 *Top and front views of the Adjusting Screw Nut*

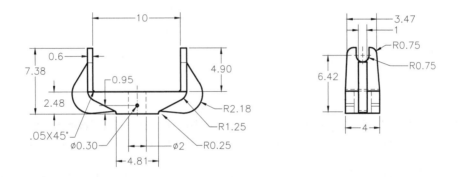

Figure 10-36 *Front and right side views of the Support Roller Bracket*

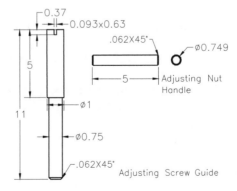

Figure 10-37 *Views of the Adjusting Nut Handle and Adjusting Screw Guide*

Creating the Assembly Components

1. Create all the components of the Stock Bracket assembly as separate part files. Specify the names of the files, as shown in Figures 10-33 through 10-39. The files should be saved in the folder *\Solid Edge\c10\Stock Bracket*.

   Make sure that the *Stock Bracket* is your current folder.

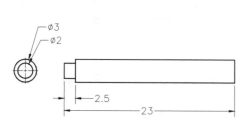

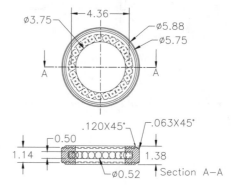

Figure 10-38 *Views of the Support Adjusting Screw*

Figure 10-39 *Top and front views of the Thrust Bearing*

Starting the Solid Edge Session in the Assembly Environment

If Solid Edge is not already running, you need to start it in the **Assembly** environment.

1. Choose the **Start** button available at the lower left corner of the screen to display a menu with additional options.

2. Choose **All Programs** (or **Programs**) **> Solid Edge V20 > Solid Edge** from the start menu to start Solid Edge.

3. Click on the **Assembly** link in the **Create** area; a new Solid Edge assembly file is started.

4. If the **EdgeBar** is not displayed, choose **Tools > EdgeBar** from the menu bar.

Assembling the Base Component with the Reference Planes

As mentioned earlier, the first part that is placed in the assembly is called the base component. The base component generally does not have any motion relative to the other components in the assembly.

1. Choose the **Parts Library** button from the top of the **EdgeBar**.

2. Browse and open the *Stock Bracket* folder.

3. Double-click on the Stock Support Base in the **EdgeBar**; the base component is assembled with the reference planes.

   Note that the assembly window should not be in the maximized state. If it is, then bring the window to the restored state. If it is in the maximized state, then the placement part window will fully overlap the target assembly window. Assembling the parts when the window is in the maximized state is not recommended because you will not be able to see both the parts at the same time.

   If the assembly window is set to **Restore**, a subwindow will be displayed at the top right corner of the main window. This method can be used to view both parts and to apply the assembly relationships easily.

Assembling the Second Component

After assembling the base component, you need to assemble the second component, which is the Thrust Bearing.

1. Before placing the second component, choose **Tools > Options** from menu bar; the **Options** dialog box will be displayed. Choose the **Assembly** tab and select the **Do not create new window during Place Part** check box, if it is not already selected and choose the **OK** button.

2. From the **EdgeBar**, drag the Thrust Bearing into the assembly window.

   You will notice that the placement part is displayed in the same window as the target part. Also the top face of the placement part is highlighted, as shown in Figure 10-40. This means that Solid Edge has automatically recognized the face that will be mated.

3. From the **Relationship** ribbon bar, choose the **Options** button to display the **Options** dialog box.

4. Select the **Use FlashFit as the default placement method** and **Use Reduced Steps when placing parts** check boxes in the dialog box, if they are not already selected, and then exit the dialog box.

5. Select the top face of the Stock Support Base; the cylindrical face of the Thrust Bearing is highlighted, indicating that you need to select the cylindrical face of the target part.

6. Select the cylindrical face of the Stock Support Base, as shown in Figure 10-41.

   The placement part is constrained to the target part, as shown in Figure 10-42. You have already applied two relationships to the parts. Next, you need to make sure the two parts are fully positioned.

7. Choose the **Assembly PathFinder** button from the **EdgeBar**. Notice that the symbol for the Thrust Bearing in the top pane of the **EdgeBar** shows that it

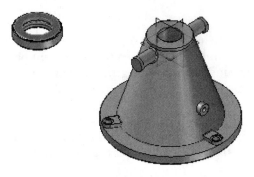

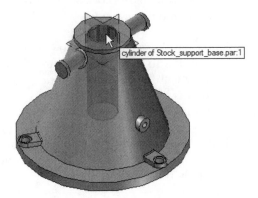

Figure 10-40 *Placement part and the target part*   ***Figure 10-41*** *Cylindrical face of the target part*
in the same window

is partially positioned. This means that you need to apply one more relationship that will constrain the rotational movement of the placement part.

8. Choose the **Planar Align** button from the **Relationship Types** flyout.

   The **Planar Align** relationship is used to align the reference plane of the placement part with any of the parallel faces of the target part.

9. Choose the **Construction Display** button from the **Relationship** ribbon bar to display the flyout.

10. Choose the **Show Reference Planes** button from the flyout to display the reference planes of the placement part.

11. Choose the **Floating Offset** button from the **Relationship** ribbon bar.

12. Select the reference plane and the face of the target part, as shown in Figure 10-42.

    Now, the Thrust Bearing is fully constrained to the Stock Support Base. The assembly at this stage is shown in Figure 10-43.

Assembling the Third Component

After assembling the second component, you need to assemble the Adjusting Screw Nut, which is the third component.

1. Before placing the third component, choose **Tools > Options** from menu bar; the **Options** dialog box will be displayed. Choose the **Assembly** tab and clear the **Do not create new window during Place Part** check box.

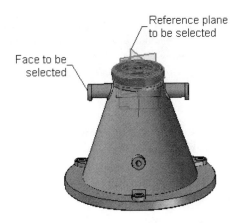

Figure 10-42 *Elements to be selected for aligning*   ***Figure 10-43*** *After assembling the components*
the reference plane and the face

2.   Choose the **Parts Library** button from the **EdgeBar**. Drag the Adjusting Screw Nut into
     the assembly window; the placement part is displayed in a separate window.

3.   Choose the **Insert** button from the **Relationship Types** flyout. Remember that
     the **Insert** relationship uses two constraints, **Mate** and **Axial Align**.

4.   Spin the placement part in its window and select the cylindrical face, as shown in
     Figure 10-44. After you select the element on the placement part, the subwindow is
     removed from the display, thus allowing you to select the corresponding element on the
     target part.

5.   Select the inner cylindrical face of the Thrust Bearing. After selecting the cylindrical
     face, the subwindow is redisplayed.

6.   Select the face on the placement part, as shown in Figure 10-45.

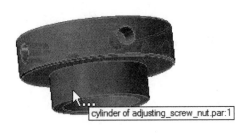

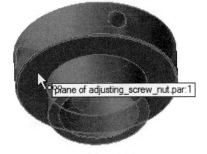

Figure 10-44 *Cylindrical face to be selected*   ***Figure 10-45*** *Face to be selected for mating*

Tip. *Generally, three assembly relationships are needed to fully constrain or fully position a component with respect to the other component. The **Insert** relationship uses two relationships and assumes the third relationship. The third relationship will lock the rotatory movement of the component. This rotatory movement can be unlocked by editing the **Insert** relationship.*

7.   Select the top face of the Thrust Bearing. The Adjusting Screw Nut is assembled with the Thrust Bearing in the assembly, as shown in Figure 10-46.

Figure 10-46 The assembly after assembling the three components

Assembling the Fourth Component

After assembling the third component, you need to assemble the fourth component, which is the Support Adjusting Screw.

1.   From the **EdgeBar**, drag the Support Adjusting Screw into the assembly window; the placement part is displayed in a separate window.

2.   Choose the **Axial Align** button from the **Relationship Types** flyout.

3.   Select any of the cylindrical faces of the placement part that are in the subwindow.

4.   Now, select the central hole in the Adjusting Screw Nut. Notice that the placement part is moved inside the assembly and is partially displayed.

5.   Choose the **Planar Align** button from the **Relationship Types** flyout.

6.   Enter the value **-19** in the dimension box available in the **Relationship** ribbon bar.

7. Select the face of the placement part and then the face of the target part, as shown in Figure 10-47.

8. Choose the **Construction Display** button from the **Relationship** ribbon bar to display the flyout.

9. Choose the **Show Reference Planes** button from the flyout, if it is not already selected. Notice that the reference planes of the placement part are displayed.

10. Choose the **Floating Offset** button from the **Relationship** ribbon bar.

11. Select the reference plane and the face of the target part, as shown in Figure 10-48.

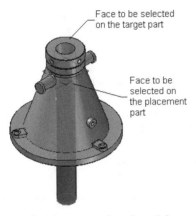
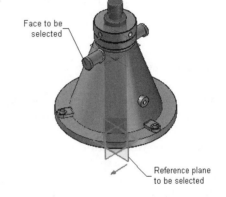

Figure 10-47 *Elements to be selected for aligning the two parts*

Figure 10-48 *Reference plane of the placement part and the face of the target part*

Note

*If you are unable to select any of the reference planes, you need to open the component in the **Part** environment. Select the planes from the **EdgeBar** and right-click to invoke the shortcut menu. Choose the **Show** option. You can now select the reference plane in the **Assembly** environment.*

The Support Adjusting Screw is fully constrained to the assembly. The assembly at this stage is shown in Figure 10-49.

Assembling the Fifth Component

The fifth component that you need to assemble is the Support Roller Bracket.

1. Drag the Support Roller Bracket from the **EdgeBar** into the assembly window; the placement part is displayed in a separate window.

2. Choose the **Axial Align** button from the **Relationship Types** flyout.

Figure 10-49 *Assembly after assembling the four components*

3.   Select the cylindrical face of the hole in the Support Roller Bracket.

4.   Select the cylindrical face of the Support Adjusting Screw. Notice that the placement part is moved inside the assembly and is partially placed.

5.   Choose the **Mate** button from the **Relationship Types** flyout.

6.   Select the bottom face of the Support Roller Bracket and then the face of the target part, that is shown in Figure 10-50.

     The assembly, after assembling these two parts, is shown in Figure 10-51. But they are not fully constrained. The rotatory movement of the Support Roller Bracket is still free and you need to constrain it.

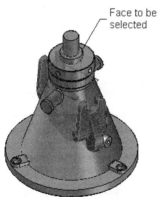

Figure 10-50 *Elements to be selected for mating the two faces*

Figure 10-51 *After assembling the components*

Note
*The rotatory movement could have been locked while applying the **Axial Align** relationship, but then the desired orientation of the placement part would not have been achieved. The desired orientation can only be achieved by aligning a plane of the placement part with the target part.*

7. Choose the **Planar Align** button from the **Relationship Types** flyout.

8. Choose the **Floating Offset** button from the **Relationship** ribbon bar.

9. Select the faces of the two components, as shown in Figure 10-52.

The Support Roller Bracket is fully constrained to the assembly, as shown in Figure 10-53.

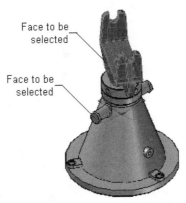

Face to be selected

Face to be selected

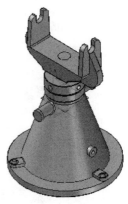

Figure 10-52 Faces to be selected for aligning *Figure 10-53 Assembly after assembling the Support Roller Bracket*

Assembling the Sixth Component

Next, you need to assemble the sixth component, which is the Stock Support Roller.

1. Drag the Stock Support Roller from the **EdgeBar** into the assembly window. The placement part is displayed in a separate window.

2. Choose the **Axial Align** button from the **Relationship Types** flyout.

3. Choose the **Lock Rotation** button from the ribbon bar.

4. Select the cylindrical face of the placement part, as shown in Figure 10-54. Then, select the cylindrical face of the target part, as shown in Figure 10-55.

The placement part is partially constrained with the assembly, as shown in Figure 10-56.

5. Choose the **Mate** button from the **Relationship Types** flyout.

6. Select the faces to mate, as shown in Figure 10-57.

Figure 10-54 Cylindrical face on the placement part to be selected for aligning the axes

Figure 10-55 Cylindrical face on the target part to be selected for aligning the axes

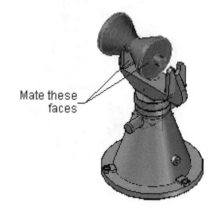

Figure 10-56 Partially positioned assembly

Figure 10-57 Elements to be selected for mating

The Stock Support Roller is fully constrained to the assembly, refer to Figure 10-58. You can check the symbol in the **Assembly PathFinder**, which shows that the Stock Support Roller is fully constrained.

Assembling the Seventh Component

Next, you need to assemble the seventh component, which is the Adjusting Nut Handle. After assembling one instance of the Adjusting Nut Handle, you will create its pattern to create the remaining instances. However, before you proceed further, you need to turn on the display of the reference planes of the Adjusting Screw Nut in the **Assembly Pathfinder**. These planes will be used to assemble the Adjusting Nut Handle.

1. Right-click on the Adjusting Screw Nut and choose **Show/Hide Component > Reference Planes**.

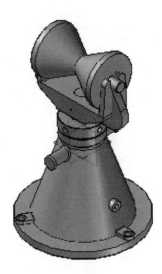

Figure 10-58 Fully constrained assembly

2. Choose the **Parts Library** button from the **EdgeBar** and then drag the Adjusting Nut Handle from the **EdgeBar** into the assembly window.

3. Choose the **Axial Align** button from the **Relationship Types** flyout.

4. Choose the **Lock Rotation** button from the ribbon bar.

5. Select the cylindrical face of the Adjusting Nut Handle.

6. Select the cylindrical face of any one of the holes in the Adjusting Screw Nut. Notice that the placement part is partially constrained to the assembly. Next, you will select the faces to mate.

   Remember that the end face of the placement part should be assembled at an offset distance of 53 from the center of the assembly.

7. Choose the **Mate** button from the **Relationship Types** flyout.

8. Enter the value **53** in the dimension box on the **Relationship** ribbon bar.

9. Select the left end face of the Adjusting Nut Handle and then select the reference plane of the Adjusting Screw Nut that is parallel to the selected surface.

10. Turn off the display of the reference planes of the Adjusting Screw Nut using the method mentioned in step 1.

    The Adjusting Nut Handle is assembled with the assembly, as shown in Figure 10-59. Also, one instance of the Adjusting Screw Nut is assembled in the assembly.

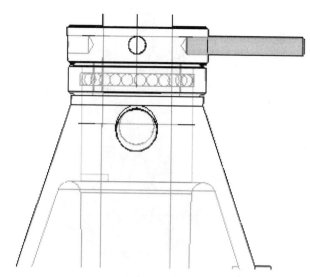

Figure 10-59 *Adjusting Nut Handle assembled with the assembly*

Creating the Pattern

You will create the pattern of the Adjusting Screw Nut to assemble the remaining instances.

1. Choose the **Pattern Parts** button from the **Assembly** toolbar; the **Pattern** ribbon bar is displayed and you are prompted to select the part that will be included in the pattern.

2. Select the Adjusting Nut Handle from the assembly and choose the **Accept** button from the ribbon bar; you are prompted to select the part or sketch that contains the pattern. This is because Solid Edge will reference the part to be patterned with the existing pattern.

3. Select the Adjusting Screw Nut from the assembly; you are prompted to select a pattern.

4. Select the existing pattern by selecting any one of the holes. Now, you are prompted to click on a reference feature in the pattern. The reference feature will be the hole that was the source while the pattern was being created on the part.

5. Select the hole in which the Adjusting Screw Nut is assembled.

6. Choose the **Finish** button from the ribbon bar; the pattern is created, as shown in Figure 10-60.

Assembling the Last Component

Finally, you will assemble the Adjusting Screw Guide with the Stock Support Base.

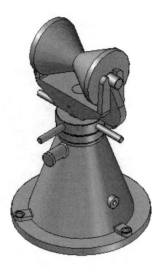

Figure 10-60 *Assembly after creating the pattern*

1. Drag the Adjusting Screw Guide from the **EdgeBar** into the assembly window.

2. Choose the **Insert** button from the **Relationship Types** flyout.

    Remember that the **Insert** relationship uses two constraints, **Mate** and **Axial Align**.

3. Select the cylindrical face of the Adjusting Screw Guide.

    After you select the element on the placement part, the subwindow is removed from the display, thus allowing you to select the corresponding element on the target part.

4. Select the cylindrical face of the hole that is on the protruded feature created on the inclined surface of the Stock Support Base. After selecting the cylindrical face, the subwindow is redisplayed.

5. Select the faces on the placement part and on the Stock Support Base, as shown in Figures 10-61 and 10-62.

    The Adjusting Screw Nut is assembled with the Thrust Bearing. The final assembly is shown in Figure 10-63.

Saving the File

1. Choose the **Save** button from the **Main** toolbar to display the **Save As** dialog box.

2. Enter the name of the assembly as Stock Bracket and choose the **Save** button to exit the dialog box.

3. Choose **File > Close** to close the file.

Figure 10-61 *Face to be selected for applying the* **Mate** *relationship*

Figure 10-62 *Face to be selected for applying the* **Mate** *relationship*

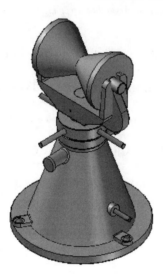

Figure 10-63 *Completed assembly of the Stock Bracket*

Tutorial 2

In this tutorial, you will create all components of the Pipe Vice and then assemble them. The Pipe Vice assembly is shown in Figure 10-64. The dimensions of the components are given in Figures 10-65 and 10-66. After completing the tutorial, save the file with the name and location given below:

Solid Edge\c10\Pipe Vice\Pipe Vice.asm   **(Expected time: 2 hrs)**

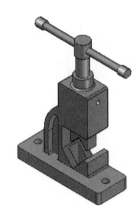

Figure 10-64 Pipe Vice assembly

The following steps are required to complete this tutorial:

a. Create all components in individual part files and save them. The part files will be saved in the *\Solid Edge\c10\Pipe Vice* folder.
b. Start a new file in the **Assembly** environment.
c. Drag the Base into the assembly window. This component will be automatically assembled with the reference planes using the **Ground** relationship.
d. Drag the Screw into the assembly window and apply the required relationships, refer to Figure 10-70.
e. Drag the Moveable Jaw into the assembly window and apply the required relationships, refer to Figure 10-72.
f. Drag the Handle into the assembly window and apply the required relationships, refer to Figures 10-73 and 10-74.
g. Drag the Handle Screw into the assembly window and apply the required relationships, refer to Figure 10-77. Similarly, assemble the other instances of the Handle Screw, refer to Figure 10-78.
h. Save the file.

Creating the Assembly Components

1. Create all components of the Pipe Vice assembly as separate part files. Specify the names of the files, as shown in Figures 10-65 and 10-66. The files should be saved in the *\Solid Edge\c10\Pipe Vice* folder. Make sure that the *Pipe Vice* is your current folder.

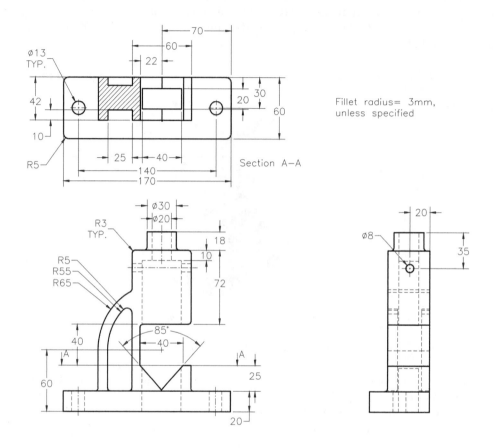

Fillet radius= 3mm,
unless specified

Section A–A

Figure 10-65 Views and dimensions of the Base

Starting Solid Edge Session in the Assembly Environment

1. Choose the **New** button from the **Main** toolbar and then double-click on **Normal.asm** to start a new assembly file.

Assembling the Base Component with the Reference Planes

As mentioned earlier, the first part that is placed in the assembly is called the base component.

1. Choose the **Parts Library** button from the **EdgeBar**.

2. Browse and open the *Pipe Vice* folder.

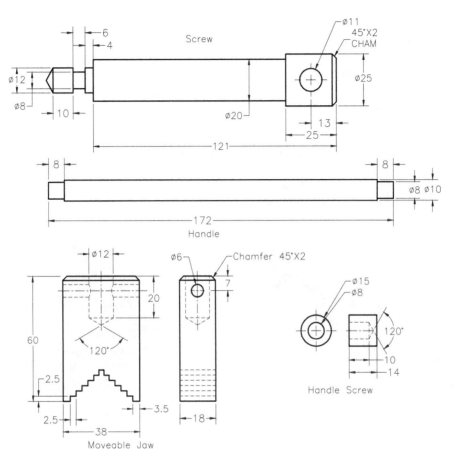

Figure 10-66 *Views and dimensions of the Screw, Handle, Moveable Jaw, and Handle Screw*

3. Double-click on the Base from the **EdgeBar** to assemble the base component with the reference planes.

Assembling the Second Component

After assembling the base component, you need to assemble the second component, which is the Screw.

1. Drag the Screw from the **EdgeBar** into the assembly window.

2. Choose the **Axial Align** button from the **Relationship Types** flyout.

3. Select the cylindrical face on the Screw. After you select the element on the placement part, the subwindow is removed from the display, thus allowing you to select the corresponding element on the target part.

4. Select the cylindrical face of the hole that is in the top cylindrical feature of the Base.

5. Choose the **Mate** button from the **Relationship Types** flyout. Enter the value **35** in the **Fixed Offset** edit box.

6. Select the face on the Screw, as shown in Figure 10-67.

7. Select the corresponding face on the top face of the Base, as shown in Figure 10-68. The Screw is assembled with the Base in the assembly.

8. Choose the **Mate** button from the **Relationship Types** flyout.

9. Choose the **Construction Display** button from the **Relationship** ribbon bar to display the flyout, if it is not already chosen.

 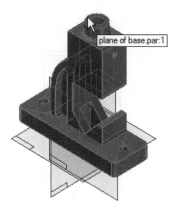

Figure 10-67 *Face to be selected for applying the* ***Mate*** *relationship*   ***Figure 10-68*** *Face to be selected for applying the* ***Mate*** *relationship*

10. Choose the **Show Reference Planes** button from the flyout to display the reference planes of the placement part.

11. Choose the **Floating Offset** button from the **Relationship** ribbon bar.

12. Select the reference plane and the face of the Base, as shown in Figure 10-69.

   The two components are assembled, as shown in Figure 10-70.

 Note
You can use the ***Mate*** *button and the* ***Axial*** *button instead of the* ***Insert*** *button for the alignment.*

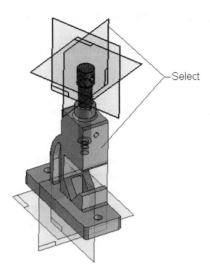

Figure 10-69 *Reference plane and the face to be selected*

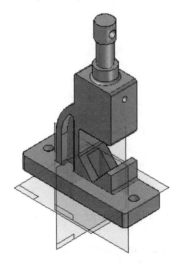

Figure 10-70 *Two components assembled*

Assembling the Third Component

Now, you need to assemble the third component, which is the Moveable Jaw.

1.   Before placing the component, you need to hide the Base component.

2.   Right-click on the Base in the **Assembly PathFinder** and choose the **Hide** option from the shortcut menu.

3.   Choose the **Parts Library** button from the top of the **EdgeBar**.

4. Drag the Moveable Jaw from the **EdgeBar** into the assembly window.

5. Choose the **Insert** button from the **Relationship Types** flyout.

6. Select the vertical cylindrical face of the hole in the Moveable Jaw.

7. Now, select the cylindrical face of the Screw; the subwindow is displayed again. You need to select the faces to mate.

8. Select the top face of the Moveable Jaw and then select the face of the Screw, as shown in Figure 10-71. Both components are assembled, as shown in Figure 10-72.

9. Choose the **Assembly PathFinder** button from the **EdgeBar**. Right-click on the Base in the **EdgeBar**. Choose the **Show** option from the shortcut menu to display the Base.

plane of Screw.par:1

Figure 10-71 Face to be selected for mating   *Figure 10-72 Two components assembled*

Assembling the Handle

Next, you need to assemble the Handle with the Screw.

1. Drag the Handle from the **EdgeBar** into the assembly window; the placement part is displayed in a separate window.

2. Choose the **Insert** button from the **Relationship Types** flyout.

3. Select the cylindrical face of the Handle.

4. Next, select the cylindrical face of the hole in the Screw, which is the second component.

5. Choose the **Construction Display** button from the **Relationship** ribbon bar to display the flyout, if it is not already chosen.

6. Choose the **Show Reference Planes** button from the flyout. Notice that the reference planes of the placement part are displayed.

7. Select the reference plane, as shown in Figure 10-73.

8. Choose the **Construction Display** button from the **Relationship** ribbon bar.

9. Choose the **Show Reference Planes** button from the flyout. Notice that the reference planes of the Handle are displayed.

10. Select the reference plane, as shown in Figure 10-74 to assemble the Handle with the Screw.

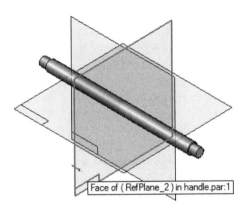 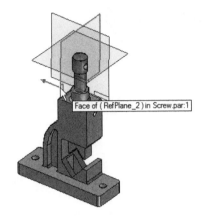

Figure 10-73   *Reference plane to be selected for mating*   *Figure 10-74*   *Selecting the reference plane on the target part*

Assembling the Handle Screw

Next, you need to assemble the Handle Screw with the Handle.

1. Drag the Handle Screw from the **EdgeBar** into the assembly window; the placement part is displayed in a separate window.

2. Choose the **Insert** button from the **Relationship Types** flyout.

3. Select the cylindrical surface of the hole in the placement part and then select the cylindrical surface on the Handle.

    Now, you need to select the faces to mate.

4. Select the front face of the placement part, as shown in Figure 10-75.

5. Next, select the face on the target part, as shown in Figure 10-76.

    The Handle Screw is assembled with the Handle, as shown in Figure 10-77.

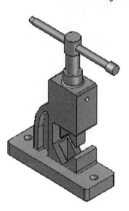

Figure 10-75 Face to be selected   *Figure 10-76* Face to be selected

6. Similarly, assemble the other instance of the Handle Screw at the other end of the Handle, refer to Figure 10-78.

Note
*To hide the assembly reference planes, right-click on the screen to invoke the shortcut menu. Choose **Hide All** > **Reference Planes**.*

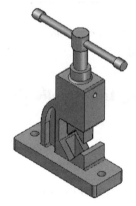

Figure 10-77 Handle Screw assembled at one end of the Handle   *Figure 10-78* Completed assembly

Saving the File

1. Choose the **Save** button from the **Main** toolbar to display the **Save As** dialog box.

2. Enter the name of the assembly as Pipe Vice and choose the **Save** button to exit the dialog box.

3. Choose **File > Close** to close the file.

Self-Evaluation Test

Answer the following questions and then compare them with those given at the end of this chapter:

1. In the top-down approach of the assembly design, all components are created within the same assembly file. (T/F)

2. The **Axial Align** relationship is generally applied to make the two faces coplanar. (T/F)

3. In Solid Edge, you can also create parts in the **Assembly** environment. (T/F)

4. The first part that is placed in the assembly is called the base component. (T/F)

5. The **EdgeBar** is used extensively while assembling the components. (T/F)

6. In Solid Edge, you can move the individual unconstrained or partially constrained components in the assembly without affecting the position and location of the other components. (T/F)

7. The _____ is the file extension of the files created in the **Assembly** environment of Solid Edge.

8. For creating a reference pattern, choose the _____ button from the **Assembly** toolbar.

9. The first assembly relationship that you apply to the two parts in an assembly restricts certain _____ of the two components.

10. For beginners, it is recommended that the assembly window should not be _____.

Review Questions

Answer the following questions:

1. Which button is used to make the **Relationship** ribbon bar available, after applying a relationship?

    (a) **Help**   (b) **Edit Definition**
    (c) **Common Views**   (d) None of the above

2. Which button in the **Relationship Types** flyout is used to constrain the two keypoints on the two parts?

    (a) **Parallel**   (b) **Mate**
    (c) **Connect**   (d) None of the above

3. Which button at the top of the **EdgeBar** is used to display the assembled parts in a chronicle in the **EdgeBar**?

    (a) **Parts List**   (b) **Alternate Assemblies**
    (c) **Assembly PathFinder**   (d) None of the above

4. Which button is used to create a new part in the **Assembly** environment?

    (a) **Create In-Place**   (b) **Assembly PathFinder**
    (c) **Standard Parts**   (d) None of the above

5. Once the relationships are applied to two parts, they cannot be edited. (T/F)

6. You cannot capture relationships of a component to place another instance of the same component. (T/F)

7. The **Axial Align** relationship is used to align the two axes. (T/F)

8. You cannot select the cylindrical surfaces to align the axes of the two cylindrical parts. (T/F)

9. The reference planes of the individual components cannot be displayed while applying assembly relationships. (T/F)

10. You can move a part only in the direction that is not constrained. (T/F)

Exercise

Exercise 1

Create the Plummer Block assembly, as shown in Figure 10-79. The exploded view of the assembly is shown in Figure 10-80 and the bill of material is shown in Figure 10-81. The dimensions of the components of the assembly are shown in Figures 10-82 through 10-84. After completing the tutorial, save the file with the name and location given below.

Solid Edge\c10\Plummer Block\Plummer Block.asm   **(Expected time: 2 hrs)**

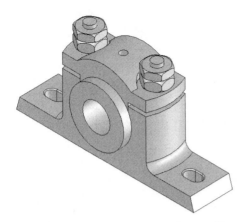

Figure 10-79 *Plummer Block assembly*

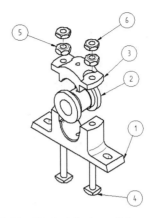

Figure 10-80 *Exploded view of the assembly with balloons*

Bill of Material		
Name	Quantity	Number
Casting	1	1
Brasses	1	2
Cap	1	3
Square headed bolt	2	4
Lock nut	2	5
Nut	2	6

Figure 10-81 *Bill of Material*

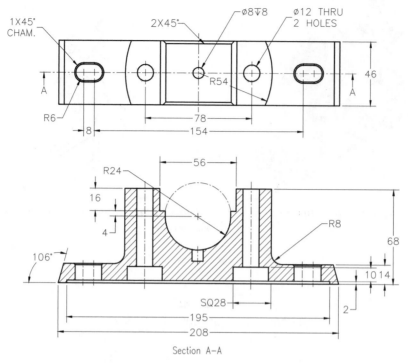

Figure 10-82 *Views and dimensions of the Casting*

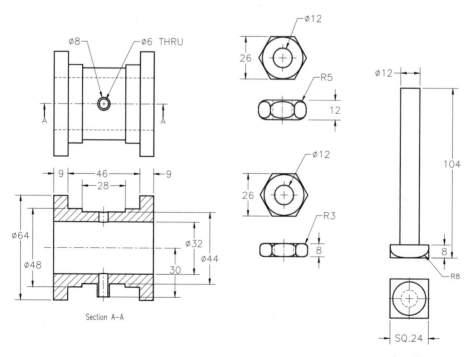

Figure 10-83 *Views and dimensions of the Brasses, Nut, Lock Nut, and Bolt*

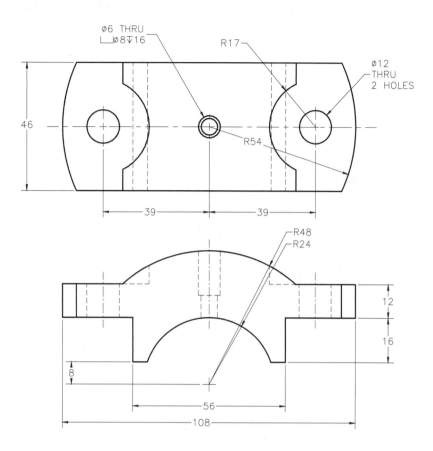

Figure 10-84 *Views and dimensions of the Cap*

Answers to Self-Evaluation Test
1. T, **2.** F, **3.** T, **4.** T, **5.** T, **6.** T, **7.** *.asm*, **8. Pattern Parts**, **9.** degrees of freedom, **10.** maximized

Chapter *11*

Assembly Modeling-II

Learning Objectives

After completing this chapter, you will be able to:
- *Create subassemblies.*
- *Edit assembly relationships.*
- *Edit assembly components.*
- *Disperse the assembly.*
- *Replace components in an assembly.*
- *Set the visibility options of the assembly.*
- *Check interference in an assembly.*
- *Create the exploded state of the assembly.*

CREATING SUBASSEMBLIES

In the previous chapter, you learned to place components in the assembly file and apply the assembly relationships to the components. In this chapter, you will learn to create subassemblies and place them in the main assembly.

Sometimes when an assembly has many parts, it becomes easy to design it by segregating it into subassemblies. To create a subassembly, you need to start a new assembly file, assemble components in it, and save it with a name. This subassembly will then be inserted into the new assembly file and assembled with the other parts. To create subassemblies, you need to follow the same procedure as that for creating assemblies. Figure 11-1 shows the subassembly of the articulated rod and piston and Figure 11-2 shows the subassembly of the master rod and the piston. Figure 11-3 shows the main assembly that is created using the two subassemblies.

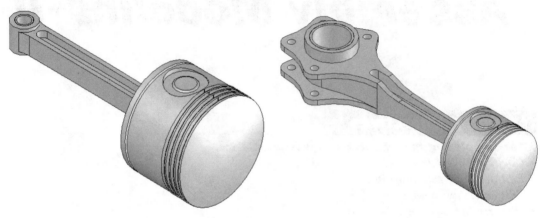

Figure 11-1 *A subassembly of articulated rod and piston*

Figure 11-2 *A subassembly of master rod and piston*

Figure 11-3 *Main assembly after assembling the two subassemblies*

To create a subassembly, you can follow the top-down approach or the bottom-up approach of the assembly design.

Note
*Right-click in the top pane of the **Parts Library** and choose the **Use Configurations** option from the shortcut menu. If this option is not chosen, the subassembly you place in the assembly document will not be activated.*

Tip. *You can also place a subassembly in the main assembly using the drag and drop method that was discussed in the previous chapter.*

*When you place a subassembly in the main assembly, an assembly icon will be displayed with the name of the subassembly in the **EdgeBar**. If you expand the subassembly in the **EdgeBar**, all parts assembled in it will be displayed.*

EDITING ASSEMBLY RELATIONSHIPS

Generally, after creating the assembly or during the process of assembling the components, you need to edit the assembly relationships. The editing operations that can be performed on the assembly relationships are listed next.

* Modifying the angle and distance offset values
* Adding relationships to a partially constrained component
* Modifying the assembly relationships

Note
*When you select a part from the top pane of the **EdgeBar**, the relationships that are applied to the selected part and the parts before it will be displayed above the dashed line. The remaining relationships that are associated with the selected part will be displayed below the dashed line.*

Modifying the Values

The following steps explain the procedure for modifying the angle or distance offset values:

1. Select a part from the **EdgeBar**; the selected part will be highlighted in the assembly window and the relationships will be displayed in the bottom pane of the **EdgeBar**.
2. You can recognize the relationship name by viewing its symbol. Select a mate relationship from the bottom pane; the faces to which the mate relationship was applied will get highlighted.
3. Enter a new offset value in the **Offset Value** edit box on the **Edit Relationships** ribbon bar. You can also enter a negative value for the offset distance. The negative value enables you to position the part in the opposite direction.
4. Choose the **OK** button to incorporate the changes.

Similarly, you can also modify the angular value of an assembly relationship.

Applying Additional Relationships

Sometimes you need to keep a part partially positioned with the other parts in the assembly.

This is because you can move the partially positioned parts along the X, Y, or Z axis. As discussed in the previous chapter, the symbol for the partially positioned part is different from that of the fully positioned part. Figure 11-4 shows a table that describes the meaning of the symbols displayed in the top pane of the **Assembly PathFinder** in the **EdgeBar**.

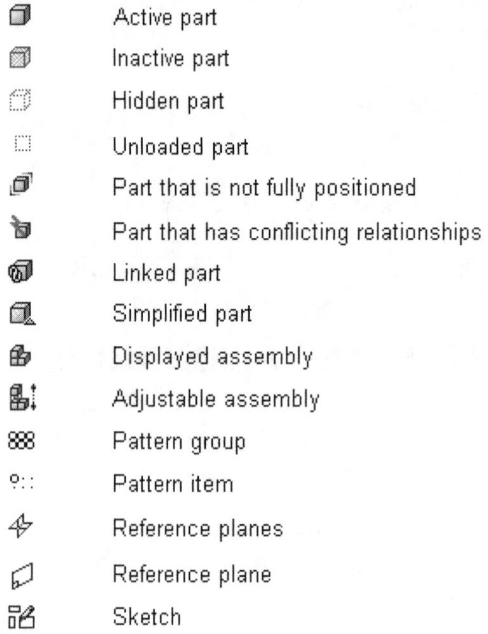

	Active part
	Inactive part
	Hidden part
	Unloaded part
	Part that is not fully positioned
	Part that has conflicting relationships
	Linked part
	Simplified part
	Displayed assembly
	Adjustable assembly
	Pattern group
	Pattern item
	Reference planes
	Reference plane
	Sketch

Figure 11-4   *Symbols that are displayed in the **EdgeBar***

The following steps explain the procedure of applying additional relationships to a part:

1. Select the partially positioned part from the **EdgeBar**; the selected part will get highlighted in the assembly window and the existing relationships will be displayed in the bottom pane of the **EdgeBar**.
2. Choose the **Edit Definition** button from the **Assembly Selection** ribbon bar to display the **Edit Part** ribbon bar. 
3. Choose the assembly relationship from the **Relationship Types** flyout to apply new relationships to the part.

Note
*When you choose the **Edit Definition** button, the **Relationship List** drop-down list will be displayed in the ribbon bar. In this drop-down list, you can view the existing relationships applied to the selected part.*

Modifying Assembly Relationships

Sometimes you may need to modify the existing assembly relationships of the parts in an assembly. For example, you may need to modify the **Mate** relationship to the **Planar Align** relationship. To do this, select the component in the **Assembly PathFinder** and choose the

Edit Definition button. Now, select the relationship that you want to replace from the **Relationship List** drop-down list. Use the **Relationship Types** flyout to choose the new relationship. Next, you can select the elements to which the new relationship needs to be applied.

You can also delete the existing relationship by selecting it from the bottom pane of the **Assembly PathFinder**. After selecting the relationship, right-click to invoke the shortcut menu and choose the **Delete Relationship** option. You can also press the DELETE key to delete the selected relationship. After deleting the relationship, you can apply a new relationship to the part.

The bottom pane of the **Assembly PathFinder** is used to view and modify the relationships between the selected part and the other parts in the assembly. Figure 11-5 shows the list of symbols that are displayed in the bottom pane. Their meanings are also mentioned in the same figure.

⟱	Ground relationship
▸|◂	Mate relationship
▸|▪	Planar align relationship
▸|◦	Axial align relationship
▪▪	Connect relationship
∠	Angle relationship
▸þ	Tangent relationship
⊘ ▸|▪	Suppressed relationship
⊟ ▸|◦	Failed relationship

Figure 11-5 Symbols of relationships

Tip: *When you modify a fixed offset type to a floating offset, you may also need to modify the other relationships to make the part fully positioned.*

Reversing the Orientation of a Part
You can reverse the orientation of a part that has been positioned using the **Axial Align**, **Planar Align**, **Mate**, **Parallel**, **Tangent**, or **Cam** relationship. To flip a part, select it and then select the relationship. Right-click to invoke the shortcut menu and choose the **Flip** option.

Note
*You can also use the **Flip** button available in the **Edit Part** ribbon bar to reverse the orientation of the part. When you flip a part assembled using the **Mate** relationship, this relationship will be converted into a **Planar Align** relationship.*

*The rotary movement of the part will be locked on applying the **Axial Align** relationship. You can unlock it by editing the relationship from the bottom pane of the **EdgeBar**. When you select* *the **Axial Align** relationship, the **Unlock Rotation** and **Lock Rotation** buttons will be displayed in the ribbon bar. Choose the **Unlock Rotation** button.*

EDITING ASSEMBLY COMPONENTS

After inserting and positioning the components in an assembly file, you may need to edit components at some later stage of your assembly design cycle. The editing of components includes editing features, editing the sketch profile, and modifying the reference planes or faces. The following steps explain the procedure of editing the components:

1. Select the component from the top pane of the **Assembly PathFinder**. Right-click on the component and choose the **Edit** option from the shortcut menu; the **Part** environment will be invoked in the assembly file.
2. Select the feature to be edited from the **EdgeBar**. You can edit or delete an existing feature. You can also add a new feature. This type of editing is known as **Editing in the Context of Assembly**.
3. After the part is edited, choose **File > Close and Return** from the menu bar.

DISPERSING SUBASSEMBLIES

Toolbar: Assembly Commands > Transfer > Disperse

 Dispersing the subassembly means that the components of the subassembly become the components of the next higher level assembly or subassembly. To disperse a subassembly, select it from the **Assembly PathFinder** and choose the **Disperse** button. The **Disperse Assembly** information box will be displayed, as shown in Figure 11-6. Choose **Yes** to accept the transfer of components of the subassembly to the next higher level assembly or subassembly.

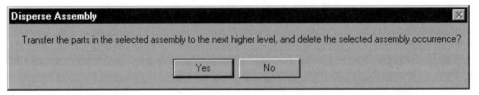

*Figure 11-6 The **Disperse Assembly** information box*

 Tip: *To edit the components separately from the **Assembly** environment, select the component and invoke the shortcut menu. Choose the **Open in Solid Edge Part** option. The component will open in the **Part** environment. Edit the component and then save the changes.*

REPLACING COMPONENTS

Toolbar:	Assembly Commands > Move Parts > Replace

Sometimes in the assembly design, you may need to replace a component of the assembly with some other component. To replace a component, choose the **Replace** button; you will be prompted to select the component to be replaced. On selecting the component, the **Replacement Part** dialog box will be displayed. Note that if the component is already selected before invoking this tool, then there will be no prompt and directly the **Replacement Part** dialog box will be displayed. Choose the **Open** button from the **Replacement Part** dialog box. To replace the components, Solid Edge compares the geometry of the two components and if their geometry matches properly, the new component will be fully positioned with the other component in the assembly. To place the new component, Solid Edge uses the same relationships that were used to place the original component. However, if there is a change in the geometry of the new component, the assembly relationships may fail and the **Replace Part** information box, as shown in Figure 11-7, will be displayed.

*Figure 11-7 The **Replace Part** information box*

If the relationships fail, their symbols will be displayed in red color in the bottom pane of the **Assembly PathFinder**. You need to delete these relationships and apply new ones to fully position the replaced component.

SIMPLIFYING ASSEMBLIES USING THE VISIBILITY OPTIONS

When you are assembling components, whether it is a large assembly or a small one, you may need to simplify it using the visibility options. By simplifying, you can hide the components at any stage of the design cycle. You can also set the transparency of any component for simplifying the assembly. The methods of simplifying the assembly are discussed next.

Tip: *You will notice that when you open an assembly by using **File > Open**, the **Activate all** parts radio button will be selected by default in the **Open File** dialog box. If you select **Inactive all** radio button from the dialog box, then the assembly will be opened with all its parts inactivated. This helps in opening the assembly faster. The symbol of an inactivated component is also different from that of the activated component.*

*To activate a component, right-click on the inactivated component and choose the **Activate** option from the shortcut menu.*

Hiding and Displaying the Components

To hide a component placed in the assembly, select it from the assembly or from the **Assembly PathFinder**. Right-click to invoke the shortcut menu and choose the **Hide** option; the display of the component will be turned off. Also, the symbol next to the component in the **Assembly PathFinder** changes, indicating that the component is hidden.

To show the hidden component, select the hidden component from the **Assembly PathFinder** and right-click to invoke the shortcut menu. Choose the **Show** option from the shortcut menu; the hidden component will be redisplayed in the assembly.

Changing the Transparency Conditions

In Solid Edge, you can change the transparency of components to simplify the assembly. Select the component to change its transparency. Select the required color from the **Face Style** drop-down list in the **Select** ribbon bar; the color of the selected component will be changed.

INTERFERENCE DETECTION IN ASSEMBLIES

Enhanced

After creating the assembly design, the most essential step is to check the interference between the components of the assembly. If there is an interference between the components, they may not assemble properly after they are manufactured. Therefore, before sending the components for manufacturing, it is essential to check the assembly for interference. To check the interference, choose **Inspect > Check Interference** from the menu bar; the **Check Interference** ribbon bar will be displayed. The tabs available in this ribbon bar are discussed next.

Interference Options

The **Interference Options** button is used to set the output options for checking the interference. When you choose this button, the **Interference Options** dialog box will be displayed, as shown in Figure 11-8. The options available in this dialog box are discussed next.

Options Tab

The options available in this tab are discussed next.

Check select set 1 against Area

The options in this area enable you to determine the method of selecting components for checking the interference. These options are discussed next.

Select set 2. This option is selected by default. When this option is selected, you need to select the second set of components individually from the **Assembly PathFinder** or from the assembly window after selecting the first set of components.

All other parts in the assembly. This option considers the remaining parts of the assembly as the second selection set.

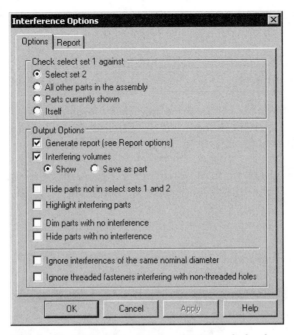

*Figure 11-8 The **Interference Options** dialog box*

Parts currently shown. This option checks the interference between the components you selected as the first set and the remaining components that are displayed in the assembly.

Itself. This option checks the interference among the first set of components.

Output Options Area

The options in this area enable you to determine the format in which you need the output from the interference check. These options are discussed next.

Generate report. This option enables you to save the interference check results into a text file; the configuration of this file can be set in the **Report** tab of the same dialog box.

Interfering volumes. This option enables you to determine the state of the interfering volumes. The **Show** radio button allows you to display the interfering volume in the assembly. Whereas, the **Save as part** option allows you to save the interfering volume as a part file. This volume is saved as a separate part and is automatically grounded.

Hide parts not in select sets 1 and 2. This option enables you to hide the parts that are not included in sets 1 and 2.

Highlight interfering parts. As the name suggests, this option highlights the parts that have an interference in the assembly.

Dim parts with no interference. If this option is selected, the parts that do not have interference with any part are displayed as dim.

Hide parts with no interference. This option enables you to hide the parts that are not in any of the selection sets and do not take part in the interference check.

Ignore interferences of the same nominal diameter. On selecting this check box, the interference is not detected, if the thread pitch does not match between a bolt and a threaded hole with the same nominal diameters.

Ignore threaded fasteners interfering with non-threaded holes. This option ignores the interference between a threaded cylinder and a non threaded hole.

Report Tab
When you choose the **Report** tab, the **Interference Options** dialog box will be displayed, as shown in Figure 11-9. The options in this tab are discussed next.

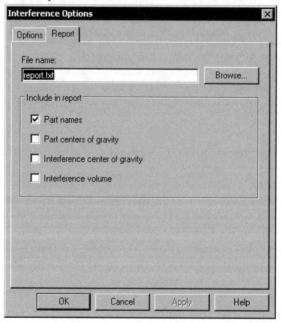

*Figure 11-9 The **Report** tab in the **Interference Options** dialog box*

File name
The **File name** edit box is used to specify the name of the report file. You can choose the **Browse** button to locate the folder in which you want to save the file.

Part names
When you select this option, the names of the parts that are causing the interference will be listed in the report file.

Part centers of gravity

When you select this option, the centers of gravity of the interfering parts will be listed in the report file.

Interference center of gravity

When you select this option, the center of gravity of the volume of the interference will be listed in the report file.

Interference volume

When you select this option, the volume of the interference will be listed in the report file.

Checking the Interference

After setting the options for the interference check, you need to select the first set of components. You can select the components from the assembly or from the **Assembly PathFinder**. After selecting the first set of components, choose the **Accept** button on the **Check Interference** ribbon bar or right-click to accept the selection. Now, you need to select the parts for set 2. After selecting the parts, right-click to process the interference check. If there is an interference, then depending on the output options you have set, the interference volume will be displayed. You can use the reference of the interference volume to edit the components for eliminating the interference.

CREATING EXPLODED STATE OF ASSEMBLIES

Menu:	Applications > Explode-Render-Animate

The exploded state of an assembly is created in the **Exploded View** environment that can be invoked from within the **Assembly** environment. To do so, choose **Applications > Explode-Render-Animate** from the menu bar. As soon as you enter this environment, the **Exploded View** toolbar will be displayed. This toolbar provides the tools to create the exploded state of an assembly. There are two methods of creating exploded state of an assembly. These are discussed next.

Automatic Explode

Toolbar:	Exploded View > Automatic Explode

The first option is to automatically create the exploded view. Whenever you explode an assembly using the automatic explode method, the flowlines will be automatically created. To create an automatic exploded state, choose the **Automatic Explode** button from the **Explode View** toolbar; the **Automatic Explode** ribbon bar will be displayed. The options in this ribbon bar are discussed next.

Select Step

 The **Select Step** button is chosen by default in the **Automatic Explode** ribbon bar. This button enables you to select the assembly you want to explode.

Select Drop-down List

There are two options in the **Select** drop-down list. These are discussed next.

Top-level assembly

By default, the **Top-level assembly** option is selected in the **Select** drop-down list. If you select this option, the subassemblies in the assembly are considered as a single component while exploding. Choose the **Accept** button to accept the **top-level assembly**. Once you accept this, the options in the **Ribbon bar** will change. Next, choose the **Automatic Explode Options** button; the **Automatic Explode Options** dialog box will be displayed, as shown in Figure 11-10. Clear the **Bind all subassemblies** check box and select the **By subassembly level** radio button in the **Explode Technique** area, if it is not already selected. Choose the **OK** button from the **Automatic Explode Options** dialog box. Choose the **Automatic Spread Distance** button from the **Automatic Explode** ribbon bar and set the distance value in the **Distance** edit box. Choose the **Explode** button from the **Ribbon bar**. Figure 11-11 shows the exploded state created using the **Automatic Explode** tool.

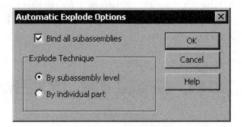

Figure 11-10 The **Automatic Explode Options** dialog box

Figure 11-11 Exploded view of the Plummer Block assembly

Tip: *The automatic explode method explodes the component of the assembly based on the relationships applied to it.*

Subassembly

This option allows you to explode the components of the selected subassembly only, as shown in Figure 11-12. The explosion procedure is similar to that discussed earlier in the top-level assemblies.

Figure 11-12 *The selected subassembly exploded*

Unexploding Assemblies

Toolbar: Exploded View > Unexplode

To unexplode the assembly, choose the **Unexplode** button from the **Exploded View** toolbar; the **Solid Edge** information box will be displayed that will inform you that the explosion will be deleted, see Figure 11-13. Choose the **Yes** button from this information box.

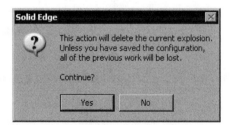

Figure 11-13 *The **Solid Edge** information box*

Manually Exploding Assemblies

Toolbar: Exploded View > Explode

The automatic explode method does not give the desired results every time. Therefore, the manual method is used to achieve the required exploded state. To explode the assembly manually, choose the **Explode** button; the **Explode** ribbon bar will be displayed and you will be prompted to select the parts you need to explode. Note that while selecting the parts, do not select the part that is stationary. Also, select only those components that will be exploded in the same direction. Remember that the order of the selection of the components should be such that the component closest to the stationary part in the exploded state is selected first. For example, in Figure 11-14, component A was selected first and then component B. The stationary part will remain stationary and the parts that were not selected will also remain at their position. After selecting the parts to be exploded, choose the **Accept** button. Now, select the part that will be stationary and then select a face or reference plane on the stationary part to specify the direction of explosion. The explosion will take place normal to the selected plane. After selecting the explode direction, the **Explode Options** dialog box will be displayed, as shown in Figure 11-15. The options in the **Explode Options** dialog box are discussed next.

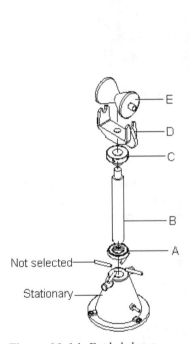

Figure 11-14 *Exploded state*

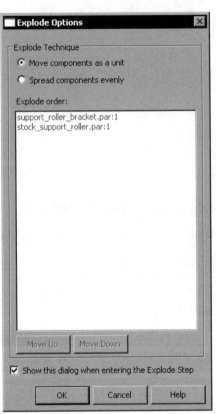

Figure 11-15 *The* ***Explode Options*** *dialog box*

Explode Technique Area
The options in this area are discussed next.

Move components as a unit
This option allows you to move the selected components as a single unit from their original position through the distance specified in the **Distance** edit box, as shown in Figure 11-16.

Spread components evenly

This option will move the selected components individually from their original position through the distance specified in the **Distance** edit box, as shown in Figure 11-17. The individual components are listed in the **Explode order** list box.

After specifying the required option, choose the **OK** button from the **Explode Options** dialog box. Next, choose the **Explode** button from the **Explode** ribbon bar; the component will explode depending upon the option specified, as shown in Figure 11-17.

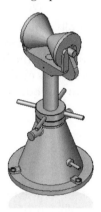

Figure 11-16 Explode as a single unit   *Figure 11-17 Explode individual parts*

Changing the Distance between the Components

Toolbar: Exploded View > Move Exploded Part

After exploding the assembly, you may need to modify the distance between the components or the orientation of the components. Choose the **Move Exploded Part** button from the **Exploded View** toolbar; the **Move Exploded Part** ribbon bar will be displayed and you will be prompted to select the part and drag it to move. In the **Move Exploded Part** ribbon bar, the **Move Dependent Parts** button is chosen by default. This button enables you to select and move a part along with its dependents. To move a single part, choose the **Move Selected Part** button from the ribbon bar. Now, select the component and drag it to move. You can change the orientation of the component by choosing the **Rotate** button from the **Move Exploded Part** ribbon bar.

Repositioning the Parts

Toolbar: Exploded View > Reposition

When you are unable to move a part beyond its parent part in the exploded state, you can invoke the **Reposition** tool from the **Exploded View** toolbar to reposition the selected component with respect to a reference part. To reposition a part, choose the **Reposition** button; the **Reposition** ribbon bar will be displayed and you will be prompted to select the part to reposition. After selecting the part, select another part, next to which the reposition part will be placed. You will notice that the reposition part changes its position in the exploded state of the assembly. Now, if required, you can move the repositioned part to the desired location.

Note
The distance and position of only the exploded parts can be modified.

Removing the Parts

Toolbar: Exploded View > Remove

The **Remove** button is available in the **Exploded View** toolbar only when you select an exploded part. When you choose this button from the **Exploded View** toolbar, the selected part will hide and move to its original position in the assembly. Note that when the part is hidden you cannot see it in the exploded state of the assembly. To redisplay the hidden component, right-click on the component in the **EdgeBar** and choose the **Show** option from the shortcut menu.

Flowlines

Toolbar: Exploded View > Flow Lines *(Customize to add)*

When you create the exploded state of an assembly, the flowlines are automatically generated. These flowlines indicate the direction of explosion of the component. The arrow at the end of the flowline is called the flowline terminator. You can set the display of the flowline and the flowline terminator using the **Flow Lines** tool or from the **View** menu in the menu bar. Figures 11-18 and 11-19 show the exploded state without and with the flowlines, respectively.

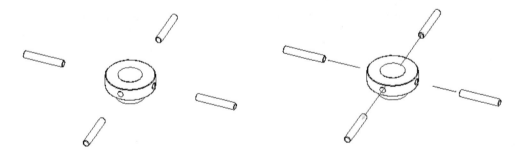

Figure 11-18 Exploded state without flowlines   *Figure 11-19 Exploded state with flowlines*

TUTORIALS

Tutorial 1

In this tutorial, you will create the exploded view of the Plummer Block assembly created in Exercise 1 of Chapter 10. The exploded state of the assembly is shown in Figure 11-20. After creating the exploded state, save the configuration with the name given below:

\Solid Edge\c11\Plummer Block\Plummer Block.cfg **(Expected time: 15 min)**

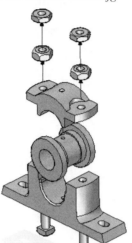

Figure 11-20 *Exploded view of the Plummer Block assembly*

The following steps are required to create the exploded state of the assembly:

a. Copy all the part and assembly files of the Plummer Block assembly from the *c10* folder to the *c11* folder. The files will be saved in the *\Solid Edge\c11\Plummer Block* folder.
b. Open the file of the Plummer Block assembly.
c. Create the exploded state of the assembly, refer to Figure 11-21.
d. Save the exploded state of the assembly in a configuration file.

Copying Files to the Current Folder

1. Copy all the part and assembly files of the Plummer Block assembly from the *c10* folder to the *c11\Plummer Block* folder. Remember that the extension of the part files is *.par* and the assembly files have an extension *.asm*.

Creating the Exploded State

To create the exploded state of the assembly, you need to invoke the **Exploded View** environment in the **Assembly** environment.

1. Open the *plummer block.asm* file in the **Assembly** environment.

2. To invoke the **Exploded View** environment, choose **Applications > Explode - Render - Animate** from the menu bar.

3. Choose the **Automatic Explode** button from the **Exploded View** toolbar. The **Select Step** button is chosen and the **Top-level assembly** option is selected by default in the **Select** drop-down list. Choose the **Accept** button to accept the selection set.

4. Choose the **Automatic Explode Options** button and clear the **Bind all subassemblies** check box from the **Automatic Explode Options** dialog box.

5. Choose the **Explode** button available in the ribbon bar to explode the assembly. Notice that the distance between the components is large.

6. Choose the **Automatic Spread Distance** button from the **Exploded View** ribbon bar and set **50** as the value in the **Distance** edit box. Now, choose the **Explode** button from the ribbon bar. The final exploded state of the assembly is shown in Figure 11-21.

7. Next, choose the **Finish** button from the ribbon bar.

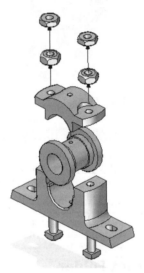

Figure 11-21 *Exploded view of the Plummer Block assembly*

Saving the Configuration

You need to save the exploded state of this assembly in a configuration file. To create the configuration file, follow the steps given next.

1. Choose **Tools > Configuration > Display Configurations** from the menu bar to display the **Display Configurations** dialog box.

2. Enter the name as **Plummer Block** in the **Configuration name** box.

3. Choose the **Save** button and then choose the **Close** button.

4. To return to the assembly window, choose the **Return** button from the ribbon bar. You will notice that the assembly is displayed in the unexploded form.

Tutorial 2

In this tutorial, you will create the exploded view of the Stock Bracket assembly created in Tutorial 1 of Chapter 10. The exploded state of the assembly is shown in Figure 11-22. After creating the exploded state, save the configuration with the name given below:

\Solid Edge\c11\Stock Bracket\Stock Bracket.cfg   **(Expected time: 30 min)**

Figure 11-22 *Exploded view of the Stock Bracket assembly*

The following steps are required to complete this tutorial:

a. Copy all the part and assembly files of the Stock Bracket assembly from the *c10* folder to the *c11* folder. The files will be saved in the *\Solid Edge\c11\Stock Bracket* folder.
b. Open the assembly file of the Stock Bracket in the **Assembly** environment.
c. Create the exploded state of the assembly, refer to Figure 11-23.
d. Save the exploded state of the assembly in a configuration file.

Copying Files to the Current Folder

1. Copy all the part and assembly files of the Stock Bracket assembly from the *c10* folder to *c11\Stock Bracket* folder. Remember that the extension of the part files is *.par* and the extension of the assembly files have an extension *is .asm*.

Creating the Exploded State

To create the exploded state of the assembly, you need to invoke the **Exploded View** environment in the **Assembly** environment.

1. Open the *stock bracket.asm* file in the **Assembly** environment.

2. To invoke the **Exploded View** environment, choose **Applications > Explode - Render - Animate** from the menu bar.

3. Choose the **Explode** button from the **Exploded View** toolbar; you are prompted to click on the parts to be exploded. Remember that the part you need to keep closest to the stationary part must be selected first. In this assembly, the stationary part is the Stock Support Base.

4. Select the components in the following order, Thrust Bearing, Support Adjusting Screw, Adjusting Screw Nut, Support Roller Bracket, and Stock Support Roller.

5. Choose the **Accept** button from the **Explode** ribbon bar; you are prompted to click on the stationary part.

6. Select the Stock Support Base as the stationary part; you are prompted to select a face of the stationary part. The face is needed to determine the direction of explosion.

7. Select the top face of the Stock Support Base; a red arrow is displayed that points in the upward direction. If the arrow does not point upward, move the cursor upward; the arrow will now point upward.

8. Click to specify the direction when the arrow points in the upward direction.

9. Select the **Spread components evenly** radio button from the **Explode Options** dialog box and choose the **OK** button. Set the value **30** in the **Spread Distance** edit box.

10. Choose the **Explode** button to explode the assembly.

11. Choose the **Fit** button from the **Main** toolbar; the exploded assembly is displayed, as shown in Figure 11-23.

12. To exit the **Explode** tool, invoke the **Select Tool** button from the **Animate** toolbar.

Note that the exploded view obtained is not the desired view. This is because the Stock Support Roller is not in the correct direction. Therefore, you need to further apply some operations on it to get the desired view.

Collapsing the Component

Ideally, the Stock Support Roller needs to be exploded on the right or left of the Stock Roller Bracket. Therefore, you need to first unexplode the Stock Support Roller and then explode it again in the horizontal direction.

Figure 11-23 Exploded view of the assembly

1. Select the Stock Support Roller from the assembly window and right-click to invoke the shortcut menu.

2. Choose the **Collapse** option from the shortcut menu; the selected component is moved to its original position with respect to its parent component, as shown in Figure 11-24.

Figure 11-24 Exploded view after collapsing the Stock Support Roller

Exploding the Stock Support Roller

Now, the Stock Support Roller will be exploded in the horizontal direction.

1. Choose the **Explode** button from the **Exploded View** toolbar; you are prompted to click on the parts to be exploded.

2. Select the Stock Support Roller from the assembly window and choose the **Accept** button. You are prompted to select the stationary part.

3. Select the Support Roller Bracket as the stationary component; you are prompted to select a face on the stationary component to specify the direction of explosion.

4. Select the face of the stationary part, as shown in Figure 11-25, to display a red arrow on the selected face.

5. When the arrow points in the direction shown in Figure 11-25, click to specify the direction; the selected component is exploded, as shown in Figure 11-26.

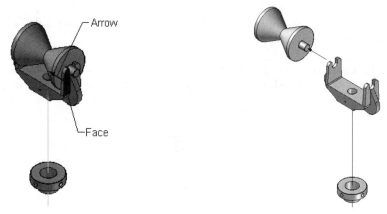

Figure 11-25 Arrow showing the direction of explosion

Figure 11-26 Selected part exploded in the specified direction

6. Enter **25** in the **Distance** edit box. Choose the **Explode** button from the **Explode View** ribbon bar.

Reducing the Gap between the Components

The distance between the components in the exploded view is large. To reduce the gap between the components, follow the steps given next.

1. Choose the **Move Exploded Part** button from the **Explode View** toolbar; the **Exploded Part** ribbon bar is displayed.

2. Select the part nearest to the stationary component and drag it so that the gap between the two components is reduced.

3. After dragging the first component, select the second component and drag it, as shown in Figure 11-27.

Figure 11-27 *Dragging the components*

4. Similarly, drag the other components to reduce the gap. The exploded state of the assembly, after reducing the gap, is shown in Figure 11-28.

Figure 11-28 *Assembly after reducing the gap*

Tip: *You can drag and place all the four instances simultaneously.*

Moving the Components

The four instances of the Adjusting Nut Handle are not at the desired location. You need to manually move the four instances one-by-one.

1. Choose the **Move Exploded Part** button from the **Exploded View** toolbar; the ribbon bar is displayed and you are prompted to select the component that you need to move.

2. Select any one of the instances of the Adjusting Nut Handle and choose the **Accept** button from the **Explode View** ribbon bar. Figure 11-29 shows the selected instance with triad.

3. Select the Z axis of the triad by clicking on it. Drag the component and place it, as shown in Figure 11-30.

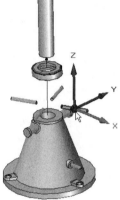 

Figure 11-29 *Moving the component along the z axis*

Figure 11-30 *Selected part placed at the required position*

 Tip: *To move the Adjusting Nut Handle more precisely to the desired location in the assembly, zoom in and view the assembly location of this part from the front view. While viewing the part from the front view, move it to the desired location. Also, change the display of the assembly by choosing the **Visible and Hidden Edges** button from the **Main** toolbar.*

4. Similarly, drag and place the other instances of the Adjusting Nut Handle. To select the next instance, choose the **Select Part** button from the **Move** ribbon bar. The assembly, after moving all instances of the Adjusting Nut Handle, is shown in Figure 11-31.

Notice that the instances still touch the Adjusting Screw Nut. Therefore, you need to move all instances of the Adjusting Nut Handle away from the Adjusting Screw Nut. To do so, you need to use the **Move Exploded Part** tool.

5. Choose the **Move Exploded Part** button from the **Exploded View** toolbar; the **Move Exploded Part** ribbon bar is displayed.

6. Select any one instance of the Screw Nut Handle and drag it to the required position. Choose the **Accept** button from the ribbon bar. Alternatively, you can enter the distance in the **Linear Distance** edit box.

7. Similarly, drag all instances of the Adjusting Nut Handle one-by-one and place them, as shown in Figure 11-32.

Figure 11-31 *Assembly after moving all instances of the Adjusting Nut Handle*

Figure 11-32 *Adjusting Nut Handle after dragging*

8. Exit the **Move Exploded Part** tool; all the parts are exploded as required.

Exploding the Last Component

The last component is the Adjusting Screw Guide and it will be exploded manually.

1. Choose the **Explode** button from the **Exploded View** toolbar.

2. Select the Adjusting Screw Guide from the assembly and choose the **Accept** button.

3. Select the Stock Support Base as the stationary part.

4. Select the face of the stationary part, as shown in Figure 11-33, to specify the direction of explosion.

5. Click when the red arrow points away from the base. After specifying its direction, the explosion takes place, as shown in Figure 11-34.

6. Exit the **Explode** tool.

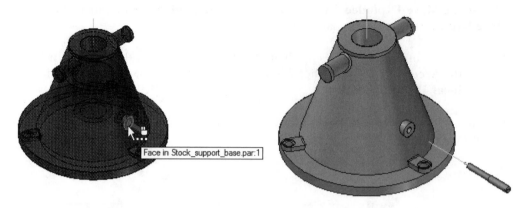

Figure 11-33 *Arrow showing the direction of explosion*

Figure 11-34 *Selected part exploded in the specified direction*

Saving the Configuration

You may need to use this exploded state of the assembly in the later chapters. Therefore, you need to save the exploded state of this assembly in a configuration file. To create the configuration file, follow the steps given next.

1. Choose **Tools > Configuration > Display Configurations** from the menu bar; the **Display Configurations** dialog box is displayed.

2. Enter the name as **Stock bracket** in the **Configuration name** box.

3. Choose the **Save** button and then choose the **Close** button.

4. To return to the assembly window, choose the **Return** button.

Tutorial 3

In this tutorial, you will create the Radial Engine assembly shown in Figure 11-35. This assembly will be created in two parts, the subassembly and the main assembly. The exploded state of the assembly is shown in Figure 11-36. The views and dimensions of all components of this assembly are shown in Figures 11-37 through 11-40. After creating the assembly, save it with the name given below:

\Solid Edge\c11\Radial Engine\Radial Engine.asm   **(Expected time: 3 hrs)**

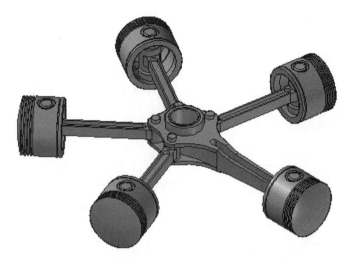

Figure 11-35 The radial engine assembly

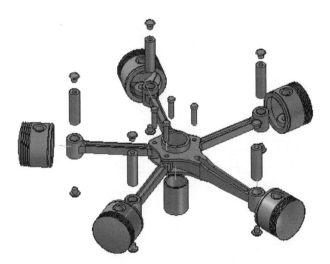

Figure 11-36 Exploded view of the assembly

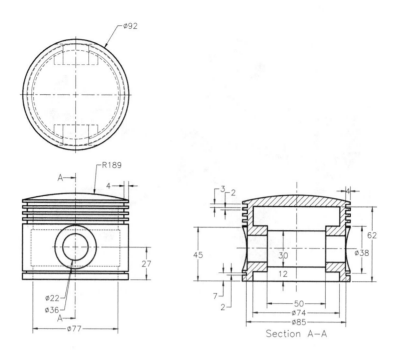

Figure 11-37 *Views and dimensions of the Piston*

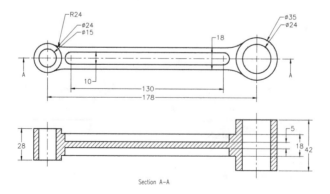

Figure 11-38 *Views and dimensions of the Articulated Rod*

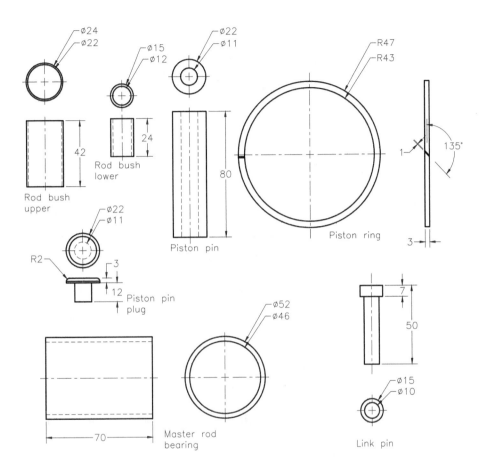

Figure 11-39 *Views and dimensions of other components*

This assembly has a large number of components, so you need to divide it into two assemblies such that one is the subassembly and the other is the main assembly. First you need to create the subassembly, which consists of the Articulated Rod, Piston, Piston Rings, Piston Pin, Rod Bush Upper, Rod Bush Lower, and Piston Pin Plug. After creating this subassembly, you will create the main assembly, in which you will assemble the Master Rod with the Piston, Piston Rings, Piston Pin, Rod Bush Upper, and Piston Pin Plug. After assembling the components in the main assembly, you will assemble the subassembly with the main assembly.

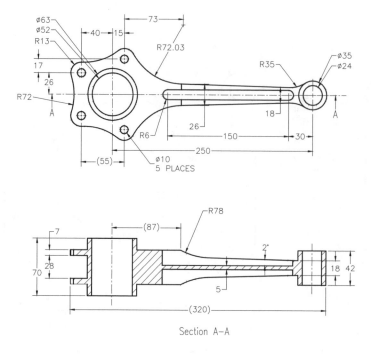

Figure 11-40 *Views and dimensions of the Master Rod*

The following steps are required to complete this tutorial:

a. Create all components of the assembly in the **Part** environment and save them in the *Radial Engine* folder.
b. Start a new assembly file and assemble the components to create the subassembly.
c. Start a new assembly file and assemble the components to create the main assembly.
d. Assemble the subassembly to the main assembly.

Creating the Components
1. Create a folder with the name *Radial Engine* in the *\Solid Edge\c11* folder. Create all the components in the individual part documents and save them in this folder.

Creating the Subassembly
As discussed earlier, you will first create the subassembly and then assemble the subassembly with the main assembly.

1. Start a new file in the **Assembly** environment. Save the file with the name *Piston Articulated Rod subassem* in the same folder where the parts are saved.

2. Choose the **Parts Library** button from the bottom of the **EdgeBar**. Now, drag and drop the Articulated Rod in the assembly window.

3. Assemble the Rod Bush Upper with the Articulated Rod using the assembly relationships. Figure 11-41 shows the sequence in which you need to assemble the components. The exploded view and the flowlines are shown only for your reference. The assembly, after assembling the Articulated Rod, Rod Bush Upper, Rod Bush Lower, Piston, Piston Pin, and Piston Pin Plug, is shown in Figure 11-42.

4. Insert the Piston Ring in the subassembly and assemble it with the Piston, as shown in Figure 11-42. Similarly, assemble the other instances of the Piston Ring with the Piston.

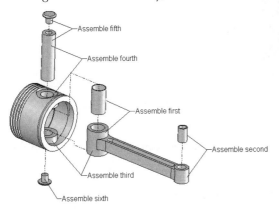

Figure 11-41 *Assembly sequence of the Articulated Rod, Piston, Piston Pin Plug, Rod Bush Upper, and Rod Bush Lower*

Figure 11-42 *First instance of the Piston Ring assembled with the Piston*

Now, you need to change the color of the Piston Ring.

5. Choose **Tools > Color Manager** from the menu bar; the **Color Manager** dialog box is displayed.

6. Select the **Use individual part styles** radio button from the dialog box and choose **OK**.

7. Now, select the Piston Ring from the **EdgeBar** or from the subassembly.

8. From the **Face Style** drop-down list in the ribbon bar, select the color you want to apply to the selected component. The subassembly, after assembling the Piston Rings and changing their color, is shown in Figure 11-43. Save and close the subassembly file.

Creating the Main Assembly

Next, you will create the main assembly and then assemble the subassembly with it.

1. Start a new file in the **Assembly** environment and save it with the name **Radial Engine Assembly** in the same folder in which the parts were saved.

Figure 11-43 *Subassembly after assembling and changing the color of Piston Rings*

2. Place the Master Rod in the assembly so that it automatically assembles with the assembly reference planes.

3. After placing the first component, use the assembly relationships to place the Piston, and then the Piston Pin, Piston Pin Plug, Piston Rings, Rod Bush Upper, and Master Rod Bearing one-by-one.

    The components, after assembling in the main assembly, are displayed in Figure 11-44.

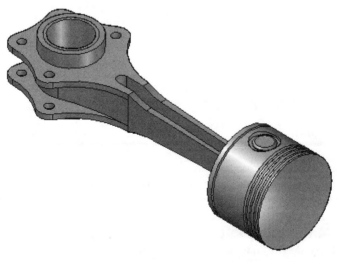

Figure 11-44 *Main assembly*

Assembling the Subassembly with the Main Assembly

Next, you will assemble the subassembly with the main assembly using the assembly relationships.

1. If the parts list is not open, then choose the **Parts Library** button from the bottom of the **EdgeBar**.

2. Right-click in the **EdgeBar** and choose the **Use Configurations** option. Otherwise, after you place the subassembly in the assembly window, some components in the subassembly will not be activated.

3. Drag and drop the *Piston Articulation Rod subassem* into the assembly window; the **Use Configuration** dialog box is displayed. In this dialog box, the **Activate all parts** radio button is selected by default.

4. Choose the **OK** button to exit the dialog box.

5. Assemble the subassembly with the main assembly using the **Mate**, **Axial Align**, and **Angle** assembly relationships. The first instance of the subassembly, after assembling with the main assembly, is shown in Figure 11-45. Note that, while applying the **Angle** relationship, you need to choose the **3** button from the **Angle Format** flyout.

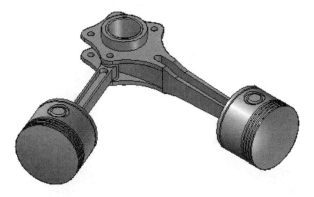

Figure 11-45 First instance of the subassembly assembled with the main assembly

6. Refer to Figure 11-46, which shows the assembly structure that will help you in assembling the instances of the subassembly.

Assembling the Link Pin

After assembling the subassembly with the main assembly, you need to assemble the Link Pin with the main assembly.

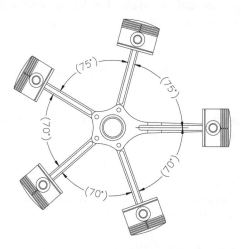

Figure 11-46 *Assembly structure*

1. Place the Link Pin in the current assembly and using the assembly relationships, assemble it with the main assembly. Figure 11-47 shows the first instance of the Link Pin assembled with the main assembly.

2. Before placing other instances of the Link Pin, select the **Automatically Capture Fit while placing parts** check box in the **Options** dialog box.

3. Figure 11-48 shows all the instances of the Link Pin assembled with the assembly.

4. Save the assembly.

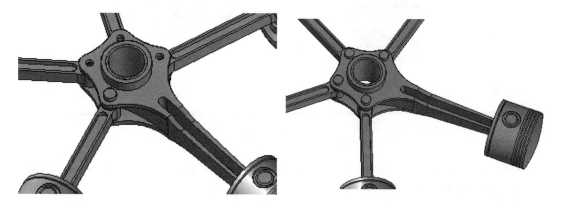

Figure 11-47 *First instance of the Link Pin assembled with the main assembly*

Figure 11-48 *All instances of the Link Pin assembled with the main assembly*

Self-Evaluation Test

Answer the following questions and then compare them to those given at the end of this chapter:

1. You can delete the existing assembly relationship by selecting it from the bottom pane of the **Assembly PathFinder** in the **EdgeBar** and pressing the DELETE key. (T/F)

2. The bottom pane of the **Assembly PathFinder** in the **EdgeBar** is used to view and modify the relationships between the selected part and the other parts in the assembly. (T/F)

3. To create subassemblies, you need to follow a different procedure than what is required for creating assemblies. (T/F)

4. By simplifying the assemblies, you can hide the components at any stage of the design cycle. (T/F)

5. Before sending the part file and assembly for detailing and drafting, it is essential to check the interference in the assembly. (T/F)

6. You cannot set the output options before starting the interference check. (T/F)

7. The _____ is the file extension of the files created in the **Assembly** environment of Solid Edge.

8. The _____ environment in the **Assembly** environment is used to create the exploded states of the assembly.

9. To turn on the display of the hidden component, select the hidden component and right-click to invoke the shortcut menu. Choose the _____ option from the shortcut menu. The hidden component will be redisplayed in the assembly.

10. To explode the assembly manually, choose the _____ button from the **Exploded View** toolbar.

Review Questions

Answer the following questions:

1. Which of the following options is used to open a component separately in the part file?

    (a) **Modify**   (b) **Open**
    (c) **Open in Solid Edge**   (d) None of the above

2. Which of the following environments within the **Assembly** environment is used to create exploded state of the assembly?

    (a) **Virtual Studio**   (b) **Explode-Render-Animate**
    (c) **Motion**   (d) None of the above

3. Which radio button is selected in the **Open File** dialog box to open all the components of the assembly as activated?

    (a) **Activate all**   (b) **Inactivate all parts**
    (c) **Use all simplified part**s   (d) None of the above

4. Which of the following options is chosen from the shortcut menu to hide a component?

    (a) **Show**   (b) **Hide**
    (c) **Activate**   (d) None of the above

5. You cannot modify the dimensions of a component in the **Assembly** environment. (T/F)

6. In the exploded state, when you choose the **Remove** button from the **Exploded View** toolbar, the selected part is hidden and moved to its original position in the assembly. (T/F)

7. The exploded state of an assembly is created by changing the environment to the **Exploded-Render-Animate** in the **Assembly** environment. (T/F)

8. You can set the transparency of any component for simplifying the assembly. (T/F)

9. The automatic explode method does not give the desired results every time. Therefore, the manual method is used to achieve the desired exploded state. (T/F)

10. When you place a subassembly in the main assembly, an assembly icon will be displayed with the name of the subassembly in the **EdgeBar**. (T/F)

Exercise

Exercise 1

Create the Shaper Tool Head assembly, as shown in Figure 11-49. After creating the assembly, create its exploded state, as shown in Figure 11-50. The dimensions of the model are given in Figures 11-51 through 11-55. After creating the assembly, save it with the name given below:

\Solid Edge\c11\Shaper Tool Head\Shaper.asm   **(Expected time: 4 hrs)**

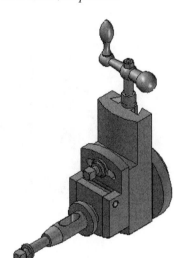

Figure 11-49   *Shaper Tool Head assembly*

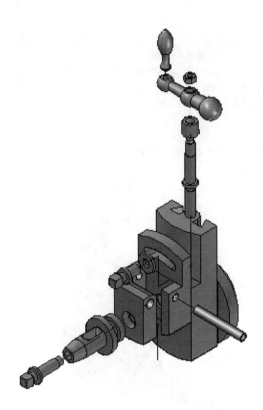

Figure 11-50 *Exploded state of the assembly*

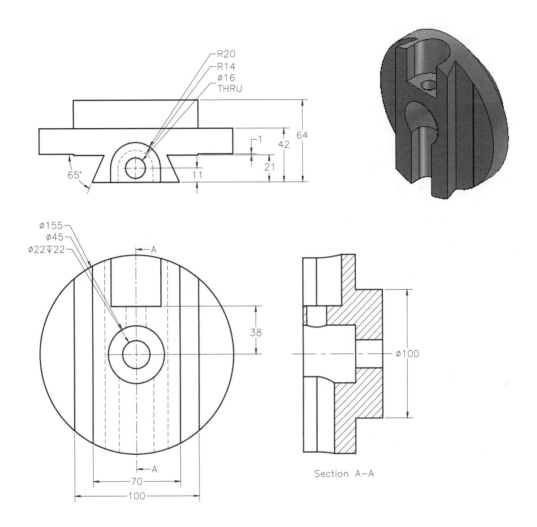

Figure 11-51 *Views and dimensions of the Back Plate*

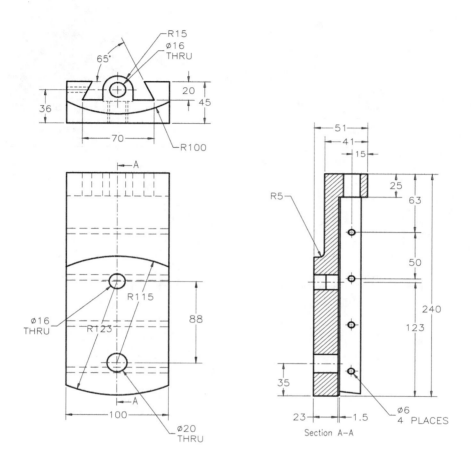

Figure 11-52 *Views and dimensions of the Vertical Slide*

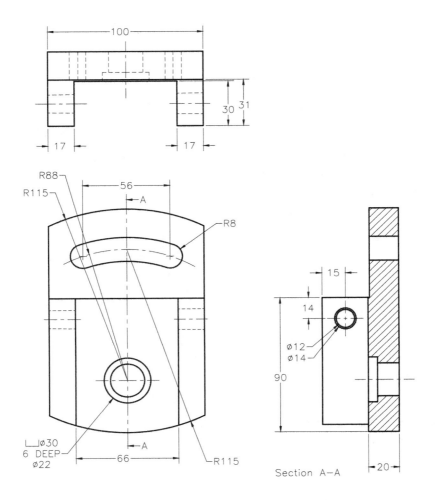

Figure 11-53 *Views and dimensions of the Swivel Plate*

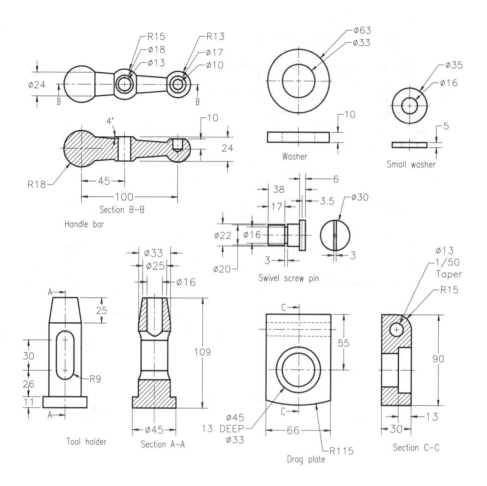

Figure 11-54 *Views and dimensions of various components*

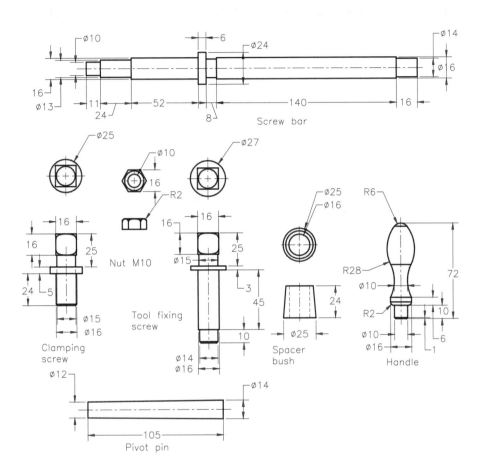

Figure 11-55 Views and dimensions of various components

Answers to Self-Evaluation Test
1. T, 2. T, 3. F, 4. T, 5. T, 6. F, 7. .asm, 8. Exploded View, 9. Show, 10. Explode

Chapter *12*

Generating, Editing, and Dimensioning Drawing Views

THE DRAFT ENVIRONMENT

After you have created a solid model or an assembly, you can generate its two-dimensional (2D) drawing views. Solid Edge has a separate environment called the **Draft** environment, which is used for generating drawing views. This environment contains the tools to generate, edit, and modify the drawing views.

To invoke the **Draft** environment, start Solid Edge and then choose the **Drawing** option in the **Create** area of the welcome screen.

If Solid Edge is running on your computer, invoke the **New** dialog box and select the **Normal.dft** template, see Figure 12-1. The *.dft* is the extension of the files created in this environment. After selecting the required template, choose **OK** in the **New** dialog box to enter the **Draft** environment. You can modify the drawing standards of the current file from the **Draft** environment.

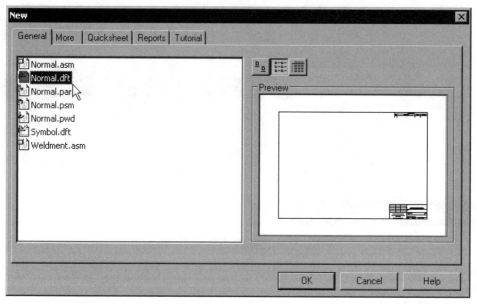

*Figure 12-1 Selecting a draft template from the **New** dialog box*

When you enter the **Draft** environment, the drawing sheet and the background sheet with the borders will be displayed, as shown in Figure 12-2. This sheet is the one on which you will generate the drawing views. The background sheet is used to add title blocks. As per the requirement, you can set parameters of the drawing sheet in the **Sheet Setup** dialog box. To display the **Sheet Setup** dialog box, choose the **File > Sheet Setup** option from the menu bar.

If you have a part file or an assembly file opened and you want to generate its drawing views, you can choose **File > Create Drawing** from the menu bar; the **Create Drawing** dialog box is displayed. Select the default template and choose **OK**; the **Drawing View Creation Wizard**

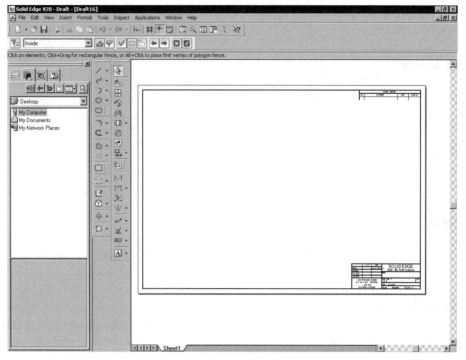

Figure 12-2 *The default screen display in the **Draft** environment*

dialog box will be displayed to generate the drawing views. You will learn more about this dialog box later in this chapter.

Tip: *To use an empty sheet without any margin lines or the title block, choose* **File** > **Sheet Setup** *from the menu bar; the* **Sheet Setup** *dialog box will be displayed. Choose the* **Background** *tab and select the blank space in the* **Background sheet** *drop-down list. The preview of the sheet in the dialog box shows an empty sheet. Choose the* **OK** *button to exit the dialog box.*

TYPES OF VIEWS GENERATED IN SOLID EDGE

In Solid Edge, there are two types of drafting techniques: generative drafting and interactive drafting. In the generative drafting, the views are generated from the part or assembly that is already created. In the interactive drafting, the views are sketched using the sketching tools.

Note

The reason for generating the drawing views is that these views are associative with their respective solid models or assemblies. Therefore, any change in the model updates the drawing views also. Similarly, any change in the dimensions of the drawing views updates the model. On the other hand, the sketched view is not associated with any model. Therefore, the editing of the views is not automatic.

In Solid Edge, you can generate six types of views from a model or an assembly. These views are discussed next.

Base View

The base view is the first view and is generated using a parent model or an assembly. This view is an independent view and is not affected by the changes made in any other view in the drawing sheet. Most of the other views are generated taking this view as the parent view.

Principal View

The principal view is an orthographic view that is generated using any other view present in the drawing sheet. This is the most common view generated after the base view.

Auxiliary View

The auxiliary view is a drawing view that is generated by projecting lines normal to a specified edge of an existing view. These views are mainly used when you want to show the true length of an inclined surface.

Section View

The section view is generated by cutting the part of an existing view using a plane or a line and then viewing the parent view from a direction normal to the section plane. These views are generally used for the models that are complicated from inside and it is not possible to display the inner portion of the part using the conventional views.

Detail View

The detail view is used to display the details of a portion of an existing view. This portion is selected from the parent view. The portion that you select will be scaled and placed as a separate view. The scale can be modified, if needed.

Broken-Out View

The broken-out view is used for the parts that have a high length to width ratio. The broken-out area is specified by adding break lines to an existing orthographic view.

GENERATING DRAWING VIEWS

Toolbar:	Drawing Views > Drawing Views Wizard

In Solid Edge, the first view that is to be generated is the base view. This view is generated using the **Drawing View Wizard** tool. The remaining views are generated by directly or indirectly using the base view. Before you proceed further, you need to set the projection type to third angle projection. To do so, choose **Tools > Options** from the menu bar to invoke the **Options** dialog box and choose the **Drawing Standards** tab. Choose the **Third** button from the **Projection Angle** area and choose **OK**.

Generating the Base View

The **Drawing View Wizard** tool is used to generate the base view. When you invoke this tool, the **Select Model** dialog box will be displayed. Using this dialog box, select the model whose drawing views you need to generate and choose the **Open** button; the **Drawing View Creation Wizard** dialog box will be displayed. Figure 12-3 shows this dialog box when a part file is selected. The options in this dialog box are discussed next.

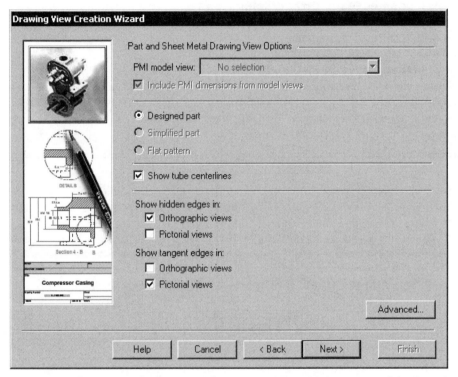

*Figure 12-3 The **Part and Sheet Metal Drawing View Options** page of the **Drawing View Creation Wizard** dialog box displayed when a part file is selected*

Part and Sheet Metal Drawing View Options Page

The options in this page enable you to specify the parameters related to the display of the drawing view.

Designed part

This radio button is selected by default and is used to specify that you need to generate the drawing views of an existing part.

Simplified part

This radio button is used to generate the drawing views of the simplified version of a model. This button will be in the inactive state if the simplified version of a model does not exist.

Flat pattern

This radio button is used to generate the drawing views of a flat pattern of the sheet metal part. It is available only for the sheet metal parts having a flat pattern.

Show tube centerlines

This check box is selected to display the centerlines in the tube components.

Show hidden edges in Orthographic views

This check box is selected by default and is used to display the hidden edges, if any, in the orthographic drawing views.

Show hidden edges in Pictorial views

Pictorial views are drawing views other than the orthogonal views. This option is used to display the hidden edges, if any, in the pictorial drawing views. Figures 12-4 and 12-5 show the isometric (pictorial) drawing views with the visible hidden edges and the suppressed hidden edges, respectively.

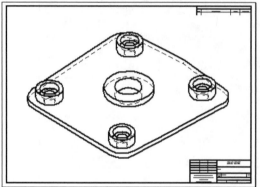 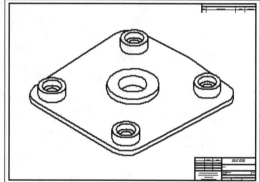

Figure 12-4 *Drawing view with hidden edges*   *Figure 12-5* *Drawing view without hidden edges*

Show tangent edges in Orthographic views

Tangent edges are the edges formed by rounds or cylindrical features. This option is used to display the tangent edges, if any in the part, in the orthographic drawing views.

Show tangent edges in Pictorial views

This option is used to display the tangent edges, if any, in the pictorial drawing views.

Drawing View Orientation Page

When you choose the **Next** button from the **Part and Sheet Metal Drawing View Options** page, the **Drawing View Orientation** area will be displayed, as shown in Figure 12-6. The options in this page enable you to specify the standard orientation of the drawing view or the pictorial view. These options are discussed next.

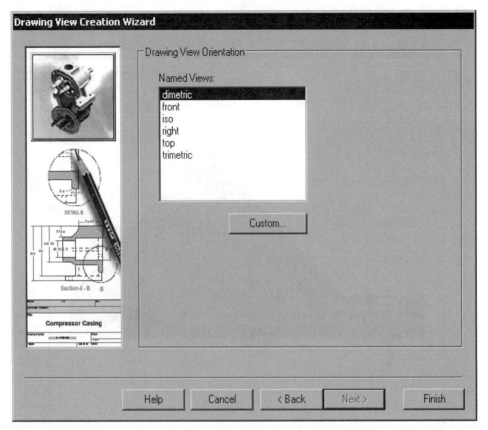

Figure 12-6 *The **Drawing View Orientation** page of the **Drawing View Creation Wizard** dialog box*

Named Views

This display box consists of options for generating views in the standard orientations. You can select any options from the standard orientations.

Custom

When you choose the **Custom** button, the **Custom Orientation** window will be displayed, as shown in Figure 12-7. This window displays the part or the assembly that you had selected earlier from the **Select Model** dialog box. You can use the drawing display tools available in this window to set the orientation of the model. You can also spin the model using the middle mouse button. After setting the orientation, choose the **Close** button to exit the window.

 Note

*The **Next** button is not activated in the **Drawing View Creation Wizard** dialog box if the **iso**, **trimetric**, or **dimetric** options are selected from the **Named Views** display box.*

If you suppress features of a model whose drawing views are generated, the suppressed features

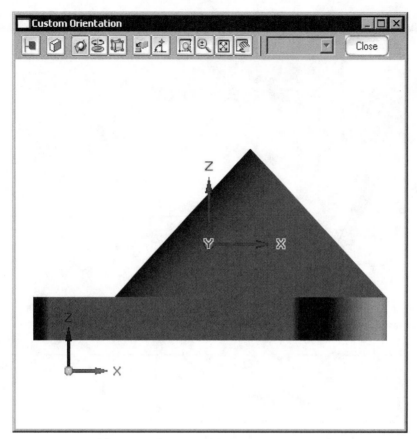

*Figure 12-7 The **Custom Orientation** window*

will not be displayed in the drawing views. When you unsuppress the features, they will be displayed in the drawing view.

Drawing View Layout Page

When you choose the **Next** button from the **Drawing View Orientation** page, the **Drawing View Layout** page will be displayed, as shown in Figure 12-8. The button in the middle represents the orientation of the model that you selected from the **Named Views** display box. You can select more than one view from the **Drawing View Layout** page and choose the **Finish** button to place the views in the drawing sheet. If you select two buttons, in addition to the middle button, three orthogonal views of the model will be displayed.

 Tip: *When you double-click on a generated drawing view, the part file associated with that view will be opened.*

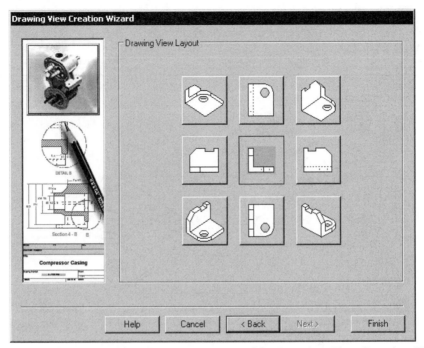

*Figure 12-8 The **Drawing View Layout** page of the **Drawing View Creation Wizard** dialog box*

Generating the Principal View

Toolbar: Drawing Views > Principal View

The principal view is generated after selecting an existing view. The views that can be selected include a base view or another principal view. To generate the principal view, choose the **Principal View** button from the **Drawing Views** toolbar; you will be prompted to select a drawing view. Move the cursor to a drawing view or the source view and select it as soon as it is enclosed in a red box. On doing so, a red crossed box will be attached to the cursor. Now, as you move the cursor up, down, left, or right, the box will also move with it. You can place the view at the bottom, top, left, or right of the source view. Note that if you move the cursor diagonally, you can generate a pictorial view, such as an isometric view, from the source view.

Note
The principal views cannot be generated from the detail view, section view, and auxiliary view.

*By default, Solid Edge generates drawing views in the first angle projection system. The third angle projection system has been used throughout this book. To change the default projection system, choose **Tools > Options** from the menu bar; the **Options** dialog box will be displayed. Choose the **Drawing Standards** tab and then select the **Third** radio button.*

Figure 12-9 shows the drawing sheet with the base view and principal views. The base view is the front view and the top and isometric views are generated from the front view using the **Principal View** tool.

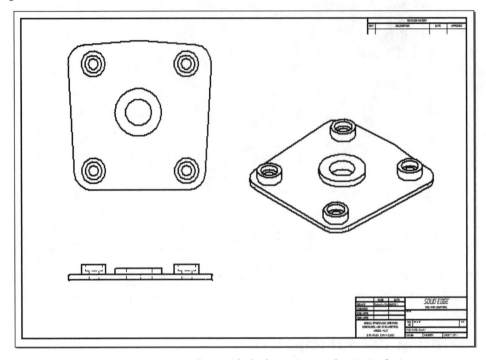

Figure 12-9 Drawing sheet with the base view and principal views

Note
*When you generate a drawing view on the drawing sheet, it will be displayed with the visible and hidden edges. You can also change the display of the drawing view to shaded. To change the display, select the drawing view; various shading buttons will be available in the **Drawing View Selection** ribbon bar. Choose any shading button and update the drawing view.*

Generating the Auxiliary View

Toolbar: Drawing Views > Auxiliary View

The auxiliary view is a drawing view that is generated by projecting the lines normal to a specified edge of an existing view. To generate the auxiliary view, choose the **Auxiliary View** button from the **Drawing Views** toolbar; you will be prompted to click on a fold line or click for the first point of the fold line. The fold line is an edge of the model or an imaginary line normal to which the view will be projected. Select an edge of the model or a keypoint on the edge and then select another keypoint. An imaginary fold line will be formed and the auxiliary view will be projected normal to this fold line. Move the cursor and then click to place the view; an arrow pointing in the direction normal to the fold line will be displayed, as shown in Figure 12-10.

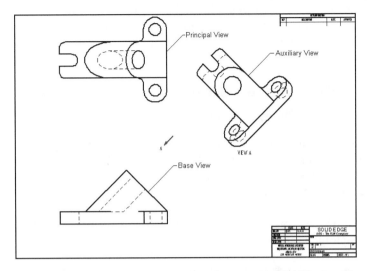

Figure 12-10 Auxiliary view generated from the principal view

The display of this arrow can be changed to a line with double arrows. To change the display, select the arrow and right-click to invoke the shortcut menu. Choose the **Properties** option from the shortcut menu; the **Viewing Plane Properties** dialog box will be displayed, as shown in Figure 12-11. Select the **Double** radio button from the **View Direction Lines** area in the dialog box and choose **OK**; the arrow will change to double arrows.

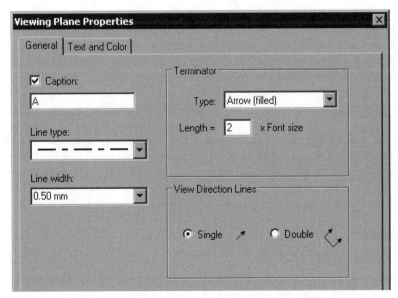

*Figure 12-11 Partial view of the **Viewing Plane Properties** dialog box*

Need for Auxiliary View

The need for auxiliary view arises when it becomes impossible to dimension a geometry in the orthographic views. For example, refer to Figure 12-10. In this model, the profile on the face of the inclined feature cannot be dimensioned until a view is generated normal to the inclination. After the auxiliary view is generated, the profile can be easily dimensioned with the true dimensions.

Generating the Section View

Toolbar:	Drawing Views > Section View

 As mentioned earlier, the section view is generated by cutting a portion of an existing view using a cutting geometry and then viewing the source view from the direction normal to the cutting geometry. In Solid Edge, various types of section views can be generated using the **Section View** tool.

To create a section view, you need a geometry that will be used to cut the source view. To create a cutting geometry, the **Cutting Plane** tool is used.

Generating a Simple Section View

The following steps explain the procedure for creating a cutting geometry and generating a simple section view:

1. Choose the **Cutting Plane** button from the **Drawing Views** toolbar; you will be prompted to select a drawing view. This view will be the source view.
2. Select the source view to activate the sketching environment. This environment contains the sketching tools that you can use to create the cutting geometry.

 Note
When you move the cursor over a drawing view to select the source view, it will be enclosed in a red box. The box indicates that the view can be selected. But sometimes, when you move the cursor on the view in the area that does not have any entity, this box will disappear. If you click at this point, the view will not be selected. So, it should be noted that the red box will appear only when the cursor is on an entity that composes the drawing view.

3. Draw the sketch for the cutting geometry. Remember that the sketch should be a continuous open sketch. You can use the alignment indicators to sketch the cutting geometry.
4. After drawing the sketch for the cutting geometry, choose the **Finish** button from the ribbon bar to exit the cutting plane environment.

 Note
When you move the cursor across the cutting geometry, the direction of arrows will also change.

5. Specify the direction of viewing by clicking in the direction pointed by the arrows.
6. Choose the **Section View** button from the **Drawing Views** toolbar; you will be prompted to select a cutting plane.

7. Select the cutting plane and place the section drawing view at the desired location in the drawing sheet. A simple section view is shown in Figure 12-12.

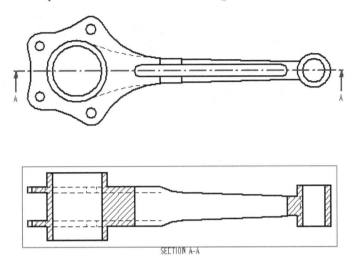

Figure 12-12 Shaded top view and the front section view

Points to Remember for Creating the Cutting Planes

The following points should be remembered while creating the cutting planes:

1. The sketch drawn can be a combination of arcs and lines, but an arc cannot be the start or the end entity of the sketch.
2. The sketch must be open and all entities should be connected to each other.
3. Relationships and dimensions can be applied between the sketched entities and the drawing view.
4. The cutting plane can be edited by double-clicking on it or by choosing the **Edit** button, which will be displayed in the ribbon bar when you select the cutting plane.

Note
When you place the section view, it does not matter on which side of the source view you place it. The section view remains the same on either sides of the source view. But it varies with the direction of arrows on the cutting plane.

Revolved Section Views

The revolved section views are needed when some features in a model are at a certain angle. In a revolved section view, the section portion revolves around an axis normal to the viewing plane such that it is straightened. For example, Figure 12-13 shows the views of a model that has three outer features at an equal angle with respect to each other. If you want to show the geometry of at least two outer features, you need to generate a revolved section view.

To generate a revolved section view, select an existing cutting plane. Because the cutting planes have entities that are at some angle to each other, you need to select the line that will

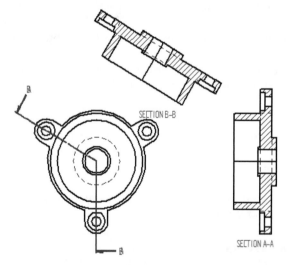

Figure 12-13 *Front view and the right-side revolved section view*

be used as a fold line for generating the section view. For example, in Figure 12-14, the inclined line is used to generate the section view at the top and the vertical line is used to generate the section view at the right. Before placing the view, choose the **Revolved Section View** button from the ribbon bar.

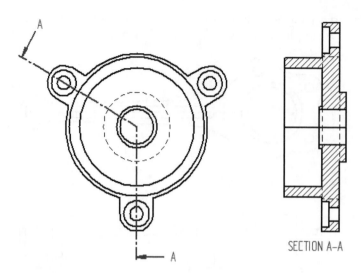

Figure 12-14 *Two different revolved section views generated by selecting two different cutting geometries*

Note

The cutting plane geometries should be multiline and they should be inclined at an angle to each other.

If a multiline cutting geometry exists, you can select only the first and last entities as the cutting plane.

*If the cutting plane geometry consists of an arc, the **Revolved Section View** button in the ribbon bar cannot be used.*

Section View that Displays only the Section Geometry

 The **Section Only** button in the ribbon bar is used to generate a section view that displays only that area of the model that is sectioned. Figure 12-15 shows the section view that displays only the section area of the model.

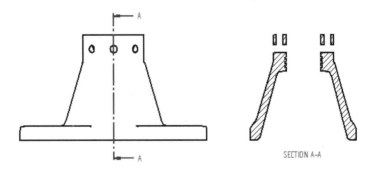

Figure 12-15 *Section view displaying only the section area*

The following steps explain the procedure for creating this type of view:

1. Choose the **Section View** button from the **Drawing Views** toolbar; you are prompted to select a cutting plane.
2. Select the cutting plane and move the cursor; a box attached to the cursor also moves along with it.
3. Choose the **Section Only** button from the ribbon bar and place the view by clicking on the desired side. The section view is placed, as shown in Figure 12-15.

Generating the Broken-Out Section View

Toolbar:	Drawing Views > Section View > Broken-Out Section View

The broken-out section view is used when you want to show a particular portion of the model in section and at the same time, not section the remaining model. The **Broken-Out Section View** button is used to generate the broken section view. This button is available on the flyout that will be displayed when you press and hold the left mouse button on the down arrow on the right of the **Section View** button. The steps given next explain the procedure for creating this type of view.

1. Choose the **Broken-Out Section View** button from the **Section View** flyout and select the drawing view where you have to draw the profile for the broken view. You automatically enter the sketching environment where all the tools that are used to draw the profile are available.
2. Draw the sketch, as shown in Figure 12-16. After drawing the sketch, choose the **Finish** button from the ribbon bar to exit.

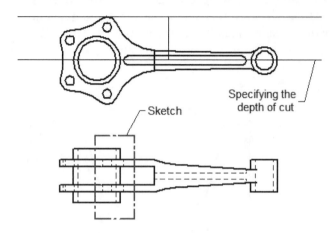

Figure 12-16 Specifying the profile and the depth of the cut

3. Next, you are prompted to specify the distance for the depth of the cut. This distance can be specified in the **Depth** edit box present on the ribbon bar or on the other orthographic view, as shown in Figure 12-16. After specifying the depth of the cut, you are prompted to select the view that needs to be broken.
4. Select the isometric view (pictorial view) to generate the broken-out section view, as shown in Figure 12-17.

Generating the Detail View

Toolbar:	Drawing Views > Detail View

Detailed views are used to provide the enlarged view of a particular portion of an existing view. In Solid Edge, the detailed view is generated by drawing a circle or any other user-defined sketch around the portion whose details are needed. When you choose the **Detail View** button, the **Detail View** ribbon bar will be displayed and the **Circular Detail View** button will be chosen by default, and you will be prompted to select the center of the circle. After specifying the center of the circle, you will be prompted to click for the edge of the circle. As soon as you click, a circle, which is actually the detail view, will be attached to the cursor. Place the view on the drawing sheet at the desired location, see Figure 12-18.

You can also choose the **Define Profile** button from the ribbon bar to define the boundary of the detail view. When you choose this button, the sketching environment will be activated.

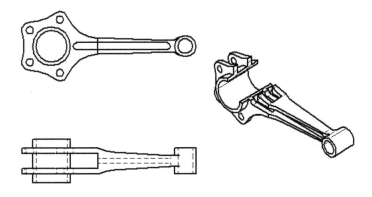

Figure 12-17 *Isometric broken section view*

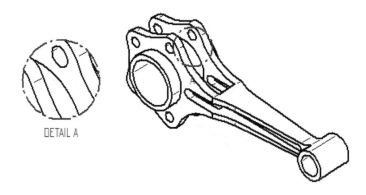

DETAIL A

Figure 12-18 *Detail view of an isometric view*

Draw the required closed profile using the tools available in this environment. Figure 12-19 shows the user-defined closed profile and the detail view created.

Tip: *If you drag and drop a part file from the **EdgeBar** on the drawing sheet, then depending on the projection angle system set for the current file, the top, front, and right-side views of the part will be generated. If you drag and drop an assembly on the drawing sheet, then an isometric view of the assembly will be generated.*

*You can right-click on a detail view and choose **Convert to Independent Detail View** to convert the view to an independent view.*

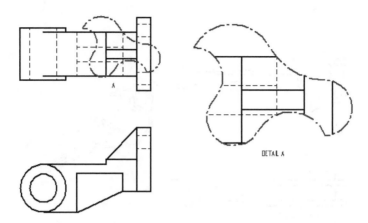

Figure 12-19 *User-defined sketch and the resulting detail view*

Generating the Broken View

This view is generated on the existing orthographic or pictorial view. It is created by breaking the existing view along the horizontal or vertical direction using the horizontal or vertical lines. This type of view is used for the parts that have a high length to width ratio. Various types of broken views are shown in Figure 12-20.

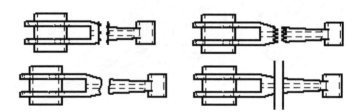

Figure 12-20 *Different types of broken views*

The following steps explain the procedure for creating this type of view:

1. Move the cursor over the drawing view where you have to add the break lines. When the view is highlighted and enclosed in a red box, right-click to invoke the shortcut menu.

2. From the shortcut menu, choose the **Add Break Lines** option; you are prompted to click in the drawing view at the point where you need to place the first break line. Notice that as you move the cursor, the break line also moves with it.

    You can set the style for the break lines from the **Style** drop-down list. By choosing the **Vertical Break** or **Horizontal Break** buttons from the ribbon bar, you can specify whether the drawing view will be broken vertically or horizontally. In the ribbon bar, there are four linetypes that can be selected for the break line type.

3. Before specifying the first point for the break line, you need to specify the line type for the break lines. Choose the **Break Line Type** button from the ribbon bar; a flyout is displayed with four buttons. Choose any of the buttons for selecting a line type. The **Break gap** edit box on the ribbon bar is used to set the distance between the pair of break lines. The **Height** edit box is used to specify the height of the zig zags in the break lines. The **Pitch** edit box is used to specify the pitch of the breaks when you select the short break line type. The **Symbols** edit box, which is available for the last break line type, is used to set the number of symbols that are added to the break lines.

Tip. *You can add the views of different parts and assemblies on a single drawing sheet. This helps you view the dimensions of the different models on a single sheet. To add a new model to the sheet, follow the same procedure that was used to generate the base view.*

4. Click on the drawing view to specify the location for the first line. After the first break line is placed, click again to specify the location for the second break line.

5. After specifying the second break line, choose the **Finish** button to exit.

Note
*When you select a view with break lines, the **Show Broken View** button will be displayed in the ribbon bar. This button toggles the display of break lines in the selected drawing view.*

WORKING WITH INTERACTIVE DRAFTING

As mentioned earlier, you can also sketch the 2D drawing views in the **Draft** environment of Solid Edge. In technical terms, sketching 2D drawing views is known as interactive drafting. The 2D drawing views can be drawn by choosing the **Draft View** button from the **Drawing Views** toolbar, after customizing the toolbar to add this button. When you do so, you will be prompted to place the view. Select a point on the drawing sheet; the sketching environment will be invoked. The tools available in the sketching environment are the same as those available in the sketching environment of the **Part** environment. After sketching the drawing view, choose the **Return** button from the ribbon bar to return to the **Drawing** environment.

MANIPULATING DRAWING VIEWS

Once the drawing views are generated, it is very important to learn how they can be modified or edited. The following editing operations can be performed on the existing drawing views:

Aligning Drawing Views

When you generate the principal views from the base views, they are aligned automatically. If you move one of the views, then the other view will also move along with the first one. This shows that the two views are aligned. Also, when you select one of the views, a center line that connects the two views will be displayed.

To unalign a view, select the view and right-click to invoke the shortcut menu. The **Maintain Alignment** option has a check mark on its left. Choose this option again from the shortcut menu; the check mark on its left is removed, suggesting that the view is no more aligned.

Now, if you move any one of the previously aligned views, the other view will not move.

To completely delete the alignment, choose the **Delete Alignment** option from the shortcut menu and then select the alignment line of the current view.

 To create a new alignment of the view, choose the **Create Alignment** option from the shortcut menu; the **Create Alignment** ribbon bar will be displayed. You can select a location for the drawing view alignment using the **Alignment position** drop-down list. The buttons available in the ribbon bar are used to specify whether you want to create a vertical, horizontal, parallel, or a perpendicular alignment. Choose the required options and buttons from the ribbon bar and then select the view to which you want to align the current view.

Modifying the Scale of Drawing Views

You can modify the scale of a drawing view by selecting it and changing the value in the ribbon bar. Alternatively, you can choose the **Properties** button from the ribbon bar. When you choose this button, the **High Quality View Properties** dialog box will be displayed. You can also invoke this dialog box by choosing the **Properties** option from the shortcut menu that will be displayed when you select a view and then right-click on it.

 Note
When you modify the scale of a drawing view that was generated by projecting a view, the scale factors of both the views are modified.

Cropping Drawing Views

Cropping is a technique that is used to view only a particular portion of the drawing view on the drawing sheet. To crop a drawing view, select a portion of the drawing view such that it is enclosed inside a boundary. Now, drag one of the boundary's handles until the portion of the drawing you want to display is visible. The portion of the view that lies inside the associated box is retained and the remaining portion is removed.

To bring back the view to its original display, right-click on the view to display the shortcut menu. Choose the **Uncrop** option from the shortcut menu; the cropping in the view is removed.

 Note
You cannot crop a detail view and a broken view.

Moving Drawing Views

To move a drawing view, select it and drag it on the drawing sheet. To place the view, release the left mouse button at the desired location on the drawing sheet.

Rotating Drawing Views

 The drawing views can be rotated by invoking the **Drawing** toolbar. Choose the **Rotate** button from this toolbar; you will be prompted to select an element to modify. Select the drawing view you need to rotate; you will be prompted to select the center of rotation. Select a point that acts as the center of rotation. Now, select a point from which you want to start the rotation and then select a point up to which you want to rotate the view. You can also specify the angle of rotation value in the dimension boxes present on the ribbon bar.

Applying the Hatch Pattern

You can also apply a hatch pattern to a closed region by using interactive drafting. To apply the hatch pattern, choose the **Fill** button from the **Drawing** toolbar; you will be prompted to select the area. As you select a closed region, it will be filled with the hatch pattern. The hatch pattern can be modified by right-clicking on it and selecting the **Properties** option.

Modifying the Properties of Drawing Views

After generating a drawing view, you can modify its properties. To set the properties, right-click on the drawing view to invoke the shortcut menu. Choose the **Properties** option to display the **High Quality View Properties** dialog box, as shown in Figure 12-21. There are eight tabs in this dialog box.

The **General** tab contains the options that are used to modify the scale, move the drawing view to another sheet, add caption or description to the drawing view, rotate the drawing view by specifying an angle, and so on. You can also select the options to add 3D dimensions to the pictorial view, retrieve dimensions on the next update of the part, process part intersections, and so on.

The **Display** tab contains the options that are used to set the display of the drawing view. The **Parts list** list box displays the components, subassemblies, and construction surfaces. You can select them in this list and choose the display options from this tab. The **Parts list options** button enables you to select the items that you want to display in the **Parts list** list box. From the **Selected Parts(s) Display** area, you can set the display style of the entities in the drawing view. The **Restore default display settings** button restores the default settings.

The **Text and Color** tab contains the options that are used to set the dimension style, color of text, font, font style, and size.

> **Tip**. *To modify the hatch pattern style of a section view, select the view and right-click to invoke the shortcut menu. Choose the **Properties** option to display the **High Quality View Properties** dialog box. Choose the **Display** tab and then from the **Show fill style** drop-down list in the **Selected Part(s) Display** area, select any one of the hatch styles. Choose **OK** to exit the dialog box.*
>
> *If you need to modify the properties of the hatch such as spacing, angle, and so on, right-click on the drawing view and choose the **Draw in View** option; the view will be opened in a separate window. Now, right-click on the hatch and choose the **Properties** option; the **Fill Properties** dialog box is displayed. Using this dialog box, you can modify the parameters of the hatch. After modifying the parameters, choose the **Return** button from the ribbon bar.*

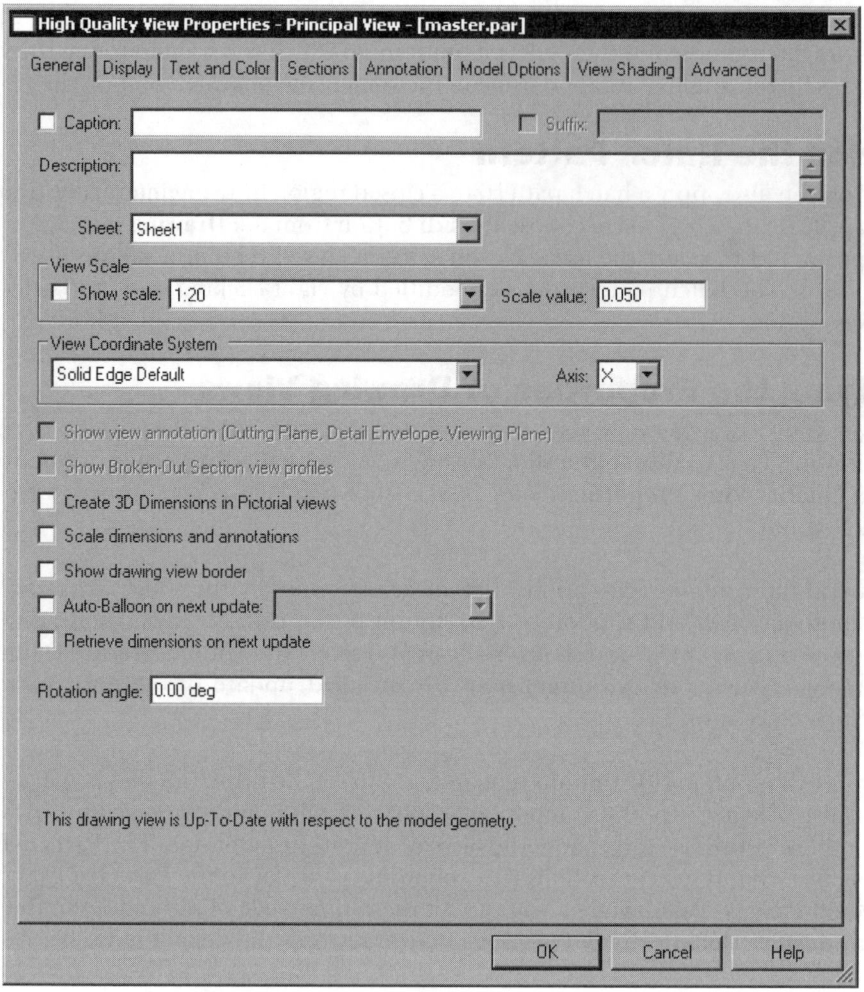

*Figure 12-21 The **High Quality View Properties** dialog box for a principal view*

The **Sections** tab lists the 3D sections that can be used to generate the section views.

The **Annotation** tab contains the options that enable you to set the style for the center lines and flowlines.

The **Model Options** tab contains the options that are used to specify whether to display the simplified representation of the part in the drawing view.

The **View Shading** tab contains the options that enable you to set the shading options for the shaded drawing view of the part.

The **Advanced** tab contains the advanced drawing options.

ADDING ANNOTATIONS TO THE DRAWING VIEWS

Once you have generated the drawing views, you need to add annotations such as dimensions, notes, surface finish symbols, geometric tolerances, and so on to them. There are two methods of displaying these annotations in the drawing views. The first method is to generate the annotations that are defined at the time of creating the model such as dimensions. These dimensions are associative in nature and so, can be used to modify or drive the dimensions of a model. The second method of displaying the annotations is to manually add them to the drawing views.

Note

*You can also create dimensions in the **Draft** environment, but these dimensions cannot drive the dimensions of the part.*

Generating Annotations

Generating annotations is the process of retrieving dimensions, notes, and so on from the parent model. The annotations that were used to create the model are displayed on the orthographic views of the model.

To retrieve dimensions, choose the **Retrieve Dimensions** button from the **Drawing Views** toolbar; the ribbon bar will be displayed with various dimensioning options and you will be prompted to select a drawing view. As soon as you select a drawing view, the dimensions will be displayed on it. Various buttons available on the ribbon bar are discussed next.

Dimension Style Mapping

This is a toggle button and is used to specify whether or not the dimension style mapping set using the **Dimension Style** tab of the **Options** dialog box will be used.

Linear

This button is used to retrieve linear dimensions in the selected drawing view.

Radial

This button is used to retrieve radial dimensions in the selected drawing view.

Angular

This button is used to retrieve angular dimensions in the selected drawing view.

Annotations

This button is used to retrieve annotations that are applied to the model.

Retrieve Duplicate Radial Dimensions

This button is used to retrieve duplicate radial dimensions that have the same value.

Hidden Line Dimensions

This button is used to retrieve dimensions of the hidden edges.

Add Dimensions

If this button is chosen, the dimensions will be added to the drawing view.

Remove Dimensions

If this button is chosen, the dimensions will be removed from the drawing view. However, note that the dimensions that are applied using the **Retrieve Dimension** tool can only be removed using this tool.

Figure 12-22 shows a drawing view after retrieving the dimensions.

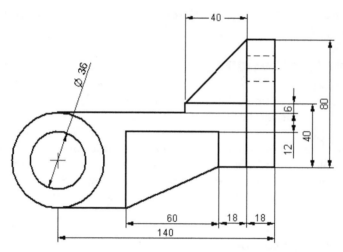

Figure 12-22 *Drawing view with dimensions*

Displaying Center Marks and Center Lines in a Drawing View

Solid Edge allows you to display center marks and center lines in the drawing views. To do this, choose the **Automatic Center Lines** button from the **Drawing Views** toolbar; the ribbon bar will be displayed with various options. If you choose the **Center Line and Center Mark Options** button from the ribbon bar, the **Center Line and Center Mark Options** dialog box will be displayed. You can select the entities on which you want to display the center marks and center lines using this dialog box.

You can set the options for adding or removing the center lines and center marks using the buttons available in the ribbon bar. It is recommended that you choose the **Center Mark** or the **Center Mark Projection Lines** button from the ribbon bar. Choosing both buttons will place the center lines above the center marks.

Figure 12-23 shows a drawing view with center mark projection lines and Figure 12-24 shows a drawing view with center lines.

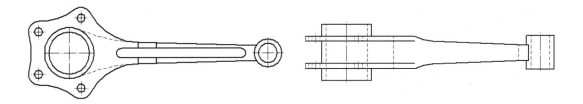

Figure 12-23 *Center marks on the holes in a drawing view*

Figure 12-24 *Center lines on the holes in a drawing view*

Adding Reference Dimensions to the Drawing Views

Although retrieving the dimensions from the parent model is the most effective way of dimensioning, but sometimes you may also need to dimension the drawing views manually. The options for dimensioning a drawing view are available in the **Drawing Views** toolbar. These options are similar to those discussed in the sketching environment. The only dimension tool that was not discussed earlier is the **Chamfer Dimension** tool, which is discussed next.

Chamfer Dimension

This button is available in the **Distance Between** flyout in the **Drawing Views** toolbar. On choosing this button, you will be prompted to select the dimension base line. This line is one of the edges of the chamfer. Next, you will be prompted to select the dimension measure line. Select the chamfer line; you will notice that the dimension is attached to the cursor. Click to place the dimension.

ADDING NEW DRAWING SHEETS

In Solid Edge, a drawing file can have multiple drawing sheets. A multisheet drawing file is generally used when you need to generate drawing views of all parts of an assembly in a single drawing file. You can easily switch between the sheets to refer to the drawing views of different parts within the same file, thus avoiding the step of opening separate drawing files.

To add a new sheet to the drawing file, right-click on **Sheet1** at the bottom of the drawing window and choose **Insert** from the shortcut menu. Alternatively, you can also choose **Insert > New Sheet** from the menu bar; a new sheet named **Sheet2** will be added to the drawing file. Using the other options available in the shortcut menu, you can rename, delete, reorder, and set up a sheet.

EDITING THE DEFAULT SHEET FORMAT

You can edit the default standard sheet format according to your design requirement. To edit the standard sheet format, choose **View > Background Sheet** from the menu bar and then choose **View > Working Sheets** to clear the check mark on the left of this option. You will notice that all entities, annotations, and views are removed from the drawing sheet and four sheet tabs, namely **A1-Sheet**, **A2-Sheet**, **A3-Sheet**, and **A4-Sheet** are displayed at the bottom of the drawing sheet. Right-click on **A1-Sheet** at the bottom of the drawing window and choose **Sheet Setup** from the shortcut menu to display the **Sheet Setup** dialog box. You can use the options in this dialog box to modify the size and units of the sheet. You can also delete the existing title block and use the sketching tools to draw a new title block. After editing the sheet, choose **View > Working Sheets** to activate this option and then choose **View > Background Sheet** to clear it.

GENERATING EXPLODED VIEWS OF ASSEMBLIES

The exploded views are generated by selecting the configuration that was saved at the time of exploding the assembly in the **Assembly** environment. The following steps explain the procedure for generating an exploded view:

1. Choose the **Drawing View Wizard** button from the **Drawing Views** toolbar to display the **Select Model** dialog box.
2. Select the assembly from the dialog box and choose the **Open** button to display the **Drawing View Creation Wizard** dialog box.
3. From the **Configuration** drop-down list in the dialog box, select the configuration that represents the exploded state of the assembly.
4. Set the other parameters and then choose the **Finish** button from the dialog box.
5. Place the view on the drawing sheet; an exploded view is shown in Figure 12-25.

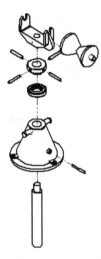

Figure 12-25 *Exploded view*

Before placing the view, you can also set the display of the parts in the exploded drawing view by choosing the **Model Display Settings** button from the ribbon bar. When you choose this button, the **High Quality View Properties** dialog box will be displayed, as shown in Figure 12-26. The options in the **Display** tab of this dialog box are discussed next.

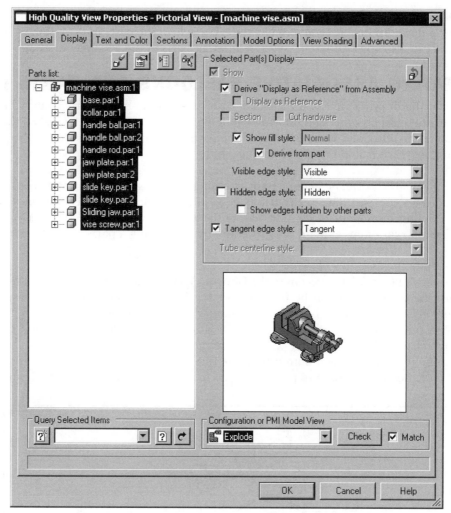

Figure 12-26 *The High Quality View Properties dialog box*

Display Tab of the Drawing View Properties Dialog Box

The **Display** tab of this dialog box contains various options for controlling the display of the assembly drawing view. These options are discussed next.

Show

Using the **Show** check box, you can control the display of one or more parts in the assembly. You will also notice that all parts, including the assembly, are selected in the **Parts list** area.

Display as Reference

This check box, when selected, enables you to display the selected part as reference. You can select the part from the **Parts list** area. The selected part is displayed as dotted in the assembly drawing view.

Visible edge style

This drop-down list enables you to select the edge style of the parts in the assembly drawing view. You can also apply different styles to different parts in the assembly drawing view.

CREATING ASSOCIATIVE BALLOONS AND PARTS LIST

Generally, the drawing view of an assembly also contains the list of parts, material of each part, quantity, and other related information in the form of a table, which is called the bill of material (BOM). In Solid Edge, it is called the parts list. Balloons are added to the parts of assembly and each balloon refers to the part in the parts list.

The parts list can be generated by choosing the **Parts List** button from the **Drawing Views** toolbar. The parts list is associative in nature, which means that any modification made in the part files of the assembly will be reflected in the parts list also. The following steps explain the procedure for generating a parts list and the balloons:

1. Generate the assembly drawing view.
2. Choose the **Parts List** button from the **Drawing Views** toolbar; the ribbon bar is displayed with the options that can be used to specify whether or not you want to display the balloons and the table. Also, you are prompted to select a drawing view.
3. Select the assembly drawing view. You can also choose the **Properties** button from the ribbon bar and set the display properties of the parts list and balloons.
4. Choose the **Auto-Balloon** button from the ribbon bar.
5. Choose the **Finish** button to place the parts list and balloons, as shown in Figure 12-27.

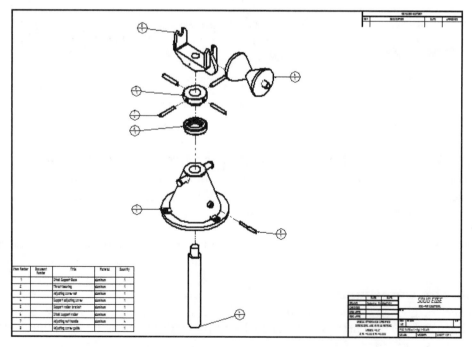

Figure 12-27 *Exploded view of the assembly with BOM and balloons*

List Properties Dialog Box

While generating the parts list on the drawing sheet and before choosing the **Finish** button, when you choose the **Properties** button from the ribbon bar, the **List Properties** dialog box will be displayed, as shown in Figure 12-28. This dialog box is used to set the parameters of the parts list and balloons. The options available in this dialog box are discussed next.

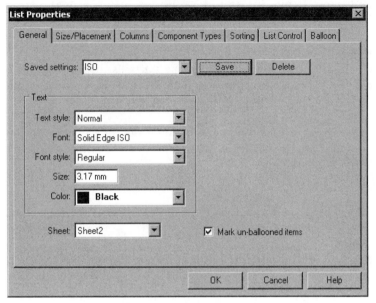

Figure 12-28 The **List Properties** *dialog box*

General Tab

The options in this tab are used to specify the text properties of the text in the parts list and are discussed next.

Saved settings

This drop-down list contains the styles that are saved for the parts list. By default, two styles, **ISO** and **ANSI**, are saved. If you need to save a new style, type a name in this drop-down list and choose the **Save** button.

Text Area

This area provides the options that are used to set the properties of the text.

Sheet

This drop-down list is used to specify the sheet on which you want to place the parts list. This option will not be active if there is only one sheet.

Mark un-ballooned items

This check box is selected by default. This indicates that if a balloon is not attached to any part of the assembly, then that part in the parts list will be marked by an asterisk. Balloons are not added to parts that are not visible in the assembly drawing view.

Size/Placement Tab

The options in this tab are used to specify the display of the parts list on the drawing sheet.

Title block

In the title block of a parts list, you can specify titles such as the item number, name, quantity, and so on. Using this drop-down list, you can specify the location of the title block in the parts list.

Maximum height of list

You can specify the maximum height of the parts list using this edit box. When the height of this list exceeds this value, the BOM list is divided into multiple sections.

Section gap

This edit box is used to specify the gap between the different sections of the parts list. This is used only when the height of the parts list exceeds the maximum height and it is divided into multiple sections.

Grid color

This drop-down list is used to specify the color of the lines that make up the parts list.

Grid line width

This edit box is used to specify the width of the lines in the parts list.

Text margin

The value in this edit box specifies the gap between the lines and the text in the parts list.

Location Area

The options in this area are used to specify the location of the parts list on the drawing sheet.

Columns Tab

The options under this tab are used to specify various properties of columns in the parts list.

Available columns

This display box lists all the column headings that you can display in the parts list.

Columns used

This display box lists all the columns that will appear in the parts list. You can add columns to this box by selecting them from the **Available columns** display box and choosing the **Add** button.

Column Format Area

The options in this area are used to specify different titles for the column headings selected from the **Columns used** display box. You can also specify the alignment of the text in various cells of the parts list.

Component Types Tab

The options under this tab are used to specify the type of components to be included in the parts list.

Sorting Tab

The options under this tab are used to specify the criteria to sort the parts in the parts list.

List Control Tab

The options under this tab are used to specify the display of parts in the parts list. From these options, you can select the parts that you want to exclude from the assembly. These options are discussed next.

Top-level list (top-level and expanded components)

When this radio button is selected, only the top-level assembly is searched for the parts to list them in the parts list. If the assembly contains subassemblies, they are listed as a single part and the parts of the subassemblies are not listed in the parts list.

 Note

Remember that the title in the parts list will be listed only if you have entered it in the file properties of that part.

Atomic List (all parts)

This radio button, when selected, specifies that all parts will be listed in the parts list. If the assembly contains subassemblies, all parts of the subassemblies will also be listed in the parts list.

Selected item Area

The options in this area are used to exclude or include the selected part from the parts list. To exclude a part, select it from the adjacent tree and then select the **Exclude** radio button.

Sub-assemblies Area

The options in this area are used to specify if a subassembly exists and also if you want it to be displayed as a single item or along with its parts in the parts list.

Include only ballooned parts

When this check box is selected, only those parts that were ballooned earlier will be listed in the parts list. This check box is cleared by default.

Exclude hidden parts

When this check box is selected, the hidden parts will be excluded from the parts list. This check box is cleared by default.

Exclude reference parts

If this check box is selected, the reference parts will be excluded from the parts list. This check box is selected by default.

Balloon Tab

The options under this tab enable you to set the display properties of the balloons that appear on the assembly drawing view.

Steps to Generate Parts List and Balloons

In this section, you will learn how to generate the parts list and balloons by setting some options in the **List Properties** dialog box. An assembly with parts list and balloons will be generated, as shown in Figure 12-29. This assembly consists of two subassemblies.

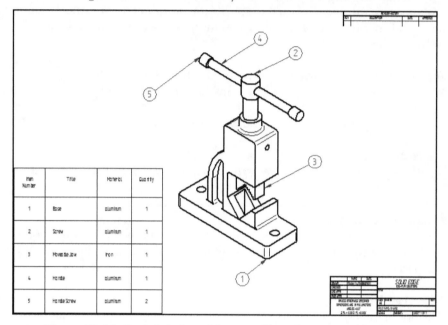

Figure 12-29 *Exploded view of the assembly with BOM and balloons*

The following steps explain the procedure for generating the parts list and balloons:

1. Choose the **Parts List** button from the **Drawing Views** toolbar; you are prompted to select the drawing view.
2. Select the drawing view that exists on the drawing sheet.
3. Choose the **Properties** button from the ribbon bar to display the **List Properties** dialog box.
4. Choose the **Columns** tab.
5. In the **Columns used** display box, select **Document Number** and choose the **Remove** button.
6. Choose the **List Control** tab.
7. From the **Global** area, select the **Atomic List (all parts)** radio button and choose the **OK** button to exit the dialog box.
8. Choose the **Auto-Balloon** button from the ribbon bar, if it is not already chosen.
9. Choose the **Finish** button from the ribbon bar to display the BOM and balloons. You will notice that the balloons are displayed showing both the item number and the quantity.

10. To remove the quantity from a balloon, select all the balloons by pressing the CTRL key; the ribbon bar is displayed.
11. Choose the **Item Count** button from the ribbon bar to clear it. Now, the balloon shows only the item number.

TUTORIALS

Tutorial 1

In this tutorial, you will generate the top view, front view, and right-side view of the part that was created in Exercise 1 of Chapter 8 and is shown in Figure 12-30. Use the standard A4 Landscape sheet format for generating the drawing views. You will also insert your company logo in the sheet.   **(Expected time: 1 hr)**

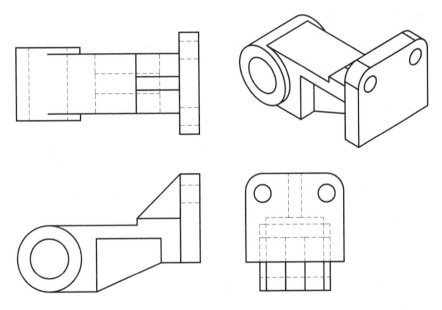

Figure 12-30 Top, front, right-side, and isometric views of the model

The following steps are required to complete this tutorial:

a. Start a new draft file.
b. Set up the drawing sheet and the background sheet, refer to Figure 12-32.
c. Set the projection angle method and save the draft template file.
d. Generate the drawing views, refer to Figure 12-34.
e. Save the draft file.

Starting a New File in the Draft Environment
1. Start Solid Edge and then select the **Drawing** option from the **Create** area of the welcome screen.

2. After entering the **Draft** environment, choose **Tools > EdgeBar** from the menu bar to hide it, if it is displayed. This is because you will not need it and moreover, turning its display off will increase the work area on the screen.

Setting the Drawing Sheet Options

The drawing sheet in Solid Edge is like a blank sheet of paper on which you can draw. You can add as many sheets as needed in the same drawing file. When you work in the **Draft** environment, you have two sheets by default. The sheet on which you place the drawing views is called the worksheet and the sheet on which you create the title blocks is called the background sheet. Based on the size of the worksheet you select, the background sheet automatically adjusts itself to the size of the worksheet. To set the worksheet and the drawing sheet for this tutorial, follow the steps given next.

1. Choose **File > Sheet Setup** from the menu bar to display the **Sheet Setup** dialog box. In the **Sheet Size** area of the **Size** tab, the **Standard** radio button is selected by default.

2. From the drop-down list, select **A2 Wide (594mm x 420mm)**, if it is not already selected. Note that in the dialog box, the units are set in millimeters.

3. Choose the **Background** tab in the dialog box. Make sure **A2-Sheet** is selected in the **Background sheet** drop-down list. Choose the **OK** button from the dialog box to exit it.

    Next, you will insert a graphic image as an object in the background sheet. Generally, a company's logo is inserted using this method. As the image has to be inserted in the background sheet, therefore, you need to deactivate the working sheet. Also, note that to insert an image, you should have an image editing program installed on your computer.

4. Choose **View > Background Sheet** from the menu bar and then choose **View > Working Sheets** to clear this option. Notice that four sheets are displayed in the bar below the drawing window.

5. Choose the **A2-Sheet** tab from the bottom of the drawing window and then zoom to fit it on the screen.

6. Select the top table, as shown in Figure 12-31. All entities in the table turn magenta in color, which indicates that they are selected.

7. Press the DELETE key to delete the selected entities.

8. Choose **Insert > Image** from the menu bar to display the **Insert Image** dialog box.

9. Choose the **Browse** button; the **Open a File** dialog box is displayed.

10. Browse and select the image file of the logo that you want to use, refer to Figure 12-32.

11. Set the transparency option for the logo, if required.

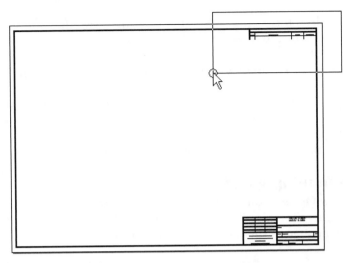

Figure 12-31 *Selecting the table*

12. After selecting the file, choose the **OK** button from the **Insert Image** dialog box; the image will be placed on the sheet.

13. Drag the image and place it, as shown in Figure 12-32. The size of the image can be modified using the handles available on the image, when it is selected.

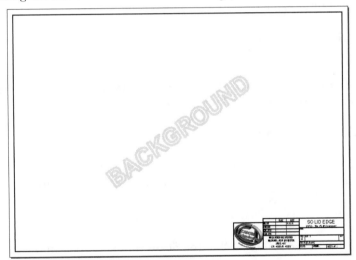

Figure 12-32 *Title block with the image*

14. After placing the image, choose **Tools > Options** from the menu bar to display the **Options** dialog box and then choose the **Drawing Standards** tab.

15. From the **Projection Angle** area, select the **Third** radio button to set the current projection type to the third angle projection. Choose **OK** to exit the dialog box.

16. Choose **View > Working Sheets** from the menu bar and then choose **View > Back-**

ground Sheet to clear this option. Now, the drawing views that you generate will be placed on the worksheet and not on the background sheet.

17. Save the drawing file as **Template.dft** in the *\Program Files\Solid Edge V20\Template* folder.

    You have successfully created a template file. In this textbook, you will further use this drawing file as the template to generate the drawing views in the **Draft** environment.

18. Close this file and then start a new file using the **Template.dft** template.

Generating the Drawing Views

The **Drawing View Orientation** page of the **Drawing View Creation Wizard** dialog box enables you to generate multiple views in a single attempt. All views required in this tutorial will be generated at the same time using this option.

1. Choose the **Drawing View Wizard** button from the **Drawing View** toolbar to display the **Select Model** dialog box.

2. Select the part created in Exercise 1 of Chapter 8 and then choose the **Open** button to display the **Drawing View Creation Wizard** dialog box.

3. Accept the default options and choose the **Next** button from the **Part and Sheet Metal Drawing View Options** page.

4. Select **front view** from the **Drawing View Orientation** page and then choose the **Next** button.

5. Select the views shown in Figure 12-33 from the **Drawing View Layout** page and then choose the **Finish** button.

6. Place the drawing views on the sheet.

    Notice that you need to increase the scale of the views. The scale of any one orthographic view, when modified, changes the scale of the other two orthographic views also.

7. Select the isometric view to display the ribbon bar.

8. Modify the value of the scale to **1.2** in the **Scale value** edit box in the ribbon bar.

9. Similarly, select any one of the orthographic views to invoke the ribbon bar. Modify the value of the scale to **1.2**.

10. You can move the views on the sheet by dragging them. Arrange all views, as shown in Figure 12-34.

Saving the File

1. Choose **File > Save As** from the menu bar to display the **Save As** dialog box. Save the file with the name *c12tut1.dft*.

2. Choose **File** > **Close** to close the file.

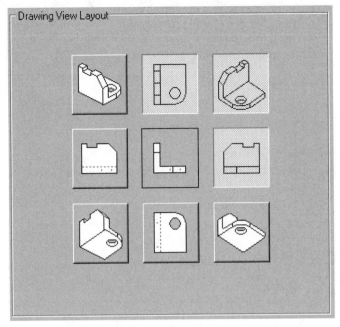

Figure 12-33 The **Drawing View Layout** *page of the* **Drawing View Creation Wizard** *dialog box*

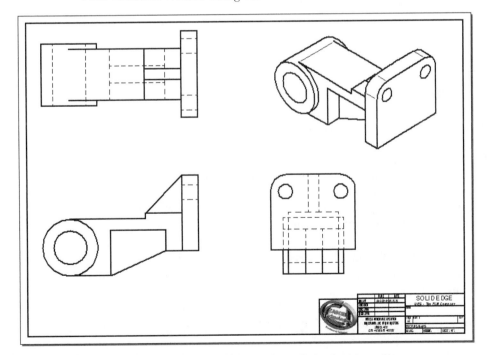

Figure 12-34 Sheet after generating all the drawing views

Tutorial 2

In this tutorial, you will generate the front view, left-side view, and auxiliary view of the part that was created in Exercise 2 of Chapter 7. You will also generate the dimensions, as shown in Figure 12-35. Use the template that was created in Tutorial 1.

(Expected time: 30 min)

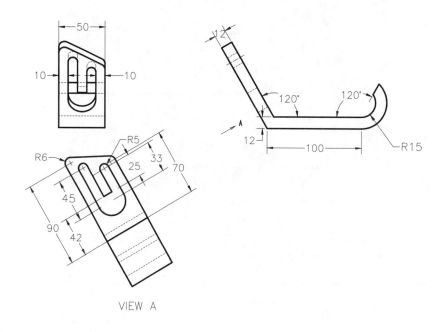

VIEW A

Figure 12-35 Left-side view, auxiliary view, and the front view of the model

The following steps are required to complete this tutorial:

a. Start a new draft file.
b. Generate the drawing views, refer to Figures 12-37 through 12-39.
c. Generate the dimensions.
d. Create the remaining dimensions that are not generated, refer to Figure 12-43.
e. Save the drawing file and close the window.

Starting a New File in the Draft Environment

You will use the template created in the previous tutorial to generate the drawing views for this tutorial.

1. Choose the **New** button from the **Main** toolbar to display the **New** dialog box.

2. Select **Template.dft** and choose the **OK** button to exit the dialog box and enter the **Draft** environment. Here, you will use the *Template.dft* file as the template.

Generating the Base Drawing Views

As mentioned earlier, the drawing views are generated from their parent part. The following steps are required for generating the drawing views:

1. Choose the **Drawing View Wizard** button from the **Drawing Views** toolbar to display the **Select Model** dialog box.

2. Select the part created in Exercise 2 of Chapter 7 and choose the **Open** button to display the **Drawing View Creation Wizard** dialog box.

3. Accept the default options and choose the **Next** button.

4. From the **Drawing View Orientation** page, select **front** and choose the **Next** button.

5. Now, choose the button of the left view in the dialog box and then choose the **Finish** button.

6. Place the drawing views on the sheet.

   Notice that you need to scale down the views. The scale of any one orthographic view, when modified, changes the scale of the other orthographic views also.

7. Select one of the views to display the ribbon bar.

8. Modify the value of the scale to **1.2** in the **Scale value** edit box.

9. You can move the views on the sheet by dragging them. Arrange the views, as shown in Figure 12-36.

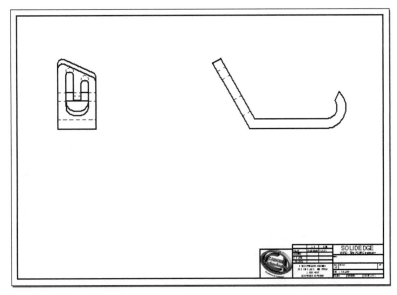

Figure 12-36 *Drawing views after reducing the scale*

Generating the Auxiliary View

The auxiliary view will be generated by selecting the edge perpendicular to which the view will be projected. This view is created because the true shape of the cut profile can be shown in this view. To generate the auxiliary drawing view, follow the steps discussed next.

1. Choose the **Auxiliary View** button from the **Drawing Views** toolbar; you are prompted to click on the first point of the fold line. The fold line is an imaginary line that is created when you select two keypoints. The view will be projected about this imaginary line.

2. Select the edge, as shown in Figure 12-37. An imaginary fold line is formed and the auxiliary view is projected normal to this fold line. Move the cursor and to place the view, see Figure 12-38. After you place the view, the arrow pointing in the direction normal to the fold line is displayed, as shown in Figure 12-39.

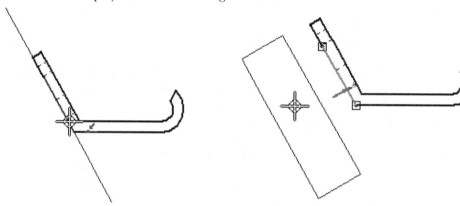

Figure 12-37 *Edge to be selected*   *Figure 12-38* *Moving the cursor to place the view*

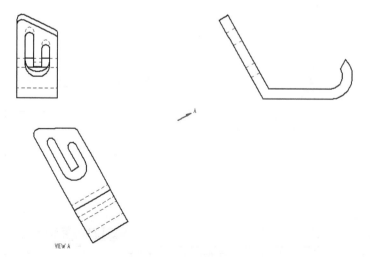

Figure 12-39 *Drawing sheet after generating the auxiliary view*

Dimensioning the Views

Now, the dimensions will be generated from the model and then the remaining dimensions will be created.

1. Choose the **Retrieve Dimensions** button from the **Drawing Views** toolbar; you are prompted to select the drawing view.

2. Select the front view; the dimensions are displayed on it. You will notice that the display of the dimensions is very small. You need to increase the font size of the dimensions.

3. Exit the current tool and then select a dimension; the current dimension style is displayed in the first drop-down list in the ribbon bar. You need to modify the text size for this dimension style.

4. Press the ESC key to remove the dimension from the selection set. Now, choose **Format > Style** from the menu bar to display the **Style** dialog box. Select the dimension style of the current dimensions from the **Styles** list box and then choose the **Modify** button.

5. Choose the **Text** tab and modify the font size to **8.5** in the **Font size** edit box. Choose **OK** and then choose **Apply** from the **Style** dialog box.

6. Place the missing dimensions, as shown in Figure 12-40, using the dimensioning tools.

7. Choose the **Distance Between** button from the **Drawing Views** toolbar and then select the **By 2 Points** option from the **Orientation** drop-down list. Dimension the auxiliary view with dimensions 90, 42, and 70, as shown in Figure 12-41.

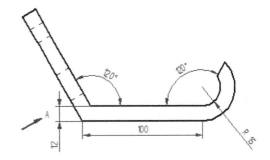

8. To dimension the auxiliary view with dimensions 45, 25, and 33, draw an axis passing through the center of the arc, as shown in Figure 12-41.

Figure 12-40 *Front view after placing the angular dimension*

9. Select the center of the arc and then the axis, and place the dimension with a value of 33, see Figure 12-42.

10. Similarly, apply the remaining dimensions to the auxiliary view so that all dimensions are displayed.

11. After dimensioning the auxiliary view, choose the **Retrieve Dimensions** button and select the left-side view to generate the dimensions. You will notice that only dimension 50 is generated. Create the remaining dimensions manually.

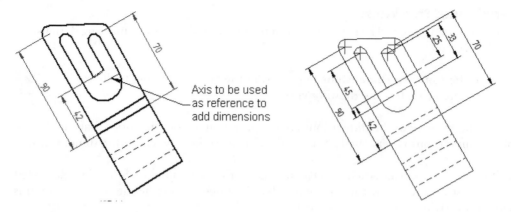

Figure 12-41 *Axis drawn to dimension*   *Figure 12-42* *Auxiliary view after dimensioning*

The drawing sheet, after dimensioning the drawing views, is shown in Figure 12-43.

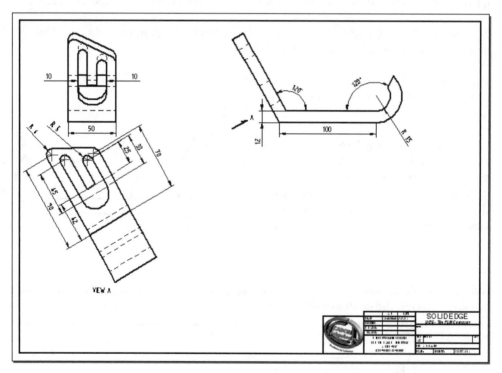

Figure 12-43 *Drawing sheet after dimensioning the views*

Saving the File

1. Save the file with the name *c12tut2.dft*.

2. Choose **File > Close** to close the file.

Tutorial 3

In this tutorial, you will generate an exploded drawing view of the assembly created in Chapter 9. You will also add the parts list and balloons to the assembly, as shown in Figure 12-44.

(Expected time: 30 min)

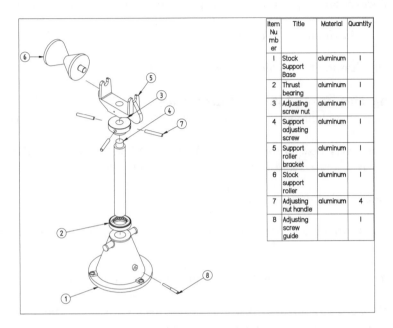

Item Number	Title	Material	Quantity
1	Stock Support Base	aluminum	1
2	Thrust bearing	aluminum	1
3	Adjusting screw nut	aluminum	1
4	Support adjusting screw	aluminum	1
5	Support roller bracket	aluminum	1
6	Stock support roller	aluminum	1
7	Adjusting nut handle	aluminum	4
8	Adjusting screw guide		1

Figure 12-44 Parts list and balloons in exploded drawing view

The following steps are required to complete this tutorial:

a. Start a new draft file.
b. Generate the exploded drawing view.
c. Generate the parts list and balloons.
d. Edit balloons.
e. Save the drawing file and close the window.

Starting a New File in the Draft Environment

1. Choose the **New** button from the **Main** toolbar to display the **New** dialog box.

2. Select **Template.dft** and choose the **OK** button to exit the dialog box. Now, you have entered the **Draft** environment.

Generating the Exploded Drawing View

1. Choose the **Drawing View Wizard** button from the **Drawing View** toolbar to display the **Select Model** dialog box.

2. Select **Assembly Document (*.asm)** from the **Files of type** drop-down list.

3. Select the Stock Bracket assembly and choose the **Open** button to display the **Drawing View Creation Wizard** dialog box.

4. In the **Assembly Drawing View Options** page, select the **Explode** configuration from the **Configuration** drop-down list. Accept the remaining default options.

5. Choose the **Finish** button to exit the dialog box.

6. Modify the drawing view scale to **0.18**.

Generating the Parts List and Balloons

The parts list and balloons are generated directly from the assembly drawing view.

1. Choose the **Parts List** button from the **Drawing Views** toolbar; the **Parts List** ribbon bar is displayed and you are prompted to select a view.

2. Select the exploded drawing view.

3. Choose the **Properties** button from the ribbon bar to display the **List Properties** dialog box.

4. In the **Text** area of the **General** tab, modify the value in the **Size** edit box to **7**.

5. Choose the **Columns** tab. In the **Columns used** display box, select the **Document Number** option and choose the **Remove** button to remove it.

6. Select the **Material** option from the **Columns used** display box.

7. Next, in the **Column Format** area, change the value in the **Column width** edit box to **42**. Similarly, change the column width value of **Quantity** to **42**.

    By default, the balloons that you place display the item number and the item count. However, in this case, you do not need to display the item count. Therefore, you need to modify the balloon properties using the **Balloon** tab.

8. Choose the **Balloon** tab to display the options related to balloons.

9. Modify the value in the **Size** edit box to **7**.

10. Next, clear the **Item count** check box to make sure the item counts are not displayed.

11. Choose the **OK** button to exit the dialog box. Choose **Finish** from the ribbon bar.

12. Drag the parts list table to the desired location on the drawing sheet and place it.

The drawing sheet after placing the parts list and balloons is shown in Figure 12-45.

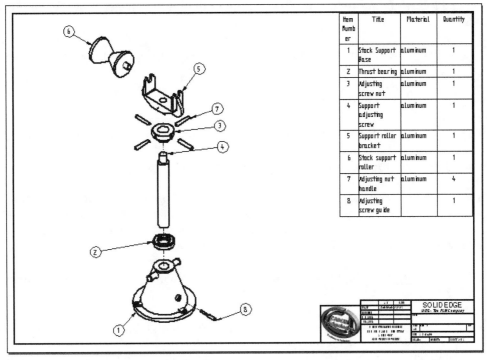

Item Number	Title	Material	Quantity
1	Stock Support Base	aluminum	1
2	Thrust bearing	aluminum	1
3	Adjusting screw nut	aluminum	1
4	Support adjusting screw	aluminum	1
5	Support roller bracket	aluminum	1
6	Stock support roller	aluminum	1
7	Adjusting nut handle	aluminum	4
8	Adjusting screw guide		1

Figure 12-45 Exploded drawing view with the parts list and balloons

Saving the File

1. Choose **File > Save** from the menu bar to display the **Save As** dialog box.

2. Save the file with the name *c12tut3.dft*.

3. Choose **File > Close** to close the file.

Self-Evaluation Test

Answer the following questions and then compare them to those given at the end of this chapter:

1. When you enter the **Draft** environment of Solid Edge, only the drawing sheet is displayed. (T/F)

2. You cannot use an empty sheet for drawing. (T/F)

3. The_____ button is used to retrieve annotations that are applied to the model.

4. The base view is the first view that is generated on the drawing sheet. (T/F)

5. A section view is generated by cutting the part of an existing view using a plane or a line and then viewing the parent view from a direction normal to the section plane. (T/F)

6. The **Drawing View Wizard** button is used to generate the base view. (T/F)

7. The _____ is the file extension of the files created in the **Draft** environment of Solid Edge.

8. The _____ view is used for parts that have a high length to width ratio.

9. A cutting plane can be edited by _____ or by choosing the _____ button from the ribbon bar.

10. To generate a section drawing view of a part, you need a _____.

Review Questions

Answer the following questions:

1. In which of the following views, the dimensions cannot be generated from the part?

    (a) Front   (b) Right-side
    (c) Top   (d) None of the above

2. Which of the following buttons in the **Drawing Views** toolbar is used to generate a BOM?

    (a) **SmartDimension**   (b) **Parts List**
    (c) **Draft View**   (d) None of the above

3. The _____ tab contains the options that are used to set the dimension style, color of text, font, font style, and size.

4. Which of the following dialog boxes is displayed when you choose the **Drawing View Wizard** button from the **Drawing Views** toolbar?

    (a) **Properties**   (b) **Select**
    (c) **Drawing View Properties**   (d) None of the above

5. Before placing the BOM on the drawing sheet, when you choose the **Properties** button from the ribbon bar, the **Parts List Properties** dialog box is displayed. (T/F)

6. When you enter the **Draft** environment, there are two sheets available by default. (T/F)

7. The technique of generating drawing views from a solid model is called generative drafting. (T/F)

8. A detail view is used to display the details of a portion of an existing view. (T/F)

9. The need for an auxiliary view arises when it becomes impossible to dimension a geometry in the orthographic view. (T/F)

10. In a revolved section view, the section portion revolves about an axis normal to the viewing plane such that it is straightened. (T/F)

Exercises

Exercise 1

Create the exploded view of the assembly that was created in Chapter 10, see Figure 12-46. Generate the BOM and balloons.   (**Expected time: 30 min**)

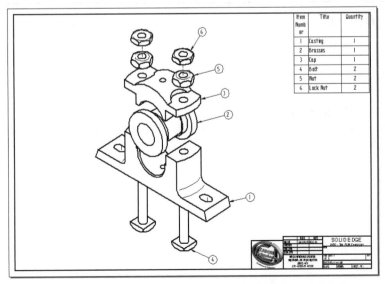

Figure 12-46 Exploded drawing view with the BOM and balloons

Exercise 2

Create the model whose drawing views are shown in Figure 12-47 and then generate the drawing views of the model. Dimension the drawing views, as shown in Figure 12-47.

(Expected time: 45 min)

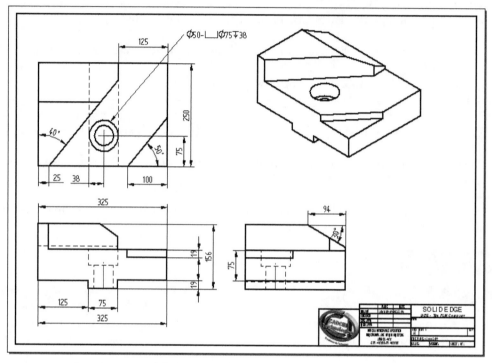

Figure 12-47 *Top, front, right-side, and isometric views of the model*

Answers to Self-Evaluation Test

1. F, **2.** F, **3. Annotations**, **4.** T, **5.** T, **6.** T, **7.** *.dft*, **8.** broken, **9.** double-clicking, **Edit**, **10.** cutting plane

Chapter 13

Surface Modeling

- *Create extruded, revolved, and swept surfaces.*
- *Create surfaces using the BlueSurf tool.*
- *Create a bounded surface.*
- *Stitch surfaces.*
- *Use the Offset Surface and Copy Surface tools.*
- *Use the BlueDot tool to join curves.*
- *Create a curve at the intersection of two surfaces.*
- *Trim surfaces.*
- *Extend a surface.*
- *Split faces.*
- *Replace faces of a part.*
- *Create curves in 3D by selecting keypoints.*
- *Create curves using a table.*
- *Project curves on surfaces.*
- *Create a curve at the intersection of two curves.*
- *Draw a curve on a surface.*
- *Derive and split curves.*
- *Split a body.*
- *Add thickness to a surface.*
- *Create rounds using the Blend and Surface Blend options.*
- *Add a draft angle from the construction surface of a parting line.*
- *Create a parting line and parting surface.*

SURFACE MODELING

Surface modeling is a technique of creating planar or nonplanar geometries of zero thickness. Surface models are the three-dimensional (3D) models that have zero thickness.

Most real-world models are created using solid models. However, some models are complex, therefore surfaces are needed to create them. After creating the required shape of a model using surfaces, you can convert it into a solid model. The techniques of creating surface models and solid models with the help of the surfaces are explained in this chapter. Remember that unlike solid models, surface models do not have mass properties. It becomes easier for readers to learn surface modeling if they are familiar with the solid modeling feature creation tools.

In Solid Edge, surface models are created in the **Part** environment using the **Surfacing** toolbar. Note that this toolbar is not available by default. To invoke this toolbar, right-click on the **Features** toolbar; a shortcut menu will be displayed. Choose the **Surfacing** option from it.

CREATING SURFACES IN SOLID EDGE

In Solid Edge, the **Surfacing** toolbar is used to create surface models. However, you will also use the **Features** toolbar to create them. To create the base feature, three tools are used. These tools are discussed next.

Creating an Extruded Surface

Toolbar:	Surfacing > Extruded Surface

To create an extruded surface, choose the **Extruded Surface** button from the **Surfacing** toolbar; the **Extruded Surface** ribbon bar will be displayed and you will be prompted to select a planar face or a reference plane. The sketch will be drawn on this planar face or reference plane. As soon as you select a planar face or a reference plane, the sketching environment will be invoked. The steps for creating an extruded surface are similar to those required for creating a solid protrusion. These steps are listed next.

1. Select a face or a sketch plane for drawing the sketch.
2. Draw the profile of the surface feature you need to create and then exit the sketching environment.
3. Define the depth and direction of extrusion by using the **Extend Step** button in the **Extruded Surface** ribbon bar.
4. Before choosing the **Finish** button, specify whether you want to create the surface extrusion with open ends or closed ends by choosing the **Open Ends** or the **Close Ends** button in the ribbon bar.

Figure 13-1 shows the surface model with open-ends and Figure 13-2 shows the surface model with closed-ends. Remember that to create a surface model with closed-ends, its profile should be closed. To provide a draft to the surfacing feature, choose the **Draft** button under the **Treatment Step**. The rest of the options are discussed in Chapter 5.

Figure 13-1 Extruded surface with open ends   *Figure 13-2 Extruded surface with closed ends*

Creating a Revolved Surface

Toolbar: Surfacing > Revolved Surface

 To create a revolved surface, choose the **Revolved Surface** button from the **Surfacing** toolbar; the **Revolved Surface** ribbon bar will be displayed and you will be prompted to select a planar face or a reference plane.

The steps required for creating a revolved surface are similar to those required for creating an extruded surface. You can also choose to close the ends of the revolved surface or keep them open. Remember that the closed or open ends option is available only when the angle of revolution is less than 360-degrees. But make sure the profile is closed. Figure 13-3 shows an open-end surface model and Figure 13-4 shows a closed-end surface model.

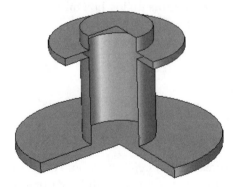

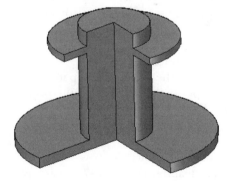

Figure 13-3 Revolved surface with open ends   *Figure 13-4 Revolved surface with closed ends*

Creating a Swept Surface

Toolbar: Surfacing > Swept Surface

When you choose the **Swept Surface** button, the **Sweep Options** dialog box will be displayed, as shown in Figure 13-5. In the **Default Sweep Type** area, there are two radio buttons that are used to specify the method of creating the swept surface. These two methods are discussed next. The rest of the options are the same as those discussed in solid sweeps.

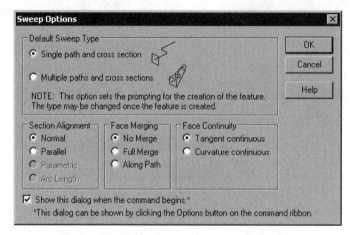

*Figure 13-5 The **Sweep Options** dialog box*

Single path and cross section Option

As the name of the radio button suggests, this method uses a single path along which the section is swept. Select this radio button in the **Sweep Options** dialog box and choose **OK**. The steps for creating a swept surface using this method are listed next.

1. After exiting the **Sweep Options** dialog box, select a face or a reference plane for drawing the sketch.
2. Draw the sketch of the path for a sweep feature.
3. Specify the location on the profile where the cross-section plane will be placed.
4. Draw the cross-section.
5. Select the start point on the cross-section.

Figure 13-6 shows the cross-section and the path to create the sweep feature, and the resulting swept feature. Figure 13-7 shows a partial view of the edge of a model and the open sketch used to create the sweep feature shown in Figure 13-8.

Multiple paths and cross sections Option

As the name suggests, when you select this method, you can use multiple paths and cross-sections to create the sweep feature. Select this radio button and choose **OK** to exit the **Sweep Options** dialog box. The steps for creating a swept surface using this option are listed next.

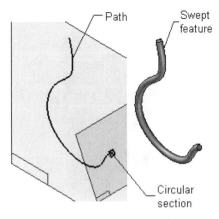 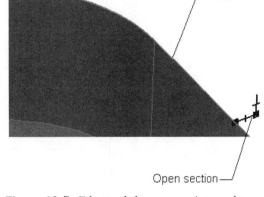

Figure 13-6 Sweep surface

Figure 13-7 Edge and the cross-section used to create the sweep feature

Figure 13-8 Sweep surface created on the top edge of the base

1. Select a reference plane or a planar face to draw the sketch of the path.
2. Draw the sketch of the first path and exit the sketching environment. Choose the **Finish** button from the ribbon bar; the **Next** button will be displayed in the ribbon bar. If you need to draw another path, select a reference plane or face. If you need to draw a cross-section, choose the **Next** button.
3. Specify the location on the profile where the cross-section plane will be placed. Draw the profile of the cross-section.
4. After exiting the sketching environment, specify the start point on the cross-section. Now, if you need to draw another cross-section, select a reference plane again and then draw the cross-section.
5. Choose the **Preview** button.

Figure 13-9 shows the cross-section and the two paths needed to create a sweep feature and Figure 13-10 shows the resulting sweep surface.

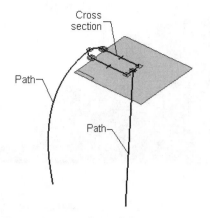
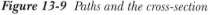

Figure 13-9 *Paths and the cross-section*   *Figure 13-10* *Resulting sweep surface*

CREATING SURFACES USING THE BLUESURF TOOL

Toolbar:	Surfacing > BlueSurf

The **BlueSurf** tool is a multipurpose tool used for creating surfaces such as complex loft surfaces with guide curves, surface patch, and so on. This tool can be invoked from the **Surfacing** toolbar. Note that this button is available only after the base feature or the sketch is created. When you choose this button, the **BlueSurf** ribbon bar will be displayed and you will be prompted to select a sketch, edge chain, or curve chain. The different methods used for creating surfaces are discussed next.

Creating Surfaces by Joining Two Curves

Create two curves, as shown in Figure 13-11. These curves are drawn using the **Sketch** button. Invoke the **BlueSurf** tool and select any one of the two curves. Now, select the second curve; a surface will be created between the two curves, as shown in Figure 13-12.

In the above case, two curves were used to create a surface. Now, you will use two curves that are connected using the **Connect** relationship to create a surface. One of the curves will be

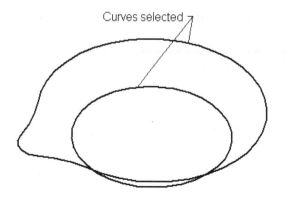

Figure 13-11 *Two curves*   *Figure 13-12* *Resulting surface*

selected as the cross-section and the other as the path, see Figures 13-13 and 13-14. To create this surface, invoke the **BlueSurf** tool and select the cross-section curve. Confirm the selection by right-clicking. Choose the **Guide Curve Step** button from the **BlueSurf** ribbon bar and select the path or the guide curve. Confirm the selection by right-clicking; the surface will be created, as shown in Figure 13-14.

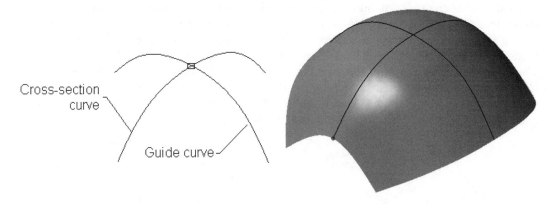

Figure 13-13 *Two curves that are used as a cross-section and a guide curve*

Figure 13-14 *Resulting surface*

Note

*In Figure 13-13, if both the curves are drawn as semicircles, you may not be able to create a surface using the **BlueSurf** tool.*

You can also use three curves to create a surface. In this case, two curves will act as cross-sections and the third curve will act as the path or the guide curve, see Figure 13-15. To create this type of surface, invoke the **BlueSurf** tool. Select the first curve and right-click to accept. Now, select the second curve and make sure the dashed line indicating the connection points does not connect the diagonal points. Now, right-click to accept it. Next, choose the **Guide Curve Step** button from the ribbon bar and select the path or the guide curve. Confirm the selection by right-clicking. The surface will be created, as shown in Figure 13-16.

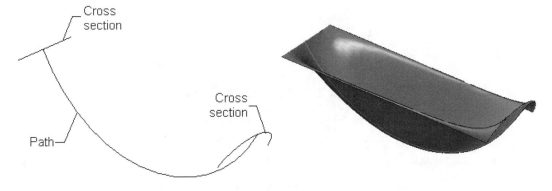

Figure 13-15 *Single path and two cross-sections*

Figure 13-16 *Resulting surface*

Controlling the Shape of the Surface by Inserting a Sketch

You can modify the shape of a surface using the **BlueSurf** tool by inserting a sketch at the desired location.

Invoke the **BlueSurf** tool and select the first curve. Right-click to accept the selection. Similarly, select the other cross-section and accept it, see Figure 13-17. You will notice that a surface is created between the selected cross-sections. Now, choose the **Insert Sketch Step** button; you will be prompted to select a planar face or a reference plane. You can create a new reference plane intersecting the surface. Using this reference plane, the geometry of the curve is created. The most widely used option for creating a reference plane is the **Parallel Plane** option. Create a parallel plane; a curve defined by the intersection of the surface and the parallel plane will be created. Similarly, define the number of planes needed to create the sketches and then exit the tool. The curve is created on the surface, see Figure 13-18.

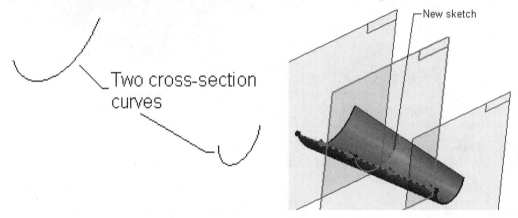

Figure 13-17 *Two cross-sections*   *Figure 13-18* *Curve created using a plane*

These curves appear as a separate sketch above the **BlueSurf** feature in the **EdgeBar**. After exiting the **BlueSurf** tool, you can select a sketch and dynamically edit it to modify the shape of the surface, see Figure 13-19.

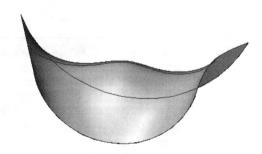

Figure 13-19 *Modified surface*

Closing the Ends

The **BlueSurf** tool is also used to close the ends of a surface. To do so, invoke the **BlueSurf** tool and select one of the edges of the surface. Accept the edge and then select the other surface to close it, see Figures 13-20 and 13-21. Note that the surface can be created by selecting an open loop or a closed loop.

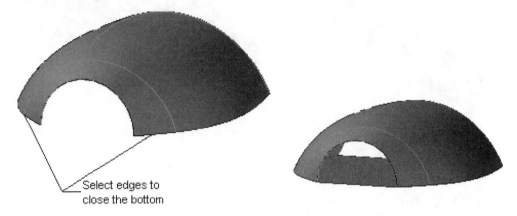

Figure 13-20 *Edges of the surface*   *Figure 13-21* *Surface created by joining the edges*

Controlling the Connection between the Two Surfaces

The **BlueSurf** tool is used to connect or join two sets of edges formed between solid or surface features, as shown in Figure 13-22. The surface, after manipulating the end conditions, is shown in Figure 13-23.

There are several end conditions that are provided in the **BlueSurf Options** dialog box, which is invoked by choosing the **BlueSurf Options** button from the ribbon bar, see Figure 13-24. The options in this dialog box can be used before or after creating the BlueSurface. The options in the **Standard** tab of this dialog box are discussed next.

Tangency Control Area

This area consists of the options that are used to specify the boundary conditions for the two end sections. The boundary condition refers to the type of joint that is required with the adjacent surface. This area has four drop-down lists, which are discussed next.

Start section

The options in this drop-down list are as follows:

> **Natural**. This option is selected by default. It does not force any tangency conditions on the surface at the start and end sections.

> **Normal to section**. This option enables the boundary conditions to be modified normal to the sketched section using the drag handles (vector).

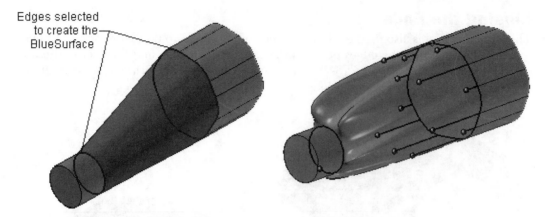

Edges selected to create the BlueSurface

Figure 13-22 *BlueSurface*   Figure 13-23 *Surface after manipulation*

 Parallel to section. This option enables you to modify the end cross-section parallel to the sketch plane. This option is generally available when a loft surface is created by joining a point. In this case, the point acts as a cross-section. The modification can be made by dragging the handles that are displayed on the boundary of the cross-sections.

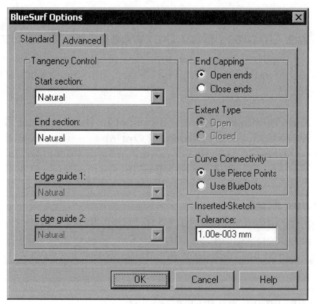

Figure 13-24 *The **Standard** tab chosen in the **BlueSurf Options** dialog box*

Tangent continuous. This option creates a surface by lofting the edges and the cross-sections such that they are tangentially continuous. The drag handles (vector) available can be used to modify the surface.

Tangent Interior. This option forces the interior surface to be tangent to the start and end sections.

Curvature continuous. This option makes the curvature of the resulting surface continuous with the adjacent surfaces.

End section
The options in this list are used to determine the end conditions of the surface with respect to the adjacent surface. These options are the same as those available in the **Start section** drop-down list. Also, their availability depends on the sections to be joined.

Edge guide 1
The options in this drop-down list are available only when a guide curve is used to create the surface. These options are the same as those available in the **Start section** drop-down list.

Edge guide 2
The options in this drop-down list are also available only when a guide curve is used to create the surface. These options are the same as those available in the **Start section** drop-down list.

End Capping Area
The options in this area are available only when the sections are closed. The **Open ends** radio button, when selected, creates a surface that has open ends. When you select the **Close ends** radio button, a surface will be created with closed ends or capped ends.

Extent Type Area
This area is available when there are at least three cross-sections. You can create a BlueSurface by closing the surface using the start section as the end section. When you select the **Open** radio button, the surface will be created by starting from the start section and ending at the end section. When you select the **Closed** radio button, a closed surface will be created between the start, end, and start sections.

Curve Connectivity Area
The options in this area are used to specify the type of connection required between the guide curve and the cross-section. These options are discussed next.

Use Pierce Points
This option uses the pierce point to connect the guide curve and the cross-section. It is used when you need to use dimensions for modifying the shape of a surface.

Use BlueDots
This option is used to connect the guide curve and the cross-section using the BlueDot. It is also used when you need to design a surface aesthetically. This is because the BlueDot enables you to modify the surface by holding it. The BlueDot is discussed later in this chapter.

CREATING SURFACES USING THE BOUNDED SURFACE TOOL

Toolbar: Surfacing > Bounded Surface

This tool is used to create a surface using one or more edges that form a closed loop. When you choose this button, you will be prompted to select the edges that form a closed loop. Select the curves, as shown in Figure 13-25, to create a surface. Next, choose the **Preview** button. The surface will be created, as shown in Figure 13-26.

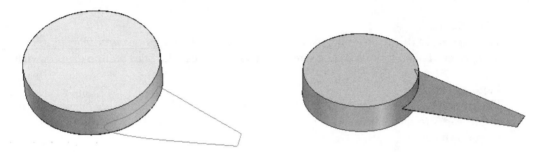

Figure 13-25 *Closed curve*   *Figure 13-26* *Surface created using the curves*

After selecting and accepting the edge that forms a closed loop, as shown in Figure 13-27, choose the **Face Tangency** button from the ribbon bar. Now, when you choose the **Preview** button, the surface will be created, as shown in Figure 13-28. It is evident from this figure that when the bounded surface is created, it maintains a tangency with the selected edge. If you choose the **Face Tangency** button again to turn it off, the surface will be created, as shown in Figure 13-29.

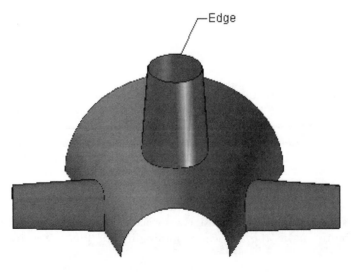

Figure 13-27 *Edge selected as a closed loop*

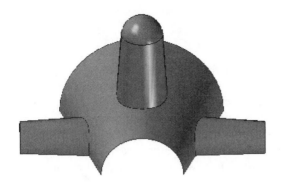

Figure 13-28 *Bounded surface created using the* **Face Tangency** *option*

Figure 13-29 *Bounded surface created after turning off the* **Face Tangency** *option*

STITCHING MULTIPLE SURFACES TO CREATE A SINGLE SURFACE

Toolbar: Surfacing > Stitched Surface

The **Stitched Surface** tool is used to join multiple individual surfaces to create a single surface. When the surface model is created, you need to join all individual surfaces and convert them into one single surface. This is because the thickness can be added to a single surface only. Remember that you cannot stitch disjoint surfaces.

To stitch surfaces, choose the **Stitched Surface** button from the **Surfacing** toolbar; the **Stitched Surface Options** dialog box will be displayed, as shown in Figure 13-30. Change the tolerance value to 1.00e-001 mm. This tolerance is the gap that is provided between the two surfaces. After exiting the **Stitched Surface Options** dialog box, you will be prompted to select two or more surfaces. Select all the surfaces that need stitching with the other surfaces and then choose the **Accept** button on the ribbon bar. The multiple surfaces are joined to form a single surface. You can check whether they are joined by selecting the model. If the surfaces are joined, the entire surface model will be selected by selecting a single surface.

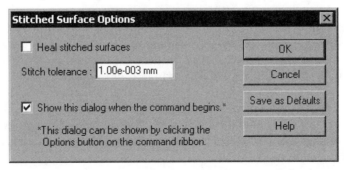

Figure 13-30 *The* **Stitched Surface Options** *dialog box*

CREATING OFFSET SURFACES

Toolbar:	Surfacing > Offset Surface

The **Offset Surface** tool enables you to offset the selected surface by a specified distance. When you choose this button from the **Surfacing** toolbar, depending on the options selected from the **Selection Type** drop-down list, you will be prompted to select a face, chain, feature, or body. After selecting a surface, you will be prompted to specify the side where the offset surface will be created. This direction is pointed by a red arrow. Click in the direction of the arrow to specify the direction of the feature creation. You can also specify the offset distance in the **Distance** edit box. The offset surface created is shown in Figure 13-31.

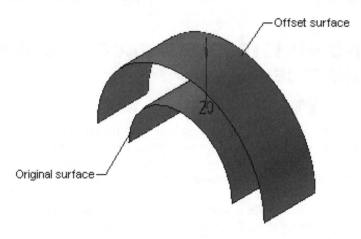

Figure 13-31 Offset surface

COPYING A SURFACE

Toolbar:	Surfacing > Offset Surface > Copy Surface

The **Copy Surface** tool is used to copy a face of a solid or a surface feature. This tool can be used in many ways. For example, you can extract the face of a solid surface that can be further used to perform surface operations. Another application of the **Copy Surface** tool is that if the file size of a solid model is too large, then you can extract the faces of the solid model and create a surface model out of a solid model. The file size of this surface model will be comparatively smaller than that of the solid model.

To extract a face of the solid model or to copy the surface model, choose the **Copy Surface** button available in the **Offset Surface** flyout of the **Surfacing** toolbar; you will be prompted to select a face. After selecting the face, choose the **Accept** button; the surface will be copied. Choose the **Finish** button to exit the tool.

When you choose the **Copy Surface** button, the ribbon bar will be displayed, as shown in Figure 13-32. The buttons in this ribbon bar are discussed next.

Figure 13-32 The ribbon bar of the Copy Surface tool

Remove Internal Boundaries

This button enables you to remove internal boundaries from the surface and create a surface by ignoring them. For example, a face having holes on it can be selected to extract the surface. This surface, when extracted using the **Remove Internal Boundaries** button, ignores the holes and creates a plane surface. In other words, the face having holes is extracted by ignoring the holes and forming a plane surface.

Remove External Boundaries

This button enables you to remove external boundaries from the surface and create a surface by ignoring them. The resulting surface will be a surface with length and width equal to the maximum length and width of the original surface. For example, a surface having a cut at the corner, when selected to copy, results in a plane surface having four corners. Figure 13-33 shows a surface that is irregular at its boundary and Figure 13-34 shows the surface created by removing the boundary.

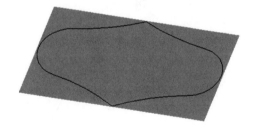

Figure 13-33 Irregular boundary surface

Figure 13-34 Surface created after removing the boundary

CREATING A BLUEDOT

Toolbar: Surfacing > BlueDot

 The **BlueDot** tool is provided by Solid Edge to help you connect two curves. These curves can only be joined by selecting their keypoints. Figure 13-35 shows a table that lists the entities and their keypoints are used to create the BlueDot. Figure 13-36 shows two splines connected using the keypoints.

When you choose the **BlueDot** button from the **Surfacing** toolbar, you will be prompted to

Entity	Keypoints to Create BlueDot
Line	Endpoints
Arc	Endpoints
Spline	Control points
Circle	None
Ellipses	None

Figure 13-35 Table specifying the keypoints of the entities that can be used to create the BlueDot

select a curve, end of sketch, or keypoint curve. Select the two curves that do not intersect in the drawing area.

After the two curves are joined, you can create a surface using them. One curve acts as a cross-section and the other as a guide curve. Figure 13-37 shows the surface formed by the **BlueDot** tool.

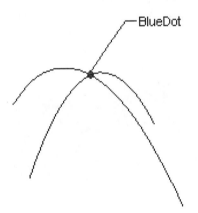

Figure 13-36 BlueDot on splines

*Figure 13-37 Surface created after joining the two curves using the **BlueDot** tool*

Note
The curves shown in Figure 13-36 are splines, therefore, they are connected using control points.

*The **BlueDot** does not appear in the **EdgeBar**.*

*The **BlueDot** cannot be added to a fully constrained sketch.*

CREATING A CURVE AT THE INTERSECTION OF TWO SURFACES

Toolbar: Surfacing > Intersection Curve

The **Intersection Curve** tool is used to create a curve at the intersection of two surfaces. When you choose this button, you will be prompted to click on a body to define set 1 and then click on the other body to define set 2. After specifying the two sets, the curve is created at the intersection of the two surfaces. Figure 13-38 shows the two surfaces that are used to create the intersect.

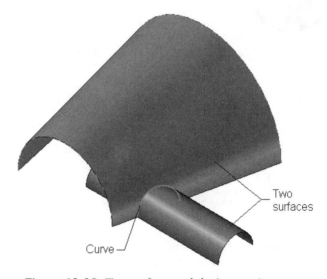

Two surfaces

Curve

Figure 13-38 Two surfaces and the intersection curve

TRIMMING SURFACES

Toolbar: Surfacing > Trim Surface

The **Trim Surface** tool is used to trim surfaces using surfaces, sketches, or reference planes. On choosing this button, you will be prompted to select the surface to trim. After selecting the surface, you will be prompted to select the curve that will be used to trim the surface. Remember that this curve should lie on the surface selected to be trimmed.

Figure 13-39 shows the surface selected to be trimmed. After selecting the surface, you will be prompted to specify the side of the surface you need to trim. Click in the direction indicated by the red arrow to select the direction. Figure 13-40 shows the trimmed surface.

EXTENDING SURFACES

Toolbar: Surfacing > Trim Surface > Extend

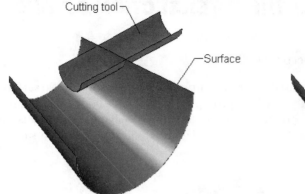

Figure 13-39 *Trimming surface using surface*   **Figure 13-40** *Trimmed surface*

The **Extend Surface** tool is used to extend the selected surface. When you choose this button, you will be prompted to select a sketch or curve chain. Select the edge from where the surface will be extended. Accept the selection and then specify the distance to extend the surface.

In the **Extent Step**, you are provided with three options that can be used to extend the surface. These options are discussed next.

Natural Extent

The surface extension also depends on whether the surface selected to be extended is created using the analytic element or the spline curve. The analytic element is an arc because the arc has only two points and cannot be modified to obtain different shapes. Whereas, the spline has control points that can be used to modify the shape of the surface.

The **Natural Extent** button is chosen by default. Figures 13-41 and 13-42 show the surface

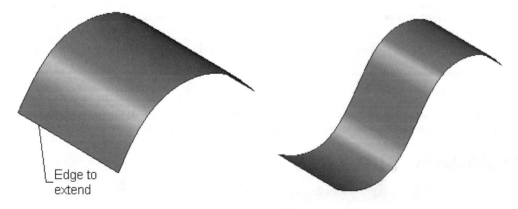

Figure 13-41 *Surface to extend*   **Figure 13-42** *Naturally extended surface*

extension obtained when a surface created using the analytic element was selected to be extended. Figure 13-41 shows the surface that is created using the spline. The resulting shape on extending the surface is shown in Figure 13-42.

Linear Extent

 This button is chosen to extend the selected surface linearly, as shown in Figures 13-43 and 13-44.

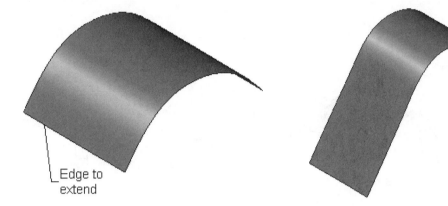

Edge to extend

Figure 13-43 Surface to extend

Figure 13-44 Surface after extending

Reflective Extent

 This button is chosen to extend the selected surface as its own reflection, as shown in Figures 13-45 and 13-46.

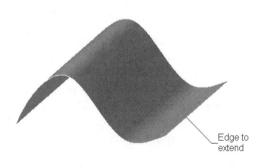

Edge to extend

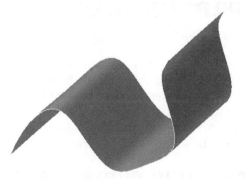

Figure 13-45 Edge of the surface selected to extend

Figure 13-46 Extended surface

REPLACING FACES OF A PART WITH A SURFACE

Toolbar: Surfacing > Replace Face

In Solid Edge, you can replace one or more faces of the solid model with a surface. To do so, the surface that is selected to replace the face should intersect the face. Figure 13-47 shows the faces of the part that are selected to be replaced with the surface. The model, after replacing its faces with a surface, is shown in Figure 13-48.

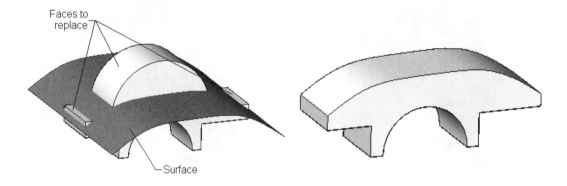

Figure 13-47 *Faces to replace*   *Figure 13-48* *Model after replacing the faces*

On choosing the **Replace Face** button from the **Surfacing** toolbar, the ribbon bar will be displayed and you will be prompted to select the faces you need to replace. After selecting the faces, you will be prompted to select the replacement surface. Remember that after the faces are replaced, the replacement surface will be automatically hidden.

SPLITTING FACES

Toolbar: Surfacing > Trim Surface > Split Face

The **Split Face** tool is used to split the surface using surfaces, edges, or curves. On invoking this tool, the **Select Surface Step** button will be activated and you will be prompted to select a single face. Select the surface to be split from the drawing area and right-click to accept the surface; the **Select Splitting Geometry** button will be activated. Next, select one or more surfaces that intersect the surface you want to split. Figure 13-49 shows the surfaces to be selected and Figure 13-50 shows the split surface.

CREATING CURVES IN 3D BY SELECTING KEYPOINTS

Toolbar: Surfacing > Keypoint Curve

The **Keypoint Curve** tool is used to create 3D curves by joining keypoints on an existing geometry. You can also use this tool to create a curve by selecting the existing points. On choosing this button, you will be prompted to select a keypoint. Select the required keypoints. After you accept the keypoints, you can choose the **End Conditions Step**

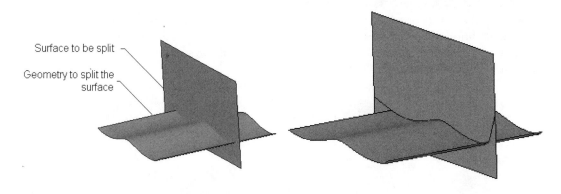

Figure 13-49 *Surfaces selected to split*   **Figure 13-50** *Split surface*

button to set the end conditions for the curve. The options available in various steps required to create this type of curve are discussed next.

Select Points Step

This button is chosen by default when you invoke the **Keypoint Curve** tool. The options in this step are discussed next.

Keypoints

If you choose this button, a flyout will be displayed that you can use to specify the type of keypoints to be selected.

Relative/Absolute Position

This is a toggle button and is used to specify whether you want to use the relative or absolute positioning of points.

Redefine Point

When you choose this button, you will be prompted to click on the point to redefine the location of an existing point. Click on the point and then click on a keypoint or in space. You can also enter the X, Y, and Z values in the corresponding edit boxes.

End Conditions Step

This button can be chosen after you accept the selected points to create a curve. The options in this step are discussed next.

Open

The **Open** button is chosen by default. When you select the keypoints with this button chosen, an open curve will be created.

Closed

The **Closed** button is chosen to create a closed curve. When you choose this button, the first keypoint will be joined with the last keypoint.

Start and End Drop-down Lists

These drop-down lists provide the options to set the end conditions of the curve. You can set the end conditions to be **Natural** or **Tangent**. Figure 13-51 shows a keypoint curve with the **Tangent** end condition at the start and end. Figure 13-52 shows the curve created with the start and end conditions set to **Natural**.

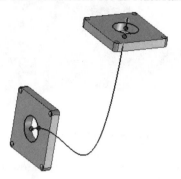

Figure 13-51 *Keypoints selected to create a curve*

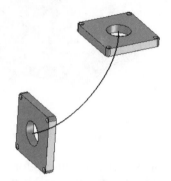

Figure 13-52 *Swept curve created*

CREATING CURVES BY TABLE

Toolbar: Surfacing > Keypoint Curve > Curve by Table

In Solid Edge, you can enter the X, Y, and Z coordinates in an MS Excel sheet and create a curve. When you choose the **Curve by Table** button from the **Surfacing** toolbar, the **Insert Object** dialog box will be displayed, as shown in Figure 13-53. You can select an existing excel file for an input to draw the curve or create a new file.

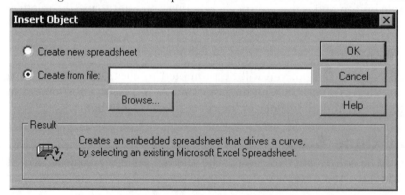

Figure 13-53 *The **Insert Object** dialog box*

When you select the **Create new spreadsheet** radio button and choose **OK**, the excel file will be opened. Enter the coordinate values in this file. Some important points related to entering the coordinates in this file are listed next.

1. The X, Y, and Z values should lie under the columns A, B, and C. Any data entered outside these columns cannot be read by Solid Edge.

2. Any cell that is blank or contains a non-numeric data will not be read by Solid Edge.

After entering the coordinate values, choose the **Close and Return** option from the **File** menu in MS Excel. You can also save the excel file to open it later, if needed.

PROJECTING CURVES ON SURFACES

Toolbar: Surfacing > Project Curve

The **Project Curve** tool is used to project curves on planar or nonplanar surfaces. When you choose this button, the ribbon bar will be displayed. Choose the **Project Curve Options** button from the ribbon bar to display the **Project Curve Options** dialog box. There are two options available in this dialog box to project curve: **Along vector** and **Normal to selected surface**. These options are discussed next.

Along vector Option

This option projects the curve in the direction of a vector that defines the normal of the plane on which the curve is sketched. If the receiving surface is inclined or nonplanar, the size of the projected curve will be different from the original curve. But, when you view the projected curve from the plane on which it was originally lying, the original and the projected curves will appear to be overlapping, see Figure 13-54. Figure 13-55 shows the sketched curve after projecting on the receiving surface. Note that the original curve is drawn on the plane that is parallel to the bottom face of the model.

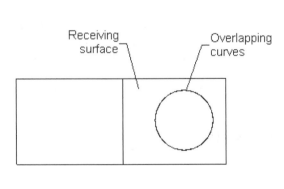

Figure 13-54 Top view of projected curve

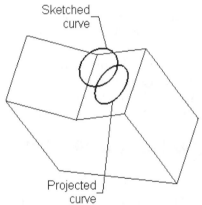

Figure 13-55 Projecting a curve

Normal to selected surface Option

This option projects the curve normal to the receiving surface. Figure 13-56 shows the curve that is selected to be projected on the receiving surface and the curve after projection. Notice that the geometry changes when viewed from the top view. Figure 13-57 shows an alternate view of the sketched curve, after projecting it on the receiving surface.

After you exit the **Project Curve Options** dialog box or when you choose the **Project Curve** option, you will be prompted to select the curve to be projected. Select the curves and then

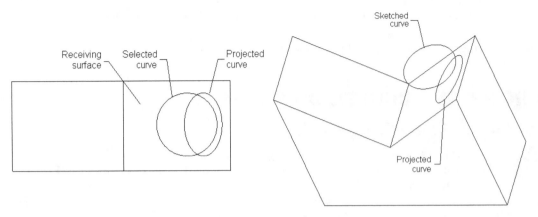

Figure 13-56 *Top view of the curve to be projected*   **Figure 13-57** *Projecting a curve*

accept their selection. Next, select a surface or face on which you need to project the curve. The curve will be projected on to the surface.

CREATING A CURVE AT THE PROJECTION OF TWO CURVES

Toolbar:	Surfacing > Project Curve > Cross Curve

The **Cross Curve** tool is used to create a 3D curve by projecting two 2D curves on each other. This tool projects imaginary lines from both 2D curves in the direction normal to the sketching planes of the 2D curves. All intersecting points are joined to get the resulting 3D curve. When you choose this button, you will be prompted to select a curve. You can select an existing curve or draw a curve. After selecting or drawing the first curve, you will be prompted to select the second curve. Select or draw the second curve to create the resulting 3D curve, as shown in Figure 13-58.

DRAWING A CURVE ON A SURFACE

Toolbar:	Surfacing > Contour Curve

The **Contour Curve** tool is used to draw a curve on the selected face. The curve is drawn by creating points on the surface. These points can be existing points such as edges, vertices, and so on, or imaginary points. The face can be planar or nonplanar. When you choose this button, you will be prompted to select a face on which you will select the points. Select the face and then select the points on it. You can use the **Open** and **Close** buttons on the ribbon bar to specify the type of curve. The curve on the surface is used to trim the surface.

Figure 13-59 shows the curve that was created on the surface and Figure 13-60 shows the spherical surface that is trimmed using the curve.

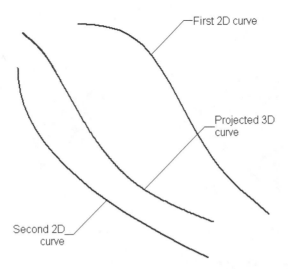

Figure 13-58 *Curve projected at the intersection of two curves*

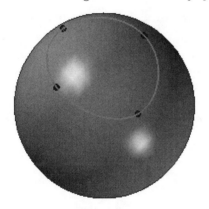

Figure 13-59 *Curve created on the surface*   **Figure 13-60** *Surface trimmed using the curve*

DERIVING CURVES

Toolbar:	Surfacing > Derived

The **Derived Curve** tool is used to derive a curve from the existing edge of a surface, solid, or an existing sketch. When you choose this button, you will be prompted to select one or more curves or edges. After selecting the curves or edges, choose the **Accept** button; the curve will be derived from the edges or curves you chose.

An application of the derived curve is shown in Figures 13-61 and 13-62. The outer edge of a rectangular box is used to create a derived curve. Then, a sweep is created along the derived curve.

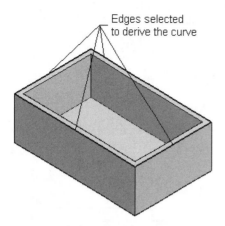

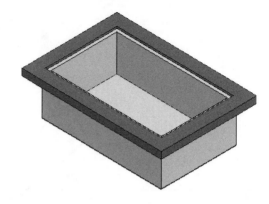

Figure 13-61 *Edges selected to derive the curve*   *Figure 13-62* *Sweep created using the derived curve*

SPLITTING A CURVE

Toolbar:	Surfacing > Derived Curve > Split Curve

The **Split Curve** tool is used to split a curve using an intersecting entity, such as a reference plane, keypoint, curve, and so on. When you choose this button, you will be prompted to select a curve that you need to split. You can select more than one curve to split. After selecting and accepting the curve to split, you will be prompted to select an axis, plane, keypoint, or a body. This entity will be used to split the curve. You can also use the options available in the **Select** drop-down list to select the elements for splitting the curve.

SPLITTING A BODY

Toolbar:	Surfacing > Divide Part

In Solid Edge, you can split a body using a surface or a plane and save the split files as separate part files. This tool can be used to create sections, a model of punch and die for sheet metal components, molds, and so on. This tool is available only when a solid feature exists on the screen and can be used only if the current file is saved.

To split a body, choose the **Divide Part** button from the **Surfacing** toolbar; you will be prompted to select a surface or a plane to divide the part. After you select a surface or a plane, a red arrow will be displayed and you will be prompted to click on the side to be divided into the new file. After you select the direction, choose the **Finish** button to display the **Divide Part** dialog box, as shown in Figure 13-63. The body that you divide is saved in two separate files. Click in one of the cells under the **Filename** column of the dialog box to enter the name of the new file with one of the split portions. After naming the two files, choose the **Save Selected Files** button to save the files.

Figure 13-64 shows the part that is divided into two parts using the surface. The resulting parts are the punch and die that are used to bend a sheet metal, see Figure 13-65.

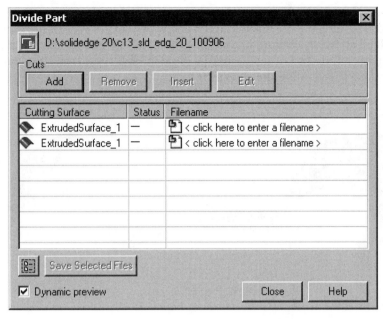

*Figure 13-63 The **Divide Part** dialog box*

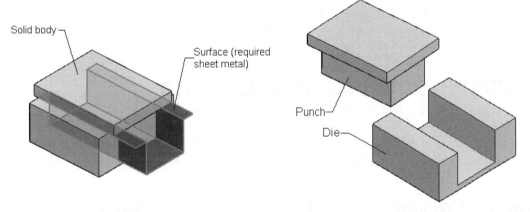

Figure 13-64 Solid body and the surface

Figure 13-65 Punch and die obtained after splitting the body

ADDING THICKNESS TO A SURFACE

Toolbar: Features > Thin Wall > Thicken

  After a surface is created, you can add thickness to it to make it a solid body. Generally, the surfaces that constitute a surface model are stitched together to form a single surface, which is then thickened using the **Thicken** tool.

On choosing the **Thicken** button from the **Features** toolbar, you will be prompted to select a body. After selecting the body, you will be prompted to select the side to which the thickness will be added. The direction is shown by a red arrow. Specify the side of the surface where the thickness will be added by clicking in that direction. You can also specify the thickness in the ribbon bar. Figure 13-66 shows a stitched surface and the side to add thickness and Figure 13-67 shows the surface after adding the thickness to it.

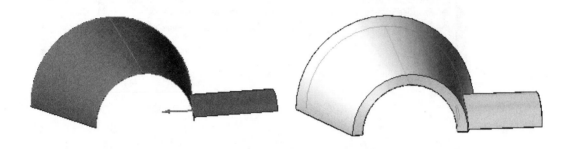

Figure 13-66 *A stitched surface and the side to*   ***Figure 13-67*** *Surface after adding the thickness*
add thickness

Tip. *An easy way of finding out whether a set of surfaces are stitched is to select any of the surfaces. If all surfaces are highlighted in red, this implies that they are stitched and are a single surface.*

CREATING ROUNDS USING BLENDING

In Chapter 6, you learned to create rounds using the **Round** tool available in the **Features** toolbar. In this chapter, you will learn to create rounds by blending two faces of a solid or a surface model. The difference between creating rounds using rounding and blending is that in rounding, you select an edge to create a round and in blending, you need to select two faces.

Creating Rounds on Solids Using the Blend Option

You can use the **Blend** option to create rounds on solid faces only. When you invoke the **Round** tool from the **Features** toolbar, the **Round** ribbon bar will be displayed. Choose the **Round Options** button from the ribbon bar to display the **Round Options** dialog box. Select the **Blend** radio button and exit the dialog box; you will be prompted to select faces. Select the two faces and specify the radius value in the Radius dimension box. Right-click to confirm the selection; the **Overflow Step** will be automatically invoked. The **Roll Along/Across** button is chosen by default in the ribbon bar and you are prompted to select an edge. The other button that is on the ribbon bar is the **Tangent Hold Line** button. These two options of creating the rounds are discussed next.

Roll Along/Across

 The **Roll Along/Across** button creates a rounded blend on any edge it encounters. When you choose this button to create a round, you will be prompted to select an edge. Select the edge, as shown in Figure 13-68; the blend round of the specified radius will be created, as shown in Figure 13-69. Remember that while creating a round blend using this option, it is necessary to specify the radius value.

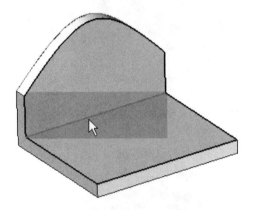   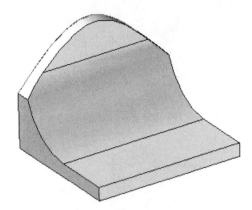

Figure 13-68 *Edge to be selected*   *Figure 13-69* *Blend round rolled across the edges*

Tangent Hold Line

 This option enables you to select the edges that will act as a hold line to control the blending. When you choose this button, you will be provided with two more options for defining the blending of the round. The function of these two buttons is explained next.

Default Radius

 This option enables you to create a blending between the tangent hold lines by maintaining the radius value. When you choose this button, you will be prompted to select an edge chain. Select the edges, as shown in Figure 13-70, and right-click to accept the selection; the blend round will be created, as shown in Figure 13-71.

Full Radius

 This option creates a full blending between the tangent hold lines. This means that the round is created using the tangent hold lines and the tangency between the faces is maintained. Figure 13-72 shows the edges selected as the tangent hold line and Figure 13-73 shows the round created.

Note
*If you do not specify the radius value in the **Select Step**, there will be no difference between the two fillets discussed above.*

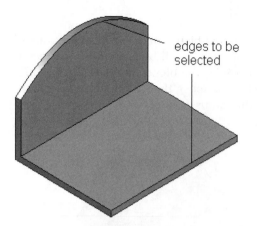

Figure 13-70 *Edges to be selected*

Figure 13-71 *Blend round between tangent hold lines with default radius*

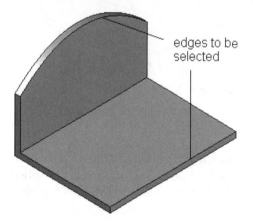

Figure 13-72 *Edges to be selected*

Figure 13-73 *Blend round between tangent hold lines with full radius*

Creating Rounds Using the Surface blend Option

You can use the **Surface blend** option to create rounds on the surfaces only. This option uses certain blend parameters that will be displayed when you choose the **Surface Blend Parameters** button from the ribbon bar. The **Surface Blend Parameters** dialog box will be displayed, as shown in Figure 13-74. The options in this dialog box are discussed next.

Figure 13-74 *The **Surface Blend Parameters** dialog box*

The **Trim and stitch input faces** check box, when selected, stitches the blend surface with the existing faces. Figure 13-75 shows the blend surface round created after clearing the check box and Figure 13-76 shows the blend surface round created with this check box selected.

Figure 13-75 *With the check box cleared*   *Figure 13-76* *With the check box selected*

The **Trim output blend** check box, when selected, trims the surface blend with the faces. Figure 13-77 shows the surface blend created when only the **Trim output blend** check box is selected. Figure 13-78 shows the surface blend round created when the check box is cleared.

Figure 13-77 *With the check box selected*   *Figure 13-78* *With the check box cleared*

Figure 13-79 shows the blend surface round, when both the check boxes in the **Surface Blend Parameters** dialog box are selected.

Roll Along/Across

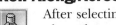 After selecting the faces to round, you are prompted to specify the side of the face where the round will be created. The **Roll Along/Across** button is chosen by default. The function of this button is the same as that discussed in the **Blend** option for creating rounds.

Tangent Hold Line

 This option of creating the surface blend rounds works in the same way as discussed in the **Blend** option for creating rounds. Figure 13-80 shows the surface blend round created using the **Default Radius** option and Figure 13-81 shows the surface

Figure 13-79 *A rounded surface*

blend round created using the **Full Radius** option. In both these cases, the tangent hold lines are the same as those selected in Figures 13-70 and 13-72.

Figure 13-80 *Surface blend round created using the* ***Default Radius*** *option*

Figure 13-81 *Surface blend round created using the* ***Full Radius*** *option*

Specifying the Blend Shape

You can also specify the shape of the blended rounds before creating them using the options available in the **Shape** drop-down list, see Figure 13-82. These options are discussed next.

Constant radius

This option uses a constant radius to create a round and is similar to creating simple rounds.

Constant width

This option creates a blend of circular cross section with a constant chord width between two selected faces.

Chamfer

The **Chamfer** option enables you to create a chamfer on two surfaces. Figure 13-83 shows the chamfer on the surfaces.

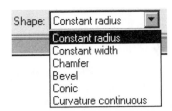

Figure 13-82 *Selecting the blend shape from the **Shape** drop-down list*

Bevel

This option creates a bevel surface between the two selected faces. When you select this option, the **Setback** and the **Value** dimension boxes will be displayed. The **Value** dimension box by default contains a value 1. This means that a bevel of 45-degrees will be created. If you enter the value 2 in this dimension box, the resulting bevel will remove an area equal to half of the dimension value you specify in the **Setback** dimension box from the face you select first. Figure 13-84 shows a bevel surface created with a dimension of 2 entered in the **Value** dimension box.

Figure 13-83 *Surface blend created using the **Chamfer** option*

Figure 13-84 *Surface blend created using the **Bevel** option*

Conic

This option uses a conic cross-section to create a surface blend. When you select this option, the **Radius** and **Value** dimension boxes will be displayed in the ribbon bar. The value in the **Radius** dimension box determines the width of the cross-section and the value in the **Value** dimension box changes the cross-section shape.

Curvature continuous

When you select this option, the **Radius** and **Value** dimension boxes will be displayed. This option enables you to vary the softness of the surface blend along the radius of the blend.

ADDING A DRAFT

Toolbar: Features > Add Draft

 In earlier chapters, you learned to add a draft angle using some of the options. In this section, you will learn to add a split draft and step draft angles using the **From parting surface** and **From parting line** options.

To add a draft, choose the **Add Draft** button from the **Features** toolbar. Next, choose the **Draft Options** button; the **Draft Options** dialog box will be displayed. The remaining options in this dialog box are discussed next.

From parting surface Option

This option enables you to select a parting geometry that acts as a pivot location about which the draft is added to the faces. To add a draft using this option, select the **From parting surface** option from the **Draft Options** dialog box. Then, select the plane that is perpendicular to the faces to be drafted; you will be prompted to select the parting surface. Select the construction surface, as shown in Figure 13-85. Right-click to accept the selection and choose the **Next** button from the ribbon bar; you will be prompted to select the faces to be added to the draft. Select the faces and then enter the draft angle value in the **Draft Angle** edit box.

Choose the **Next** button and specify the direction where the draft is needed; the draft will be added, as shown in Figure 13-86. This figure shows the four vertical faces that are selected to add the draft.

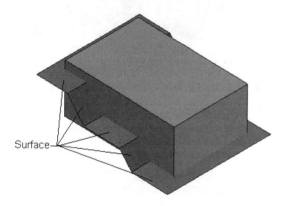

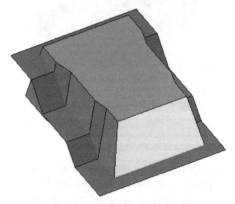

Figure 13-85 *Construction surface*

Figure 13-86 *Draft added to the faces*

 Note
The first plane or the face you select to add the draft is also called as neutral plane.

After the draft is added to the selected faces in Figure 13-86, the single face is divided into five faces. This is because of the geometry of the construction surface that was used as the parting surface.

Split draft

The **Split draft** option available in the **Draft Options** dialog box is used to split the selected face into two faces using the split surface so that different draft angles can be applied to both the faces. The parting surface acts as a hinge about which the draft angles will be added. Figure 13-87 shows the construction surface that is used as a parting surface. The parting surface splits the selected faces and two different draft angles are added to them, as shown in Figure 13-88.

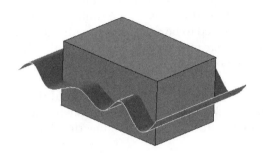

Figure 13-87 Construction surface   *Figure 13-88 Draft added to the faces*

From parting line Option

This option enables you to select a construction curve that acts as a pivot location about which the draft is added to the faces.

To add a draft by using a parting line, select the **From parting line** radio button from the **Draft Options** dialog box. The method of adding the draft angle is the same as followed earlier while using the **From parting surface** option. Figure 13-89 shows the curve and the face selected to add the draft and Figure 13-90 shows the draft added to the faces.

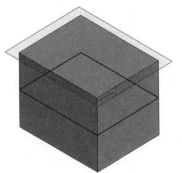

Figure 13-89 Curve and the face selected to add the draft

Figure 13-90 Draft added to the faces

Split draft

As discussed earlier, the **Split Draft** option enables you to specify two different draft angles on the selected faces. The parting line acts as a pivot about which the draft is added. The parting line can be created by projecting a curve on the faces or by creating an intersection curve on the faces.

Step draft

The **Step draft** option will be available in the **Draft Options** dialog box when you select the **From parting line** radio button. This option is used to add a step to the draft created. The step faces can be added perpendicular to the face selected to be drafted or tapered along the draft. This can be done by selecting the **Perpendicular step faces** check box or the **Taper step faces** check box from the **Draft Options** dialog box.

Figure 13-91 shows the neutral plane, the curve that is projected on the face, and the face selected to be drafted. Figure 13-92 shows the step draft added perpendicular to the face selected to be drafted. The front view is also shown in this figure to show the difference between the two options of the step draft.

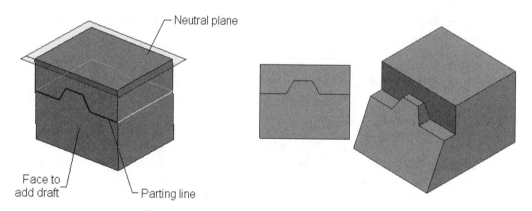

Figure 13-91 *Parting line, neutral plane, and the face selected to add a draft*

Figure 13-92 *Draft added to the faces using the* **Perpendicular step faces** *option*

Figure 13-93 shows the tapered step draft added. The front view is also shown in this figure to show the difference between the two options of the step draft. Figure 13-94 shows a split line draft created on the cylindrical face.

USING THE PARTING SPLIT TOOL

Toolbar:	Surfacing > Parting Split

The **Parting Split** tool enables you to split the selected faces along a silhouette edge. Note that parting edges cannot be created on the planar faces. To create a parting edge, choose the **Parting Split** button; you will be prompted to select a reference plane or a face. Select a reference plane or a face to split the faces, as shown in Figure 13-95. Now, you will be prompted to select a face. Select all the faces of the part, except the two end faces. The parting edge is created, as shown in Figure 13-96. You can check that the selected faces are divided by the parting edge.

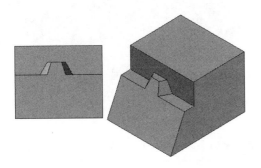

Figure 13-93 *Draft added to the faces using the* **Taper step faces** *option*

Figure 13-94 *Draft added using the split line*

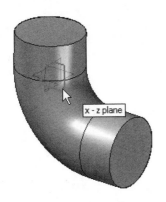

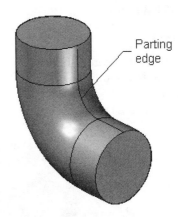

Figure 13-95 *Reference plane selected*

Figure 13-96 *Parting edge created*

USING THE PARTING SURFACE TOOL

Toolbar:	Surfacing > Parting Split > Parting Surface

The parting surface is used for creating molds, core, and cavity. The **Parting Surface** tool enables you to create a parting surface from a parting edge or from an edge chain. When you choose this button, you will be prompted to select a face or a reference plane to which the parting surface will be parallel. Then, you will be prompted to select an edge, sketch, or a curve chain. Select the curve chain; you will be prompted to specify the extent and direction of the parting surface. Figure 13-97 shows the parting surface created after selecting the parting edge shown in Figure 13-96. Figure 13-98 shows the parting surface created by selecting the edge chain.

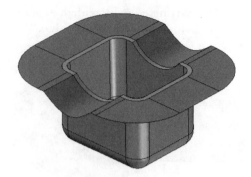

Figure 13-97 *Parting surface created using the parting edge*

Figure 13-98 *Parting surface created using the edge chain*

TUTORIALS

Tutorial 1

In this tutorial, you will create the surface model shown in Figure 13-99. Its orthographic views are shown in Figure 13-100. After creating the model, save it with the name and location given below:

> *Solid Edge\c13\c13tut1.par*   **(Expected time: 30 min)**

Figure 13-99 *Isometric view of the surface model*

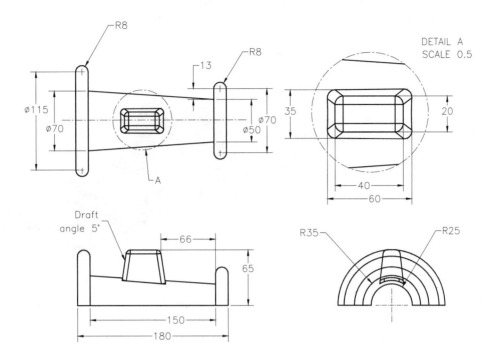

Figure 13-100 *Top, front, right-side, and the detailed views of the surface model*

The following steps are required to create this model:

a. The base feature is a revolved surface, see Figure 13-102.
b. The second feature is an extruded surface that will be created on a plane parallel to the top plane and at a distance of 65. A draft angle will also be applied to this surface, see Figure 13-104.
c. The third feature is the trim feature that will trim the bottom part of the extruded surface, see Figure 13-105.
d. The fourth feature is also a trim feature that will trim the bottom surface of the revolved surface, see Figure 13-106.
e. The fifth feature is the stitch feature that will stitch the revolved surface and the extruded surface.
f. The sixth feature is the round feature that will be created on the edges of the extruded surface, see Figure 13-107.

Creating the Base Feature

The base feature is the revolved surface whose profile is drawn on the top plane.

1. Open a new file in the **Part** environment and choose the **Revolved Surface** button from the **Extruded Surface** flyout in the **Surfacing** toolbar; you are prompted to select a plane. Select the top plane.

2. Draw the profile for the revolved feature and apply the relations and dimensions, as shown in Figure 13-101.

3. Revolve the sketch through 180-degrees to create the revolved surface, as shown in Figure 13-102.

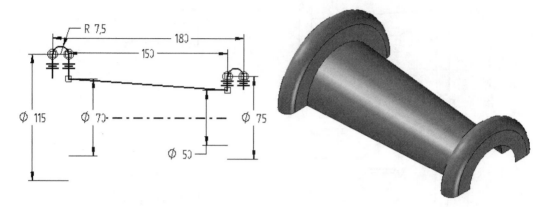

Figure 13-101 Sketch of the base feature   *Figure 13-102 Revolved surface*

4. Exit the **Revolve** tool.

Creating the Second Feature

The second feature is the extruded surface whose sketch will be drawn at an offset plane parallel to the top plane.

1. Choose the **Extruded Surface** button from the **Features** toolbar; you are prompted to select a plane.

2. Create a parallel plane at an offset of 65 from the top plane and select it as a sketching plane.

3. Draw the sketch, as shown in Figure 13-103.

4. Exit the sketching environment.

5. Specify the depth of extrusion such that the surface is extruded up to the bottom edge of the base feature. Also, choose the **Close Ends** button in the ribbon bar, if it is not already chosen.

6. Choose the **Treatment Step** button from the ribbon bar and then choose the **Draft** button.

7. Enter **5** as the value in the **Angle** edit box and choose the **Flip 2** button.

8. Choose the **Preview** button from the ribbon bar; the extruded surface with a draft is created, as shown in Figure 13-104.

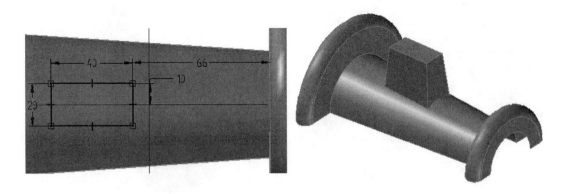

Figure 13-103 *Sketch with dimensions*   *Figure 13-104* *Extruded surface with the draft*

Trimming the Extruded Surface

1. Choose the **Trim Surface** button from the **Surfacing** toolbar; you are prompted to select a body.

2. Select **Single** from the **Select** drop-down list. Now, select the four vertical faces and the bottom face of the extruded surface. Right-click to accept; you are prompted to select a curve, face on a surface, or a plane to trim along.

3. Select the middle portion of the revolved surface and right-click to accept.

4. After selecting the surface, you are prompted to select the side of the surface that needs to be trimmed. This direction is shown by a red arrow. Click on the screen when the arrow points downward.

    The extruded surface is trimmed, as shown in Figure 13-105. You will notice that the extruded surface is closed from the bottom. Therefore, you need to remove the bottom end surface of the revolved surface.

5. Choose the **Trim Surface** button, if it is not already chosen and select the revolved surface.

6. Select the four faces of the extruded surface; a red arrow is displayed.

7. Click on the screen when the arrow points toward the surface that needs to be removed; the bottom of the extruded surface that was covered with the revolved surface is removed, as shown in Figure 13-106. Exit the **Trim** tool.

Stitching the Two Surfaces

It is necessary to stitch the two surfaces before creating the round. If the two surfaces are not stitched, the resulting round will have gaps, as shown in Figure 13-107. This figure shows that the two surfaces were not stitched, therefore the edge of the BlueSurface is rounded without involving the revolved surface.

Figure 13-105 *Extruded surface after trimming*   *Figure 13-106* *The trimmed bottom surface*

1. Choose the **Stitched Surface** button from the **Surfacing** toolbar; the **Stitched Surface Options** dialog box is displayed. Make sure that the value of 1.00e+000 mm is displayed in the **Stitch tolerance** edit box.

2. Choose **OK** and exit the dialog box; you are prompted to select the surfaces.

3. Select the revolved surface and the drafted extruded surface. Choose the **Accept** button from the ribbon bar; the two surfaces are stitched.

Creating a Round

1. Choose the **Round** button from the **Features** toolbar; you are prompted to select the edges to round.

Figure 13-107 *Gaps after creating rounds and before stitching the surfaces*

2. Select the four vertical edges and the four edges of the top face of the extruded surface. Enter **5** in the **Radius** edit box.

3. Choose the **Accept** button from the ribbon bar; the round is created, as shown in Figure 13-108.

4. Save the model with the name *c13tut1.par.*

Figure 13-108 *Final surface model*

Tutorial 2

In this tutorial, you will create the surface model shown in Figure 13-109. Its orthographic views are shown in Figure 13-110. After creating the model, save it with the name and location given below:

\Solid Edge\c13\c13tut2.par   **(Expected time: 45 min)**

Figure 13-109 *Surface model*

The following steps are required to create this model:

a. First, examine the model and determine the number of features in it. You will notice that the model is composed of 15 features.

b. The base feature is an extruded surface that will be created on the right plane, see Figure 13-112.

c. The second and third features are sketches that will be used to create the fourth feature. The fourth feature is the BlueSurface that is used to connect the two sketches, see Figures 13-113 and 13-114.

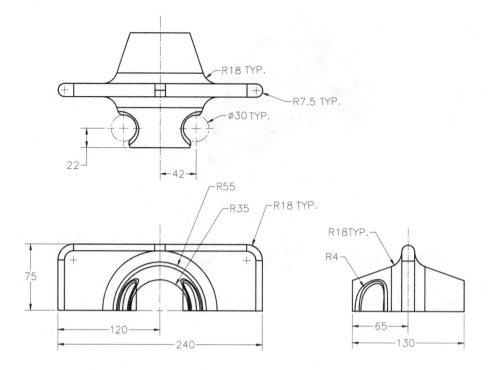

Figure 13-110 Top, front, right side, and the isometric views of the surface model

d. The fifth feature is the mirror copy of the BlueSurface, see Figure 13-115.
e. The sixth feature is the BlueSurface that is used to cap the end of the extruded surface, see Figure 13-116. The seventh feature is the mirror copy of the BlueSurface.
f. The eighth feature is the extruded cylinder with open ends, see Figure 13-118. This cylindrical surface will be used to create the cut in the BlueSurface created earlier. The ninth and tenth features are the trim features, see Figures 13-119 and 13-120.
g. The eleventh feature is the mirror copy of the trimmed feature (tenth feature).
h. The twelfth feature is the stitch feature that will stitch all the surfaces. The rest of the features are round features, see Figures 13-125 and 13-126.

Creating the Base Feature

The base feature is an extruded surface whose profile is drawn on the right plane.

1. Open a new file in the **Part** environment and choose the **Extruded Surface** button from the **Surfacing** toolbar; you are prompted to select a plane. Select the right plane.

2. Draw the profile for the extruded surface and apply the relationships and dimensions to it, as shown in Figure 13-111.

3. Extrude the sketch symmetrically to a depth of 240 to create the extruded surface, as shown in Figure 13-112.

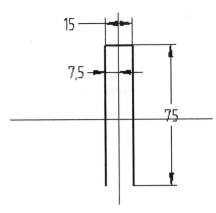

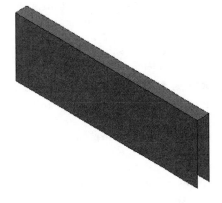

Figure 13-111 Sketch with dimensions

Figure 13-112 Extruded surface

Creating the BlueSurface by Joining Two Sketches

The second feature is the sketch that will be created on the front face of the extrude surface. The third feature is also a sketch that will be created on a parallel plane, which is at an offset distance of 65 mm from the right plane. Then, the BlueSurface is created by joining the two sketches.

1. After drawing the two sketches, as shown in Figure 13-113, choose the **BlueSurf** button from the **Surfacing** toolbar; you are prompted to select a sketch, edge chain, or a curve chain.

2. Select the sketches that were created earlier, refer to Figure 13-113. While selecting the sketches, remember that the keypoints should not overlap.

3. After selecting the sketches, the BlueSurface is created with open ends, as shown in Figure 13-114.

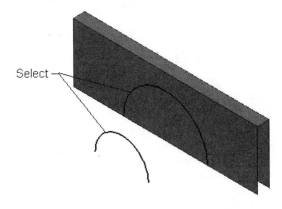

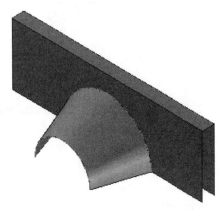

Figure 13-113 Two sketches

Figure 13-114 BlueSurface

4. Choose the **Mirror Copy** button from the **Mirror Copy Features** flyout in the **Features** toolbar; you are prompted to select a surface or a curve.

5. Create the mirror copy of the BlueSurface, as shown in Figure 13-115.

Creating the BlueSurface at the End of the Extruded Surface

This BlueSurface will be created to close the ends of the extruded surface.

1. Choose the **BlueSurf** button from the **Surfacing** toolbar; you are prompted to select a sketch, edge chain, or a curve chain.

2. Select the edge of the surface, as shown in Figure 13-116, as the cross-section and choose the **Accept** button.

3. Choose the **Guide Curve Step** button from the ribbon bar and select the edge, refer to Figure 13-116. Choose the **Accept** button and exit the tool; the surface is created, as shown in Figure 13-116.

4. After creating the BlueSurface, create a mirror copy of it so that the other end of the extruded surface is also closed.

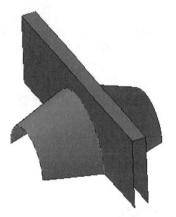

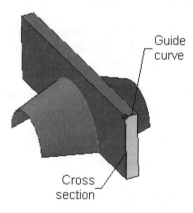

Figure 13-115 *Mirror copy*   *Figure 13-116* *BlueSurface*

Creating the Cut on the BlueSurface

To create the cut on the BlueSurface, you will create a cylindrical surface. Then, this surface will be used to trim the BlueSurface, thus creating the cut.

1. Choose the **Extruded Surface** button and create the cylindrical surface by drawing the sketch on the top plane. To draw the sketch and dimension it, refer to Figure 13-110.

2. Extrude the sketch up to the vertex of the bottom edge of the BlueSurface, see Figure 13-117.

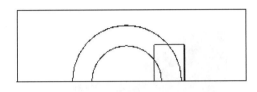

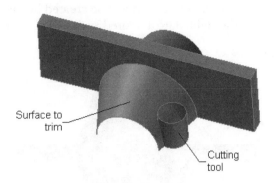

Figure 13-117 Cylindrical surface   *Figure 13-118 Surfaces used for trimming*

 Note

If the sketch that is drawn to create the cylindrical surface is not extruded up to the vertex of the BlueSurface, then you will not be able to trim the surfaces later.

3. After creating the cylindrical surface, choose the **Trim Surface** button from the **Surfacing** toolbar; you are prompted to select a body.

4. Select the BlueSurface; you are prompted to select a curve, face, or a plane that lies on the surface to trim along.

5. Select the cylindrical surface, as shown in Figure 13-118, and choose the **Accept** button from the ribbon bar; you are prompted to select the side of the surface that will be trimmed. This direction is shown by a red arrow.

6. Click on the screen when the arrow points toward the cylinder.

    The BlueSurface is trimmed, as shown in Figure 13-119. You will notice that a part of the cylindrical surface needs to be removed. Therefore, you need to apply another trimming operation.

7. Choose the **Finish** button and select the cylindrical surface. Right-click to accept it.

8. Select the BlueSurface; a red arrow is displayed.

9. Click on the screen when the arrow points upward. The part of the cylindrical surface that was not needed is removed, as shown in Figure 13-120.

Creating the Cut on the Left Side of the BlueSurface

The cut on the left will be created by mirroring the trimmed surface feature created on the right. The mirrored surface will be used to trim the other side of the BlueSurface.

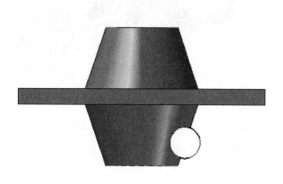

Figure 13-119 *Cylindrical surface from the top view*

Figure 13-120 *Trimmed BlueSurface*

1. Mirror the cut feature to the left side, see Figure 13-121. Choose the **Trim Surface** button; you are prompted to select a body.

2. Select the BlueSurface and right-click; you are prompted to select a curve that lies on the surface to trim along.

3. Select the mirrored surface and choose the **Accept** button from the ribbon bar; you are prompted to select the side of the surface that will be trimmed. This direction is shown by a red arrow.

4. Click on the screen when the arrow points toward the left; the mirrored surface is trimmed, as shown in Figure 13-122.

Trimming the Extruded Surface

To trim the extruded surface, you will use the semicircular edge of the BlueSurface that intersects the extruded surface.

1. Choose the **Trim Surface** button from the **Surfacing** toolbar.

2. Select the extruded surface and then right-click; you are prompted to select a curve, face, or a plane that lies on the surface to trim along.

3. Select the semicircular edge of the BlueSurface that intersects the extruded surface and choose the **Accept** button from the ribbon bar; you are prompted to select the side of the surface that will be trimmed.

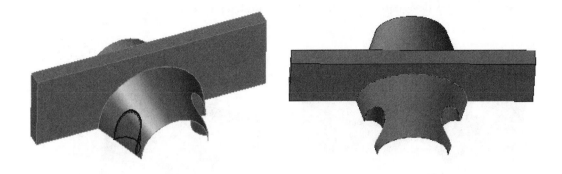

Figure 13-121 *Surface after mirroring*   **Figure 13-122** *Trimmed surface*

4. Click on the screen when the arrow points downward.

5. Similarly, trim the other side of the extruded surface. The model, after trimming the extruded surface, is shown in Figure 13-123.

Stitching the Surfaces

It is necessary to stitch all the surfaces before creating the round.

1. Choose the **Stitched Surface** button from the **Surfacing** toolbar; the **Stitched Surface Options** dialog box is displayed. Make sure that the value of 1.00e+000 mm is displayed in the **Stitch tolerance** edit box.

2. Choose **OK** and exit the dialog box; you are prompted to select the surfaces.

3. Select all the surfaces one by one. Choose the **Accept** button from the ribbon bar; the surfaces are stitched.

Creating a Round

After stitching the surfaces, create the rounds of radii 4 and 18.

1. Choose the **Round** button from the **Features** toolbar; you are prompted to select the edges to round.

2. Select the edges of the trim feature on the BlueSurface designated by 1, see Figure 13-124, and enter **4** in the **Radius** edit box.

3. Choose the **Accept** button from the ribbon bar and then choose the **Preview** button; the round is created, as shown in Figure 13-125.

4. Choose the **Finish** button. Select the two edges designated by 2, as shown in Figure 13-124 and the edges designated by 1 at the front and back face of the extruded surface.

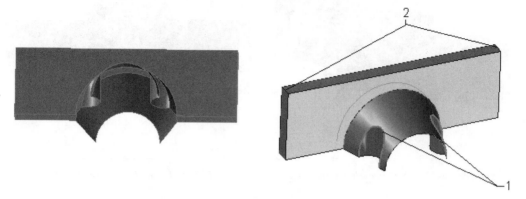

Figure 13-123 Extruded surfaces after trimming   *Figure 13-124* Edges to be selected

5. Enter **18** in the **Radius** edit box and choose the **Accept** button.

6. Choose the **Preview** and then the **Finish** button.

7. Similarly, create the remaining rounds. For dimensions, refer to Figure 13-110. The surface model, after creating all rounds, is shown in Figure 13-126

Figure 13-125 Round of radius 4   *Figure 13-126* Model after creating all rounds

8. Choose the **Save** button to save the model with the name *c13tut2.par*.

Self-Evaluation Test

Answer the following questions and then compare them to those given at the end of this chapter:

1. You can create a surface with closed ends by drawing an open sketch. (T/F)

2. Surface models have no thickness. (T/F)

3. The **BlueSurf** tool has only one function and that is creating surfaces. (T/F)

4. You can trim two surfaces by selecting them individually. (T/F)

5. The _____ tool is used to connect two sketched curves.

6. The _____ button is used to create a curve at the intersection of two surfaces.

7. In Solid Edge, the _____ and _____ methods of extending a surface are available.

8. Remember that after the faces are replaced using the _____ button, the replacement surface is automatically hidden.

9. The _____ button is used to project the curves on the surfaces.

10. The _____ button is available only when a solid feature exists on the screen.

Review Questions

Answer the following questions:

1. What is the range of the stitch tolerance available in the **Stitched Surface** tool?

   (a) **120**   (b) **1.00e+005 to 1.00e-000**
   (c) **1.00e-005 to 1.00e+000**   (d) **1.00e-000 to 1.00e+005**

2. How many tools are available to create a base feature?

   (a) two   (b) three
   (c) one   (d) None of the above

3. Which of the following toolbars is used to create surface models?

   (a) **Surfacing**   (b) **Features**
   (c) **Main**   (d) None of the above

4. Which of the following dialog boxes is used to set the stitch tolerance?

    (a) **Sweep Options**   (b) **Stitched Surface Options**
    (c) **Stitched**   (d) None of the above

5. Before adding thickness to a set of surfaces, they should be _____.

    (a) trimmed   (b) merged
    (c) stitched   (d) None of the above

6. The ends of a surface can be closed using the **BlueSurf** tool. (T/F)

7. The surface models do not have mass properties. (T/F)

8. You can select an open sketch to create a bounded surface using the **Bounded Surface** tool. (T/F)

9. Thickness can be added to a surface. (T/F)

10. To trim a surface, a curve must lie on it. (T/F)

Exercises

Exercise 1

Create the surface model shown in Figure 13-127. Its orthographic views and dimensions are shown in Figure 13-128. After creating the model, save it with the name and location given below:

    Solid Edge\c13\c13exr1.par   **(Expected time: 30 min)**

Figure 13-127 *Surface model*

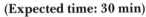
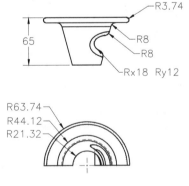

Figure 13-128 *Top and front views*

Exercise 2

Create the surface model shown in Figure 13-129. The orthographic views with the dimensions are also shown in the same figure. After creating the model, save it with the name given below:

Solid Edge\c13\c13exr2.par   **(Expected time: 30 min)**

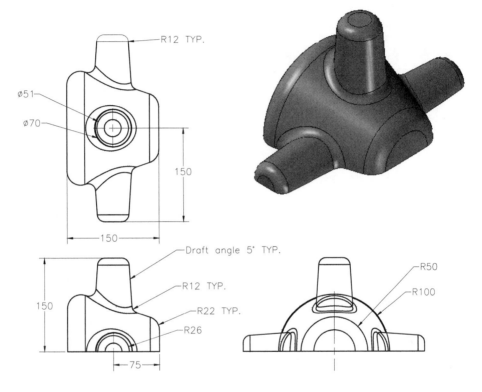

Figure 13-129 Top, front, right side, and the isometric views of the surface model

Answers to Self-Evaluation Test

1. F, **2.** T, **3.** F, **4.** T, **5. BlueDot**, **6. Intersection Curve**, **7.** natural extent and linear extent, **8. Replace Face**, **9. Project Curve 10. Replace Face**

Chapter *14*

Sheet Metal Design

Learning Objectives

After completing this chapter, you will be able to:
- *Set the parameters for creating the sheet metal parts.*
- *Create the base of the sheet metal part.*
- *Add various types of flanges to the sheet metal part.*
- *Add a jog to the sheet metal part.*
- *Bend or unbend a part of the sheet metal part.*
- *Add corner bends to the sheet metal parts.*
- *Create dimples, louvers, drawn cutouts, and beads in the sheet metal component.*
- *Convert solid parts to sheet metal parts.*
- *Create the flat pattern of the sheet metal parts.*

THE SHEET METAL MODULE

The component with a thickness greater than 0 and less than 12 mm is called a sheet metal component. Sheet metal fabrication is a chipless process and is an easy way to create components by using the manufacturing processes such as bending, stamping, and so on.

A sheet metal component of uniform thickness is shown in Figure 14-1. It is not possible to machine such a thin component. Therefore, after creating the sheet metal component, you need to flatten it in order to find the strip layout. Based on this layout detail, you can design the punch and die. Figure 14-2 shows the flattened view of the sheet metal component.

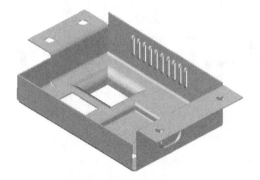

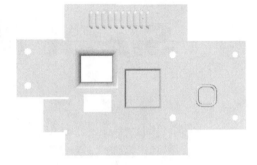

Figure 14-1 *Sheet metal component*   *Figure 14-2* *Flattened view of the sheet metal*
                                                                             component

Note

Not all features of a sheet metal component can be flattened. For example, features such as louvers, dimples, and so on cannot be flattened because they are created using a punch and a die.

Solid Edge allows you to create the sheet metal components in a special environment called the **Sheet Metal** environment, provided specially for the sheet metal components. This environment provides all the tools that are required for creating the sheet metal components.

To start a new document in the **Sheet Metal** environment, choose **Sheet Metal Part** from the **Create** area of the welcome screen, as shown in the Figure 14-3. Alternatively, you can double-click on **Normal.psm** from the **General** tab of the **New** dialog box to start this environment, see Figure 14-4.

On selecting this file, you will proceed to the **Sheet Metal** environment. In the **Sheet Metal** environment, the **Features** toolbar provides the tools required to create the sheet metal components. The default screen is shown in Figure 14-5. Only the **Tab** and **Contour Flange** sheet metal tools are activated in the **Features** toolbar. This is because you have not yet created the base of the sheet metal part. Once you create the base of the sheet metal part using the available tools, the remaining tools will be activated in the **Features** toolbar.

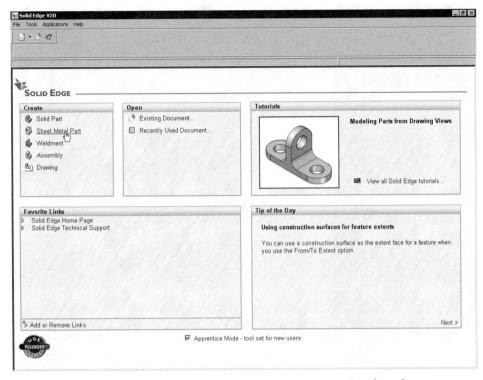

Figure 14-3 *Starting the **Sheet Metal Part** environment using the welcome screen*

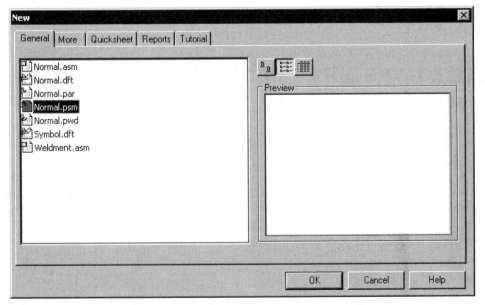

Figure 14-4 *Starting a new sheet metal document*

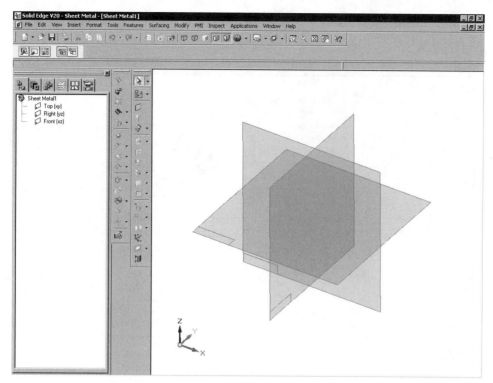

Figure 14-5 *Default screen displayed before creating the base of the sheet metal part*

Note
Sheet metal parts are saved in the *.psm format.

SETTING THE SHEET METAL PART PROPERTIES

Menu bar: Tools > Material Table

Before proceeding with creating the base of the sheet metal part, it is recommended that you set the options related to them. These options control the default values of the sheet thickness, bend radius, relief depth, and relief width that will be displayed in various tools.

To set these options, choose **Tools > Material Table** from the menu bar; the **Solid Edge Material Table** dialog box will be displayed with the **Material** tab chosen. Choose the **Gage** tab to display the parameters related to the sheet metal part, see Figure 14-6. The options available in the **Gage** tab are discussed next.

Sheet metal gage

This drop-down list is used to set the default gage size for the sheet metal part. The other parameters are automatically defined once you set the default sheet gage from this drop-down

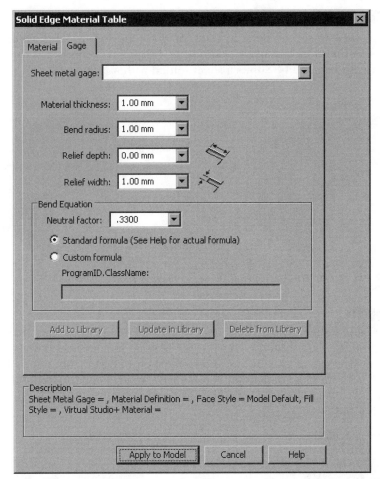

Figure 14-6 The **Gage** tab of the **Solid Edge Material Table** dialog box

list. By default, no gage size is selected. As a result, you can set the custom parameters for the sheet metal part.

Material thickness

This edit box is used to set the default thickness for the sheet metal part. The thickness specified in this edit box will be displayed as the default thickness whenever you invoke a tool to create the sheet metal part.

Note

While creating the sheet metal part, you can modify the default thickness. You do not necessarily need to accept the default sheet thickness.

Bend radius

This edit box is used to set the default value for the bend radius. This value is used while adding flanges to the model or while bending it. Figure 14-7 shows a sheet folded with a radius of 1 mm and Figure 14-8 shows a sheet folded with a radius of 5 mm.

Figure 14-7 *Sheet with 1 mm bend radius*   *Figure 14-8* *Sheet with 5 mm bend radius*

Relief depth

Whenever you bend a sheet metal component or create a flange such that the bend does not extend throughout the length of the edge, a groove is added at the end of the bend so that the walls of the sheet metal part do not intersect when folded or unfolded. This groove is known as relief. You can set a predefined depth for the relief using the **Relief depth** edit box. Figure 14-9 shows a sheet metal part with relief depth of 2 and Figure 14-10 shows a sheet metal part with relief depth of 5.

Figure 14-9 *Relief depth = 2*   *Figure 14-10* *Relief depth = 5*

Relief width

The **Relief width** edit box is used to enter the value of the width of the relief. The default value of the relief width is equal to the thickness of the sheet. You can enter the value of the relief width in this edit box. Figure 14-11 shows a sheet metal component with a relief width of 1 mm and Figure 14-12 shows a sheet metal component with a relief width of 4 mm.

Figure 14-11 *Relief width = 1*   *Figure 14-12* *Relief width = 5*

CREATING THE BASE OF THE SHEET METAL PARTS

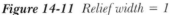

Toolbar: Features > Tab

The **Tab** tool is used to create the base of the sheet metal component. You can also use this tool to add additional faces on the sheet metal component. To create the base of the sheet metal part, invoke this tool; the **Tab** ribbon bar will be displayed and the **Plane or Sketch Step** will be activated. You can draw the sketch for the base or select an existing sketch.

After drawing or selecting the sketch, the **Thickness Step** will be activated and the **Thickness** edit box will be displayed. You can enter the thickness value of the sheet in this edit box. Figure 14-13 shows the sketch for the base and Figure 14-14 shows the base of the sheet metal component.

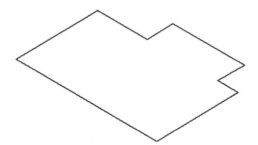

Figure 14-13 *Sketch for the base*   *Figure 14-14* *Base of the sheet metal component*

Note
*If you use the **Tab** tool to create additional faces of the sheet metal part, you cannot use an existing sketch. In this case, you need to sketch the face using the **Plane or Sketch Step** of the* **Tab** *tool.*

ADDING FLANGES TO A SHEET METAL PART

Toolbar:	Features > Flange

Flange is the bend section of the sheet metal. Solid Edge allows you to directly add a folded face to the existing sheet metal part. This is done using the **Flange** tool. When you invoke this tool, the **Flange** ribbon bar will be displayed. It is recommended that before you create the flange, you should set its options. To do so, choose the **Flange Options** button from the ribbon bar; the **Flange Options** dialog box will be displayed, as shown in Figure 14-15.

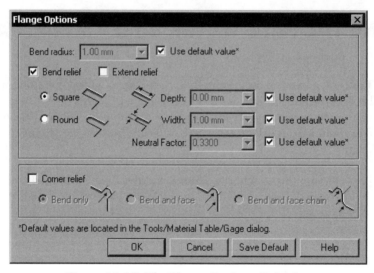

*Figure 14-15 The **Flange Options** dialog box*

Flange Options Dialog Box

The options in the **Flange Options** dialog box are discussed next.

Bend radius

This edit box is used to specify the bend radius. By default, the **Use default value** check box is selected. As a result, the default value that was set using the **Gage** tab of the **Solid Edge Material Table** dialog box will be used as the bend radius. If you want to modify the value, clear the **Use default value** check box and then enter the value in the **Bend radius** edit box.

Bend relief

This edit box is used to specify whether or not the bend relief will be added. If this check box is selected, the other options to add the relief will be activated. You can add a square shape relief or a round shape relief. You can use the default value of the relief depth, width, and neutral factor or enter a new value in the edit boxes. Figure 14-16 shows a sheet metal part with a square relief and Figure 14-17 shows a sheet metal part with a round relief.

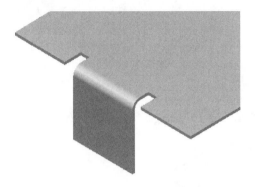

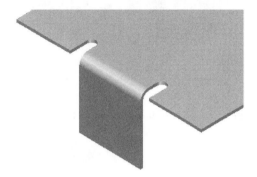

Figure 14-16 *Square relief*   *Figure 14-17* *Round relief*

Extend relief

Select this check box to extend the relief to the entire face of the sheet metal part. By default, this check box is cleared. As a result, the relief is applied only to the portion that is adjacent to the flange that you are creating.

Corner relief

This check box is selected to add a corner relief to the flange. A corner relief is added when the flange termination forms a corner with another flange. By default, this check box is cleared. As a result, no corner relief is added, as shown in Figure 14-18. If you select the **Corner relief** check box, you can add three different types of corner reliefs by selecting their radio buttons. Figure 14-19 shows the bend only corner relief. Note that the corner relief is added to the existing flange and not to the one that you are creating now. Figure 14-20 shows the bend and the face corner relief.

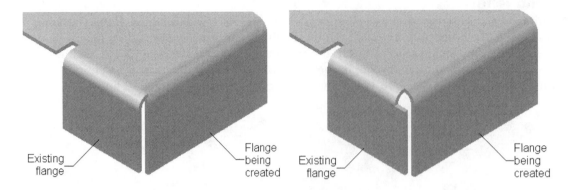

Figure 14-18 *Flanges with no corner relief*   **Figure 14-19** *Flanges with bend only corner relief*

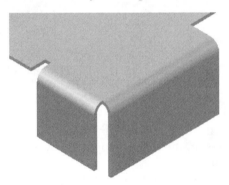

Figure 14-20 *Flanges with bend and face corner relief*

The third type of corner relief is used when the first flange has a chain of faces. In this case, the corner relief is applied to the face chain. Figure 14-21 shows a sheet metal part in which the first flange forms a chain with another flange. In this figure, the bend and face corner relief is added. Figure 14-22 shows the same model after adding the bend and face chain corner relief.

After setting the flange parameters, you can proceed with various steps for creating the flange. These steps are discussed next.

Edge Step
This step is activated by default when you invoke the **Flange** tool. In this step, you need to select the edge to which the flange will be added. As soon as you select the edge, the preview of the flange will be displayed. The size of the flange is changed dynamically as you move the cursor. Also, note that when you select the edge, additional options are displayed in the ribbon bar. Before clicking in the drawing area to place the flange, you can use these options to modify the shape and size of the flange. These options are discussed next.

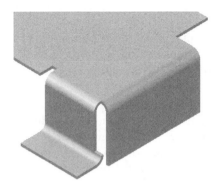 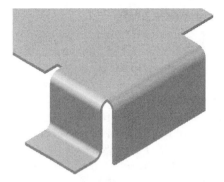

Figure 14-21 *Flanges with bend and face corner relief*

Figure 14-22 *Flanges with bend and face chain corner relief*

Material Inside

 This button is chosen by default and creates the flange such that the material is added inside the profile of the flange. The profile is automatically displayed when you place the flange. This button is chosen by default.

Material Outside

 Choose this button to add the material outside the profile of the flange. You can also choose this button after placing the flange.

Bend Outside

 If this button is chosen, the bend of the flange will be placed outside the profile of the flange.

Full Width

 This button is chosen to create the flange of the width equal to the width of the edge selected to create the flange. This button is chosen by default.

Centered

 Choose this button to create the flange at an equal distance from the center of the flange. After choosing this button, modify the distance of the flange and then click in the drawing area to place it. After you place the flange, its width will be displayed on the screen. You can click on the width value and modify it to the required value.

At End

 Choose this button to create the flange at one of the ends of the selected edge. When you choose this button, you will be prompted to select the desired end of the edge. Select one of the endpoints of the edge; the preview of the flange will be displayed. Click on the screen to place the flange; the width of the flange will be displayed. Click on this value to modify the width of the flange.

From Both Ends

 Choose this button to create the flange at a certain offset from both ends of the selected edge. After you place the flange, its dimensions from both the ends are displayed. You can click on these dimensions to modify their values.

From End

 Choose this button to create the flange at a certain offset from one of the endpoints of the selected edge. When you choose this button, you will be prompted to select the desired end. Select the end and place the flange. After you place the flange, its distance from the selected end and its width will be displayed. You can click on these dimensions to modify their values.

Distance

This edit box is used to specify the distance of the flange. This value is modified dynamically as you move the cursor in the drawing window. This value is also displayed when you place the flange. You can modify the value in the drag window also.

Inside Dimension

 This button is chosen to dimension the distance of the flange from inside the base sheet. This button is chosen by default.

Outside Dimension

 This button is chosen by default to dimension the flange from outside the base sheet.

Angle

This edit box is used to specify the angle of the flange. The default value is 90-degrees. You can enter the desired value in this edit box.

Profile Step

After you place the flange, the button of this step will be activated. You can choose this button to modify the profile of the flange. As soon as you choose this button, the sketching environment is invoked. The default profile is rectangular. If needed, you can remove some of the entities of the profile and add additional sketched entities to create the profile.

Offset Step

This step is used when you want to add some offset between the flange and the edge selected to create it. When you choose this button, the **Distance** edit box will be displayed. As you move the cursor, the value in this edit box is modified .

 Note
When you create a flange at an offset, the bend relief is not added.

CREATING CONTOUR FLANGES

Toolbar: Features > Contour Flange

 Contour flanges are the ones that are created by using an open sketched shape. To create a contour flange, invoke the **Contour Flange** tool; you will be prompted to select the end of an edge at which a normal plane will be placed to create the profile of the contour flange. Select the endpoint of the edge at which you want to place the plane. Next, you will be prompted to select a keypoint or enter the offset distance. Specify the location of the plane. After you specify the location, the sketching environment will be invoked. You can draw the profile of the contour flange using lines and arcs. Note that you cannot use splines in the sketch.

After drawing the open sketch for the contour flange, exit the sketching environment; the **Extent Step** will be invoked and the preview of the contour flange will be displayed. The **Extent Step** is discussed next.

Extent Step

This step is automatically invoked when you exit the sketching environment. The options in this step are discussed next.

Finite Extent

This button is chosen to specify the extent of the contour flange using a distance value. This button is chosen by default. As a result, the **Distance** edit box is displayed in which you can enter the value. If this button is chosen, the **Symmetric Extent** button will be available in the ribbon bar. You can use this button to create a contour flange with the symmetric extent. Figure 14-23 shows the preview of a contour flange being created. This figure also shows the open profile for the contour flange. Figure 14-24 shows the resulting contour flange with the bend relief.

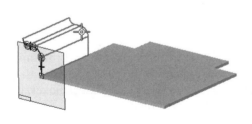

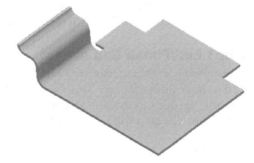

Figure 14-23 Preview of a contour flange being created

Figure 14-24 The resulting contour flange

To End

 Choose this button to terminate the contour flange at the end of the selected edge. When you choose this button, you will be prompted to specify the side for the feature creation.

Chain

 Choose this button to select a chain of edges on which the contour flange will be created. Figure 14-25 shows the base of the sheet metal component and the sketch to be used to create the contour flange. Figure 14-26 shows the contour flange created by selecting all four edges on the top face of the base.

Figure 14-25 Sketch for the contour flange

Figure 14-26 The resulting contour flange created by selecting all four edges on the top face

Modifying the Contour Flange Options

You can choose the **Contour Flange Options** button from the ribbon bar to modify the contour flange options. When you choose this button, the **Contour Flange Options** dialog box will be displayed, refer to Figure 14-27. This dialog box has two tabs, **General** and **Miters and Corners**. The options in the **General** tab are the same as those discussed while creating flanges. The options in the **Miters and Corners** tab are discussed next.

Start End/Finish End Areas

The options in these areas are used to create a miter corner at the start end and the finish end of the contour flange. By default, the **Miter** check boxes in both the areas are cleared. As a result, the options in these area will not be available. Once you select these check boxes, the options in this area will be available. These options are discussed next.

Angle

The **Angle** edit boxes in both the areas are used to specify the miter angle at the start and finish ends. The default value is -45-degrees. Figure 14-28 shows the preview of a contour flange with miters of 45 degrees at both the ends.

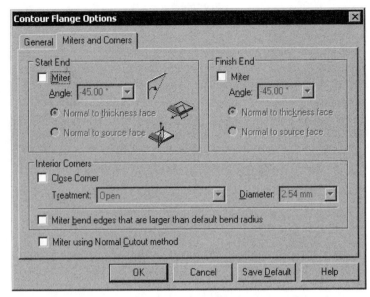

Figure 14-27 *The Miters and Corners tab of the Contour Flange Options dialog box*

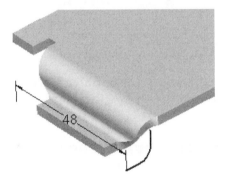

Figure 14-28 *Preview of the flanges with -45-degrees miter at the two ends*

Normal to thickness face

This radio button is used to create the miter normal to the thickness face, as shown in Figure 14-29.

Normal to source face

This radio button is used to create the miter normal to the source face, as shown in Figure 14-30.

Interior Corners Area

The options in this area are used to specify the corner treatment while creating the contour flange at multiple edges. You need to select the **Close Corner** check box to enable the

Figure 14-29 *Top view of the miter normal to the thickness face*   *Figure 14-30* *Top view of the miter normal to the source face*

Treatment drop-down list. The options available in this drop-down list are discussed next.

Open

This option is selected to create an open corner.

Close

This option is selected to create a close corner.

Circle cutout

This option is selected to create a circular cutout at the corner. You can enter the diameter of the circle in the **Diameter** edit box that is available when you select the **Circular cutout** option.

Miter bend edges that are larger than default bend radius

This check box is selected to add a miter to the rounds that did not exist earlier.

Miter using Normal Cutout method

This check box is selected to add a miter by creating a normal cutout.

CREATING LOFTED FLANGES

Toolbar:	Features > Contour Flange > Lofted Flange

The **Lofted Flange** tool is used to create a transition of sheet between two selected profiles. Note that the profiles that you use should be open and they may or may not have the same number of elements. Figure 14-31 shows the sketches for creating the lofted flange and the parallel planes on which the two sketches are drawn. Figure 14-32 shows the preview of the resulting lofted flange.

When you invoke this tool, the **Lofted Flange** ribbon bar is displayed. Various steps required to create a lofted flange are discussed next.

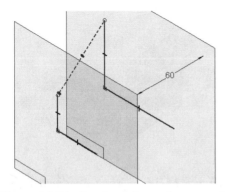

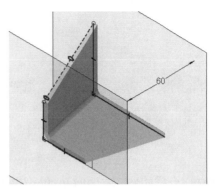

Figure 14-31 Sketches to be used to create the lofted flange

Figure 14-32 Preview of the resulting lofted flange

Cross Section Step

This step is activated when you invoke the **Lofted Flange** tool. This step can be used to create or select the profiles for the lofted flange. To draw the profile, select the sketching plane and then draw the first profile. Exit the sketching environment and then define the start point at the first profile. Choose the **Finish** button from the ribbon bar. Next, create a parallel plane and draw the second profile. Exit the sketching environment and specify the start point at this profile also. Next, choose the **Finish** button; the **Side Step** will be activated.

Side Step

This step is used to specify the side of the material addition. The side is displayed by a red arrow. You can move the cursor on either side of the profiles to specify the side. Once you specify the side, the preview of the contour flange will be displayed. Choose the **Finish** button to complete the feature.

 Note
*You can also modify the lofted flange options using the **Flange Options** button from the ribbon bar.*

ADDING THE JOG TO THE SHEET

Toolbar:	Features > Jog

 The **Jog** tool is used to add a jog to an existing sheet metal part using a sketched line segment. Figure 14-33 shows the base of the sheet metal part and the line to be used to add the jog. Figure 14-34 shows the sheet after adding the jog.

To add a jog, invoke the **Jog** tool; the **Jog** ribbon bar will be displayed. Various steps required to add the jog are discussed next.

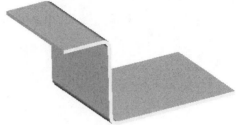

Figure 14-33   *Base sheet and the line to add the jog*

Figure 14-34   *Sheet after adding the jog*

Plane or Sketch Step

This step is used to select the plane or the face of the base feature to draw the line segment for adding the jog.

Draw Profile Step

This step is automatically activated when you select a planar face or a plane to draw the sketch. Draw a single line that will define the jog line at the base sheet and then exit the sketching environment.

Side Step

This step is automatically activated when you exit the sketching environment. In this step, you need to define the side of the sheet on which the jog will be added.

Extent Step

This step is automatically activated when you define the side of the jog. In this step, you will be prompted to set the distance value. You can move the cursor on the screen to specify the distance of the jog. Alternatively, you can enter the value in the **Distance** edit box. Click on the screen to specify the distance; the preview of the jog will be displayed with the distance value. You can modify the distance value at this stage also.

Note
The buttons available in the ribbon bar in the **Extent** *step are the same as those discussed earlier.*

BENDING THE SHEET METAL PART

Toolbar:	Features > Bend

 The **Bend** tool is used to bend an existing sheet metal part using a sketched line segment. Figure 14-35 shows a sheet metal part and the line to be used to bend it. Figure 14-36 shows the sheet after bending.

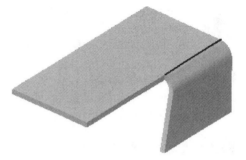

Figure 14-35 Base sheet and the line to bend the sheet

Figure 14-36 Model after adding the bend

To bend the sheet, invoke the **Bend** tool; the **Bend** ribbon bar will be displayed. Various steps required to bend the sheet are discussed next.

Plane or Sketch Step

This step is used to draw the line segment to bend the sheet or to select an existing entity to be used for bending. Select a face of the sheet to be used for drawing the sketch or select an existing sketch.

Draw Profile Step

This step is automatically activated when you select a planar face or a plane to draw the sketch. Draw a single line segment that will define the bend line at the base sheet and then exit the sketching environment.

Bend Location

This step is automatically activated when you exit the sketching environment. In this step, you need to define the side of the sheet that will be bent. A red arrow is displayed on the bend line. You can use this line to specify the side to bend.

Moving Side

This step is automatically activated when you define the side of the bend. In this step, you need to define the side of the sheet that will be moved after bending.

Bend Direction

This step is automatically activated when you define the side to be moved. You can bend the selected side on either side of the line segment.

UNBENDING THE SHEET METAL PART

Toolbar:	Features > Bend > Unbend

 The **Unbend** tool is used to unbend the portion of the sheet bent using the **Bend** or **Flange** tools. This tool is highly useful when you want to create a feature on the bent portion of the sheet. This tool works in the following two steps:

Fixed Face Step

This step is used to specify the portion of the sheet that will be fixed and will not move after unbending. Generally, the base of the sheet metal part is selected in this step.

Select Bends Step

This step is automatically invoked when you select the face to fix. In this step, you need to select the rounds of the bends or flanges. Note that moving the cursor over the linear portion of the bend or flange will not select them. Select the **All Bends** option from the **Select** drop-down list to unbend all the bends in the sheet metal part.

After selecting the rounds, accept the selection and then choose the **Preview** button to preview the unbend feature. Next, choose the **Finish** button to exit the **Unbend** tool.

REBENDING THE SHEET METAL PART

Toolbar:	Features > Bend > Rebend

The **Rebend** tool is used to rebend the portion of the sheet that was unbent using the **Unbend** tool. When you invoke this tool, you will be prompted to select the bends to be modified. Move the cursor over the location where the bend was placed originally; the bend will be highlighted. You can also select the **All Bends** option from the **Select** drop-down list in the ribbon bar to rebend all the bends. Choose the **Accept** button to accept the selection and then choose the **Preview** button. Next, choose the **Finish** button to exit the **Rebend** tool.

Figure 14-37 shows an unbent sheet with the cut features created at the bends and Figure 14-38 shows the sheet after rebending.

FILLETING OR CHAMFERING CORNERS OF A SHEET METAL PART

Toolbar:	Features > Break Corner

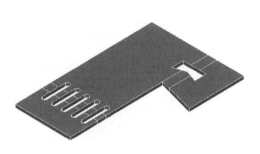

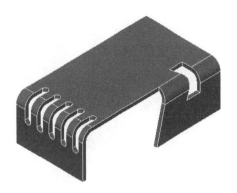

Figure 14-37 Cut features created on the unbent sheet metal part

Figure 14-38 Model after creating the cuts and then rebending

The **Break Corner** tool is used to add fillets or chamfers to the selected corners of the sheet metal part. When you invoke this tool, the **Break Corner** ribbon bar will be displayed and you will be prompted to select the edges to treat. You can select the edges that you want to fillet or chamfer. By default, the **Radius Corner** button is chosen from the ribbon bar. As a result, a fillet is added to the model. If you want to add a chamfer, choose the **Chamfer Corner** button from the ribbon bar. It creates a 45-degrees chamfer. You can enter the fillet or chamfer value in the **Break** edit box. This edit box will be enabled after you select the corners.

You can select the **Face** option from the **Select** drop-down list to select all the corners of the selected face.

TREATING 2 BEND CORNERS OF A SHEET METAL PART

Toolbar: Features > Break Corner > Close 2-Bend Corner

The **Close 2-Bend Corner** tool is used to treat the corner created by two bends. When you invoke this tool, you will be prompted to click on the bends to be modified. Select the curved portion of the two bends to treat. The **Treatment** drop-down list, can be used to perform three types of treatments on the selected bends. These types of bend corner are discussed next.

Open Treatment

This type of treatment is performed using the **Open** option from the **Treatment** drop-down list. In this type of treatment, the walls are closed but the corner is kept open. Figure 14-39 shows the two bends of a sheet metal part selected for treatment and Figure 14-40 shows the corner after treatment.

You can also add a gap to the corner treatment by entering the value of the gap in the **Gap** edit box. Figure 14-41 shows the open corner treatment with a gap of 2mm.

Figure 14-39 *Two bends selected for the open corner treatment*

Figure 14-40 *Model with the open corner treatment of the two bends*

Figure 14-41 *Model with the open corner treatment with a gap of 2 mm*

 Note

The gap value should be less than the sheet thickness.

Close Corner Treatment

This type of treatment is performed using the **Close** option from the **Treatment** drop-down list. In this type of treatment, the corners are also closed along with the walls, as shown in Figure 14-42.

Circle Cutout Corner Treatment

This type of treatment is performed using the **Circle cutout** option from the **Treatment** drop-down list. In this type of treatment, a circular cutout is created at the corner, as shown in Figure 14-43. You can enter the diameter of the circle in the **Diameter** edit box.

You can also overlap one wall on the other by choosing the **Overlap** button from the ribbon bar. Figure 14-44 shows the model with the overlap.

Figure 14-42 *Close corner treatment*

Figure 14-43 *Model with the circular cutout corner treatment of the two bends*

Figure 14-44 *Overlapping of walls in the corner treatment*

CREATING DIMPLES IN A SHEET METAL PART

Toolbar:	Features > Dimple

Solid Edge allows you to sketch a user-defined shape and then use it to create a dimple in the sheet metal component. To create the dimple, invoke the **Dimple** tool. It is recommended that before you start proceeding with sketching the dimple, you should set the dimple options. To do so, choose the **Options** button from the ribbon bar; the **Dimple Options** dialog box will be displayed, as shown in Figure 14-45.

Dimple Options Dialog Box

The options available in this dialog box are discussed next.

Taper angle

This edit box is used to specify the taper angle for the dimple. Figure 14-46 shows a dimple with no taper angle and Figure 14-47 shows a dimple with a taper angle of 25-degrees.

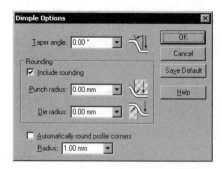

Figure 14-45 The **Dimple Options** *dialog box*

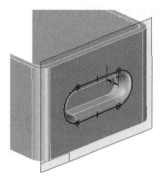

Figure 14-46 *Dimple with no taper*

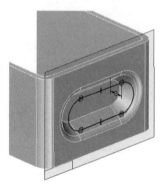

Figure 14-47 *Dimple with a 25-degrees taper*

Rounding Area

The options in this area are used to specify the punch and die radius for creating the dimple. By default, these values are set to zero. You can set any desired value for the punch and die radius.

Automatically round profile corners

If the profile that you have drawn for the dimple has sharp corners, you can select this check box to automatically round those corners. The radius of the round can be specified in the **Radius** edit box below this check box.

After specifying the dimple options, you can proceed with creating the dimple. Various steps to create the dimple are discussed next.

Plane or Sketch Step

By default, this step is activated when you invoke the **Dimple** tool. As a result, you are prompted to select a planar face. Select a face on which you want to sketch the profile of the dimple.

Draw Profile Step

This step is automatically activated when you select a planar face to draw the sketch. Draw the profile of the dimple and then exit the sketching environment.

Extent Step

If you draw a closed profile for the dimple and exit the sketching environment, this step is automatically activated. In this step, you can specify the distance of the depression of the dimple and the direction in which the feature will be depressed. You can specify the distance of the dimple dynamically on the screen or by entering the value in the **Distance** edit box. Figure 14-48 shows a 25-degrees taper dimple created in the forward direction.

After you place the dimple, its preview will be displayed and the **Sidewalls Inside** and **Sidewalls Outside** buttons will be available in the ribbon bar. These buttons, are used to specify whether the dimple walls will be placed inside the profile or outside the profile.

Solid Edge also allows you to create open profiles for the dimple. Note that the open profile should be created such that when extended, the open entities intersect the edges of the model. When you exit the sketching environment after drawing the open profile, the **Side** step will be activated and you will be prompted to specify the side of the feature creation. Note that you need to specify the side inside the profile. Figure 14-49 shows the preview of the dimple created using an open profile. The open profile is also shown in the same figure. Note that in this profile, when the two inclined lines are extended, they intersect with the top edge of the sheet metal part.

Figure 14-48 *25-degrees taper dimple created in the forward direction*

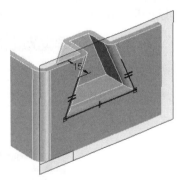

Figure 14-49 *Dimple created with an open profile*

CREATING LOUVERS IN A SHEET METAL PART

Toolbar: Features > Dimple > Louver

Louvers are created in a sheet metal part to provide openings in it. Figure 14-50 shows a sheet metal part with a rectangular pattern of louvers on its top face.

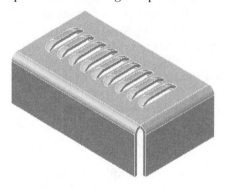

Figure 14-50 Sheet metal part with a pattern of louvers on the top face

In Solid Edge, louvers are created by sketching a single line segment defining the length of the louver. To create the louver, invoke the **Louver** tool; the **Louver** ribbon bar will be displayed. It is recommended that before you start creating the louver, you should set the louver options. To do so, choose the **Louver Options** button from the ribbon bar; the **Louver Options** dialog box will be displayed, as shown in Figure 14-51.

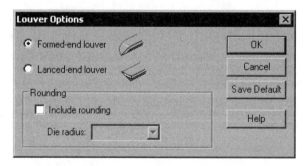

*Figure 14-51 The **Louver Options** dialog box*

Louver Options Dialog Box

The options available in the **Louver Options** dialog box are discussed next.

Formed-end louver

This radio button is selected to create a formed-end type of louver. Figure 14-52 shows a pattern of the formed-end louvers.

Lanced-end louver

This radio button is selected to create a lanced-end type of louver. Figure 14-53 shows a pattern of the lanced-end louvers.

Figure 14-52 *Formed-end louvers*   *Figure 14-53* *Lanced-end louvers*

Rounding Area

The options available in this area are used to set the die rounding. The radius for the round can be specified in the **Die radius** edit box.

After specifying the louver options, you can proceed with creating the louver. Various steps to create the louver are discussed next.

Plane or Sketch Step

This step is activated by default when you invoke the **Louver** tool. As a result, you are prompted to select a planar face. Select a face on which you want to sketch the profile of the louver.

Draw Profile Step

This step is automatically activated when you select a planar face to draw the sketch. Draw the profile of the louver and then exit the sketching environment. Note that the profile has to be a single line segment.

Depth Step

This step is automatically activated when you exit the sketching environment. In this step, you need to specify the depth of the louver. You can enter the depth in the **Distance** edit box or specify it dynamically in the drawing window. Note that the distance value is specified along the face on which the sketch is drawn. You need to dynamically specify the side of the line on which the depth of the louver will be added.

Height Step

This step is automatically activated when you specify the depth of the louver. In this step, you need to specify the height of the louver. The height is specified normal to the face on which the sketch is drawn. You can enter the height in the **Distance** edit box or specify it dynamically in the drawing window. You need to specify the side of the sheet on which the louver will be added. Note that the height should be less than or equal to the difference of the depth of the louver and the sheet thickness. Also, the height should be more than the sheet thickness. For example, if the depth of the louver is 6mm and the sheet thickness is 2 mm, the height of the louver can be more than 2 and less than or equal to 4. Figure 14-54 shows the preview of a formed-end louver. The depth of the louver is 6mm and its height is 3.85mm.

Figure 14-54 Preview of the formed-end louver

CREATING DRAWN CUTOUTS IN A SHEET METAL PART

Toolbar: Features > Dimple > Drawn cutout

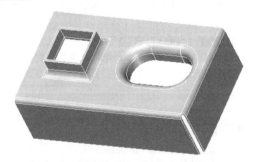

The drawn cutouts are exactly the same as the dimples, with the only difference being that for drawn cutouts, the end face is open. Figure 14-55 shows a sheet metal part with two different shape drawn cutouts. In this figure, the rectangular cutout is created in the upward direction and the oblong cutout is created in the downward direction.

 Note
*The working of this tool is exactly the same as that of the **Dimple** tool.*

Figure 14-55 Drawn cutouts of various shapes

CREATING BEADS IN A SHEET METAL PART

Toolbar: Features > Dimple > Bead

 The **Bead** tool is used to create an embossed or an engraved bead on a sheet metal part using a single entity or a set of tangentially connected entities. Figure 14-56 shows an embossed bead and Figure 14-57 shows an engraved bead.

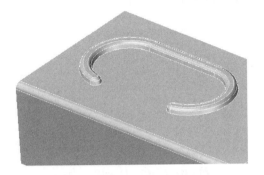 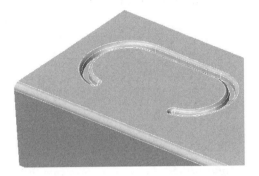

Figure 14-56 Bead created in the upward direction, resulting in the embossed feature

Figure 14-57 Bead created in the downward direction, resulting in the engraved feature

When you invoke this tool, the **Bead** ribbon bar is displayed. It is recommended that before you proceed with creating the bead, you should set its options. To set the bead options, choose the **Bead Options** button from the ribbon bar; the **Bead Options** dialog box will be displayed, as shown in Figure 14-58.

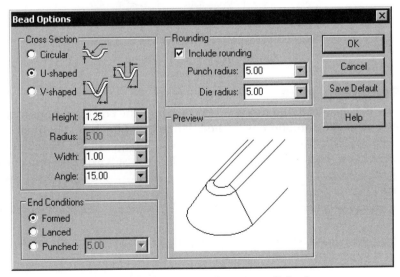

*Figure 14-58 The **Bead Options** dialog box*

Bead Options Dialog Box

The options available in this dialog box are discussed next.

Cross Section Area

The options available in this area are used to specify the cross-section of the bead. You can specify the height, radius, width, and the angle of the bead using the edit boxes available in this area. Figures 14-59 through 14-61 show beads with different cross-sections.

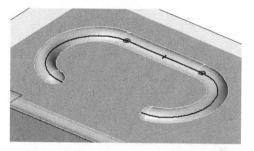

Figure 14-59 *Circular cross-section bead*

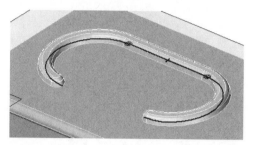

Figure 14-60 *U-shaped bead*

Figure 14-61 *V-shaped bead*

End Conditions Area

The options available in this area are used to specify the end conditions of the bead. You can specify the end condition as formed, lanced, or punched. The punch gap can be specified in the edit box that will be available on the right of the **Punched** radio button when you select it. Figures 14-62 through 14-64 show beads with different end conditions.

Note
*The remaining options in the **Bead Options** dialog box are similar to those discussed earlier.*

After specifying the bead options, you can proceed with creating the bead. Various steps to create the bead are discussed next.

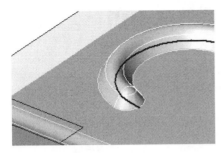

Figure 14-62 Formed end condition

Figure 14-63 Lanced end condition

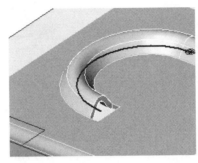

Figure 14-64 Punched end condition with a gap of 2 mm

Plane or Sketch Step

This step is activated by default when you invoke the **Bead** tool. As a result, you are prompted to select a planar face. Select a face on which you want to sketch the profile of the bead.

Draw Profile Step

This step is automatically activated when you select a planar face to draw the sketch. Draw the profile of the bead and then exit the sketching environment. Note that the profile has to be a single line segment or a set of tangentially connected open or closed entities.

Side Step

This step is automatically activated when you exit the sketching environment. In this step, you need to specify the side of the feature creation. The side is displayed by a red arrow on the screen. You can specify the required side by clicking on either side of the sketch.

ADDING GUSSETS TO A SHEET METAL PART

Toolbar: Features > Dimple > Gusset

Gussets are rib like stiffeners that can be added to the sheet metal part to increase its strength. In Solid Edge, you can create an automatic gusset of round or square shape or a gusset with a user-defined profile. Figures 14-65 through 14-68 show various types of gussets that can be created.

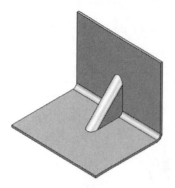

Figure 14-65 Front view of a round gusset

Figure 14-66 Back view of the round gusset

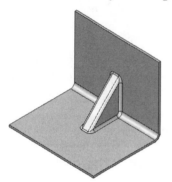

Figure 14-67 A square gusset

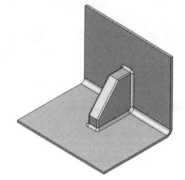

Figure 14-68 A user-defined gusset

To add a gusset, invoke the **Gusset** tool from the **Dimple** flyout in the **Features** toolbar; the **Gusset** ribbon bar will be displayed and the **Select Bend Step** will be activated. As a result, you will be prompted to select a bend along which the gusset will be placed. Select the rounded portion of a bend or a flange; the **Gusset Placement Step** will be invoked and the preview of the gusset created using the current values will be displayed as you move the mouse along the selected bend.

Place the gusset and then choose the **Gusset Options** button from the ribbon bar to modify the gusset options. When you choose this button, the **Gusset Options** dialog box will be displayed, as shown in Figure 14-69.

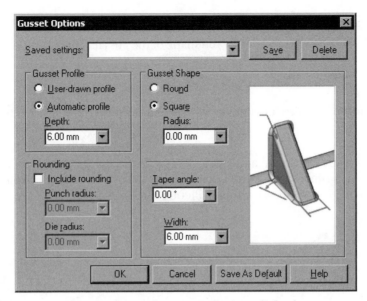

*Figure 14-69 The **Gusset Options** dialog box*

The options available in this dialog box are discussed next.

Gusset Profile Area

The options in this area are used to define the profile of the gusset. These options are discussed next.

User-drawn profile

This is the first radio button available in the **Gusset Profile** area. You can select this radio button to create a user-drawn profile. When you exit the **Gusset Options** dialog box after selecting this option, the **Plane or Sketch Step** will be invoked. The working of this tool will then become similar to that of the **Rib** tool discussed in the earlier chapters.

Automatic profile

By default, the **Automatic profile** radio button is selected in this area. As a result, an automatic profile of a single inclined line is drawn as the profile of the gusset. The depth of the automatic profile can be specified in the **Depth** edit box provided below this radio button.

Rounding Area

The options in this area are used to specify the punch and die radius to create the gusset. Select the **Include rounding** check box to enable the **Punch radius** and **Die radius** edit boxes. You can enter the desired values in the edit boxes of this area.

Gusset Shape Area

The options in this area are used to define the shape of the gusset. These options are discussed next.

Round

This radio button is used to create a gusset with a round shape, as shown in Figure 14-70.

Square

This radio button is used to create a gusset with a square shape. You can also apply fillets to the sharp edges of a square gusset by entering the radius value in the **Round** edit box. Figure 14-71 shows a square gusset without filleting the edges.

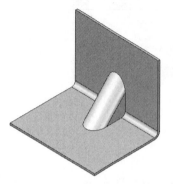

Figure 14-70 *A round gusset*

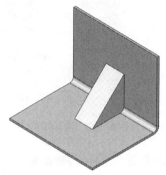

Figure 14-71 *A square gusset*

Taper angle

This edit box is used to enter the taper angle for the gusset. Figure 14-72 shows a gusset with a taper angle of 25-degrees.

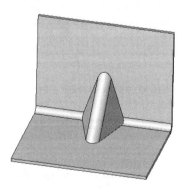

Figure 14-72 *A gusset with a taper angle of 25-degrees*

Width

This edit box is used to specify the width of the gusset. Figure 14-73 shows a gusset with a width of 10 mm and Figure 14-74 shows a gusset with a width of 20 mm.

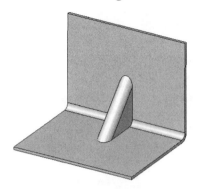

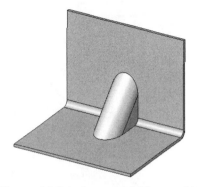

Figure 14-73 *A gusset of 10 mm width*   *Figure 14-74* *A gusset of 20 mm width*

ADDING HEMS

Toolbar:	Features > Contour Flange > Hem

Hems are defined as the rounded faces created on the sharp edges of a sheet metal component in order to reduce the area of the sharpness in a sheet metal component. This makes the sheet metal component easy to handle and assemble. To create a hem, invoke the **Hem** tool; the **Hem** ribbon bar will be displayed and you will be prompted to select an edge for the hem. Before you select the edge, it is recommended that you choose the **Hem Options** button to set the hem options. When you choose this button, the **Hem Options** dialog box will be displayed, as shown in Figure 14-75.

The options in this dialog box are discussed next.

Hem Profile Area

The options available in this area are used to specify the profile of the hem. These options are discussed next.

Hem type

This drop-down list is used to specify the type of hem. There are seven different types of hems available in this drop-down list. These are discussed next.

Closed

This option is used to create a closed hem, as shown in Figure 14-76. The flange length can be specified in the **Flange length 1** edit box available on the right of the preview window.

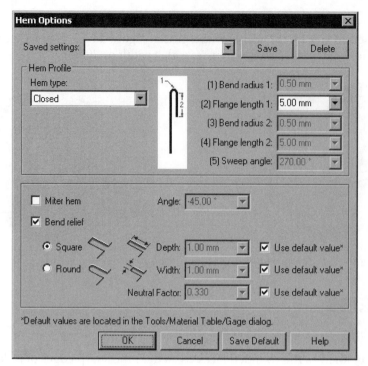

Figure 14-75 The **Hem Options** *dialog box*

Open

This option is used to create an open hem, as shown in Figure 14-77. The bend radius and the flange length can be specified in the **Bend radius 1** and **Flange length 1** edit boxes, respectively.

Figure 14-76 A closed hem

Figure 14-77 An open hem

S-Flange

This option is used to create a hem with an S shape, as shown in Figure 14-78. The bend radii and the flange lengths can be specified in their respective edit boxes.

Curl

This option is used to create a curled hem, as shown in Figure 14-79. The bend radii and the flange lengths can be specified in their respective edit boxes.

Figure 14-78 An S-shaped hem

Figure 14-79 A curled hem

Open Loop

This option is used to create a hem that has an open loop, as shown in Figure 14-80. The bend radius and the included angle of the open loop can be specified in the **Bend radius 1** and **Sweep angle** edit boxes, respectively.

Closed Loop

This option is used to create a hem that has a closed loop, as shown in Figure 14-81. The bend radius and the flange length can be specified in their respective edit boxes.

Figure 14-80 An open loop hem

Figure 14-81 A closed loop hem

Centered Loop

This option is used to create a hem with a centered loop, as shown in Figure 14-82. The bend radii and the included angle can be specified in their respective edit boxes.

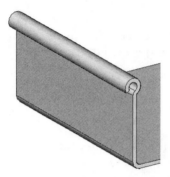

Figure 14-82 A centered loop hem

Miter Hem

This check box is selected to miter a hem. You can specify a negative or a positive miter angle for the hem, as shown in Figures 14-83 and 14-84, respectively.

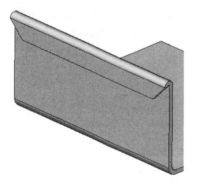

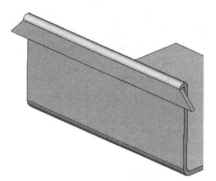

Figure 14-83 An open hem with a negative miter

Figure 14-84 An open hem with a positive miter

 Note
The remaining options in this dialog box are the same as those discussed earlier in this chapter.

After specifying the hem options, exit the dialog box and then select the edge on which you want to place the hem. Note that the hem will be placed on the face on which the selected edge lies.

CONVERTING A SOLID PART TO A SHEET METAL PART

Toolbar:	Features > Convert to Sheet Metal

Solid Edge allows you to convert a solid part to a sheet metal part. However, to do so, the part has to be created in the solid modeling environment of a sheet metal file. Start a new sheet metal file and then choose **Applications > Switch to Part** from the menu bar; the **Sheet Metal to Part** information dialog box is displayed. Choose **Yes** from this information box. The part modeling environment will be invoked. Now, create the solid part that you want to use. Note that you can use only a part, such as a shelled box, to be converted into a sheet metal part. After creating the part, switch back to the sheet metal environment by choosing **Applications > Switch to Sheet Metal** from the menu bar. Figure 14-85 shows a shelled solid box with the top face removed and Figure 14-86 shows the same box after converting into a sheet metal part.

Figure 14-85 Shelled box to be converted into a sheet metal part

Figure 14-86 Box after converting into sheet metal part

Various steps used to convert a solid part into a sheet metal part are discussed next.

Select Face Step

When you invoke the **Convert to Sheet Metal** tool, the **Select Face** step will be activated and you will be prompted to select the base face. Select the face that will act as the base of the sheet metal part. Depending on the type of model selected to be converted, the **Solid Edge** information box will be displayed, as shown in Figure 14-87. Choose **OK** from this dialog box.

Select Rip Edges Step

You need to invoke this step manually to select the edges to be ripped in the sheet metal part. Generally, the side edges of the joined faces are selected to be ripped. The corner relief is also applied automatically to the corners of the edges selected to be ripped. Figure 14-88 shows the preview of the four vertical edges selected to be ripped and Figure 14-89 shows the resulting sheet metal part.

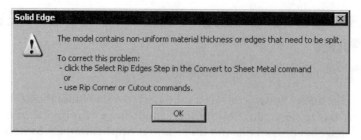

Figure 14-87 The **Solid Edge** *information box*

Figure 14-88 Edges selected to be ripped

Figure 14-89 Sheet metal part after ripping the corners

RIPPING CORNERS OF A SOLID PART

| **Toolbar:** | Features > Convert to Sheet Metal > Rip Corner |

You can also rip the corners of a solid part using the **Rip Corner** tool. Note that when you use this tool, no corner relief is added to the model. To rip the corners, invoke this tool and select the edges whose corners you want to rip.

Note
*You can also use the other tools such as **Cutout**, **Normal Cutout**, **Mirror**, and so on in the sheet metal environment. These tools are discussed in detail in the part modeling environment.*

CREATING THE FLAT PATTERN OF A SHEET METAL PART

As mentioned earlier, you need to flatten a sheet metal part after creating it to generate its drawing views. Solid Edge provides a number of options to flatten a sheet metal part. Some of the options are discussed next.

Creating the Flat Pattern in the Flat Pattern Model Environment

Menu:	Applications > Flatten Model

Choose **Applications > Flatten Model** from the menu bar, the **Flat Pattern Model** environment will be invoked. When you invoke this environment, the **Flatten** ribbon bar will be displayed and you will be prompted to select the face that will be oriented upward in the flat pattern. You can also invoke this ribbon bar by choosing the **Flatten** button from the **Modify** toolbar that is displayed in this environment. Select the base face of the sheet metal part. Next, you will be prompted to select an edge that will define the X axis and the origin. Click on an edge close to one of its endpoints to define the orientation of the X axis.

Figure 14-90 shows a sheet metal part and Figure 14-91 shows the top view of its flat pattern. Note that in the flat pattern, the lower horizontal edge was selected close to the left endpoint to define the X axis and the origin.

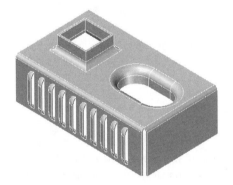

Figure 14-90 *Edges selected to be ripped*

Figure 14-91 *Sheet metal part after ripping the corners*

After creating the flat pattern, you can restore the sheet metal modeling environment by choosing **Applications > Design Model** from the menu bar. The flat pattern will be displayed under the **Flat Pattern** heading in the **Feature Pathfinder** tab from the **Edgebar**. You can again restore the flat pattern environment using the **Application** menu.

Note

As evident in Figure 14-91, the features such as louvers, dimples, drawn cutouts, beads, and so on are not flattened as these features are created using a punch and a die.

Saving a Sheet Metal Part in the Flat Pattern Format

Menu:	File > Save as Flat

The other method of creating a flat pattern is to save the sheet metal part as a flat pattern in a separate file. You can save the file in the AutoCAD (*.dxf), Solid Edge part, or Solid Edge sheet metal format. To save the flat pattern file, choose **File > Save as Flat** option from the menu bar in the sheet metal environment; the **Flatten** ribbon bar is displayed. Select the face that will be oriented upward, the edge to define the origin, and the X axis; the **Save as Flat** dialog box will be displayed. Select the file type from the **Save as type** drop-down list and then specify the name and the location of the flat pattern file. Figure 14-92 shows the flatten sheet metal part. As evident in this figure, the features such as louvers, dimples, drawn cutouts, and so on are removed from the model.

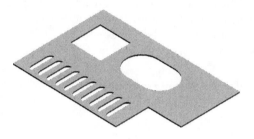

Figure 14-92 *Flat pattern saved as a separate sheet metal file*

TUTORIALS

Tutorial 1

In this tutorial, you will create the sheet metal component shown in Figure 14-93. The flat pattern of the component is shown in Figure 14-94. The dimensions of the model are shown in Figure 14-95. The material thickness, bend radius, relief depth, and relief width is 1mm. Assume the missing dimensions. Save the model with the name given below:

Solid Edge\c14\c14tut1.psm   **(Expected time: 30 min)**

The following steps are required to complete this tutorial:

a. Start a new sheet metal file and set the sheet metal parameters.
b. Draw the sketch of the front face of the sheet metal part, refer to Figure 14-96.
c. Convert the sketch into the sheet metal face using the **Tab** tool, refer to Figure 14-97.
d. Add the flange on the top face of the base, refer to Figure 14-98.
e. Add the flanges on the left face of the feature, refer to Figure 14-99.
f. Similarly, create the rest of the flanges, refer to Figure 14-100.
g. Close the corner of the flanges, as shown in Figure 14-101.
h. Create the holes, as shown in Figure 14-102.
i. Create the flat pattern of the sheet metal part, as shown in Figure 14-103.
j. Save the model.

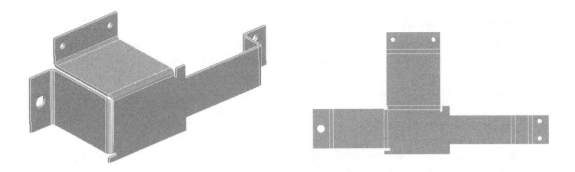

Figure 14-93 *Sheet metal part for Tutorial 1*   *Figure 14-94* *Flat pattern of the part*

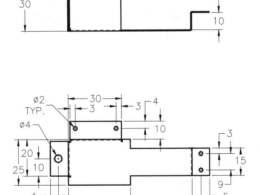

Figure 14-95 *Dimensions of the sheet metal part*

Starting a New Sheet Metal File

1. Start a new sheet metal file.

2. Choose **Tools > Material Table** from the menu bar to invoke the **Solid Edge Material Table** dialog box.

3. Choose the **Gage** tab and set the value of the material thickness, bend radius, relief depth, and relief width to **1 mm**.

4. Press the ENTER key or choose the **Apply to Model** button.

Creating the Front Face

1. Choose the **Tab** button from the **Features** toolbar to invoke this tool; you will be prompted to click on a planar face or a reference plane.

2. Select the **Front (xz)** plane as the sketching plane and invoke the sketching environment.

3. Draw the sketch for the front face of the part, as shown in Figure 14-96.

4. Exit the sketching environment and specify the thickness of the sheet metal part in the backward direction. Exit the **Tab** tool to create the base of the sheet metal part, as shown in Figure 14-97.

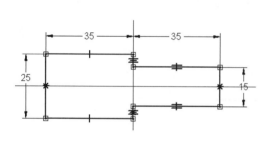

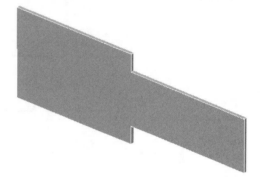

Figure 14-96 Sketch for the front face   *Figure 14-97 Front face of the part*

Creating the Flanges

Next, you need to create various flanges on the front face of the sheet metal part. These flanges will be created using the **Flange** tool.

1. Choose the **Flange** button from the **Features** toolbar to invoke this tool; you will be prompted to click on a thickness face edge.

2. Select the top horizontal edge to create the flange and then choose the **At End** button from the ribbon bar. Select the left endpoint of the top edge to locate the flange.

3. Specify the distance of the flange as **30mm**; the preview of the flange will be displayed. In the preview of the flange, modify the width to **30 mm**. Figure 14-98 shows the preview of the flange after modifying the width. Choose the **Finish** button to create the flange.

4. Select the left vertical edge and specify the distance of the flange as **30 mm**.

5. Choose the **At End** button and select the top endpoint of the edge to locate the flange. Modify the width of the flange to **20 mm** in the preview.

6. Choose the **Flange Options** button to invoke the **Flange Options** dialog box and select the **Corner relief** check box. Select the **Bend and face** radio button and exit the dialog box; the preview of the second flange will be displayed, as shown in Figure 14-99. Choose the **Finish** button to create the flange.

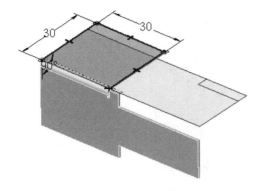
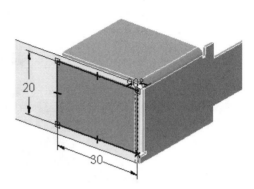

Figure 14-98 Preview of the top flange   *Figure 14-99* Preview of the left flange

7. Similarly, create the third, fourth, fifth, and the sixth flanges. For dimensions refer to Figure 14-95. The model after creating all the flanges is shown in Figure 14-100.

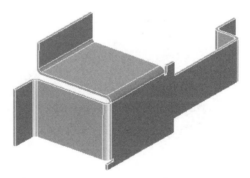

Figure 14-100 Model after creating all the flanges

Closing the Corner between the First Two Flanges

The corner between the first two flanges needs to be closed. This is done using the **Close 2-Bend Corner** tool.

1. Choose the **Close 2-Bend Corner** button from the **Features > Break Corner** toolbar to invoke this tool; you will be prompted to click on the bend to be modified.

2. Select the bend of the two flanges to define the corner to be closed.

3. Select the **Circle Cutout** option from the **Treatment** drop-down list. Specify the gap value as **0.25mm** and the diameter as **2mm**.

4. Choose the **Preview** button and then the **Finish** button to close the corner. The part after closing the corner is shown in Figure 14-101.

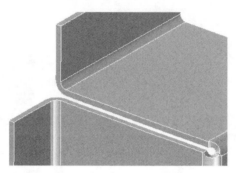

Figure 14-101 Partial view of the part after closing the corner

Creating Holes

1. Create five holes in the sheet metal part. For dimensions, refer to Figure 14-95. The final sheet metal part is shown in Figure 14-102.

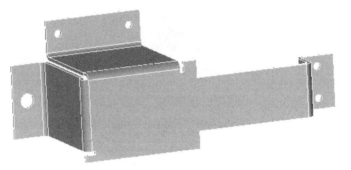

Figure 14-102 Final sheet metal part after creating the holes

Generating the Flat Pattern

Next, you need to generate the flat pattern of the sheet metal part. The flat pattern will be generated in the **Flat Pattern Model** environment.

1. Choose **Applications > Flatten Model** from the menu bar; the **Flat Pattern Model** environment will be invoked and the **Flatten** tool will be activated by default. As a result, you will be prompted to click on a face to be oriented upward.

2. Select the front face of the sheet metal part; you will be prompted to click on an edge to define the X-axis and the origin.

3. Select the top horizontal edge of the front face close to the left endpoint of the edge; the flat pattern of the model will be created, as shown in Figure 14-103.

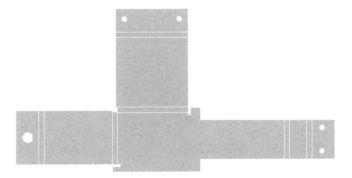

Figure 14-103 *Flat pattern of the sheet metal part*

Saving the Model

1. Save the model in the location and with the name *Solid Edge\c14\c14tut1.psm* and then close the file.

Tutorial 2

In this tutorial, you will create the sheet metal part of the Holder Clip shown in Figure 14-104. The flat pattern of the component is shown in Figure 14-105 and the dimensions are given in Figure 14-106. Assume the missing dimensions of the part. The material thickness, bend radius, relief depth, and relief width is 1mm. After creating the sheet metal component, create its flat pattern. Save the component with the name given below.

Solid Edge\c14\c14tut2.psm   **(Expected time: 45 min)**

The following steps are required to complete this tutorial:

a. Start a new sheet metal file and set the sheet metal parameters.
b. Draw the sketch of the top face of the sheet metal part, refer to Figure 14-107.
c. Convert the sketch into the sheet metal face using the **Tab** tool, refer to Figure 14-108.
d. Add the flange on the front face of the base, refer to Figure 14-109.
e. Add the flanges on the right face of the feature, refer to Figure 14-110.
f. Add the remaining flanges in the model, refer to Figures 14-109 through 14-114.
g. Create one louver on the top face and then create a rectangular pattern of louvers, refer to Figures 14-115 and 14-116.
h. Create the five holes, as shown in Figure 14-117.
i. Create the drawn cutout on the right face of the model, refer to Figures 14-118 and 14-119.
j. Generate the flat pattern of the model, refer to Figure 14-120.
k. Save the model.

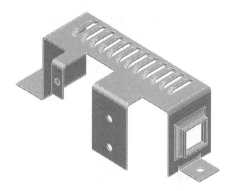

Figure 14-104 Sheet metal part for Tutorial 2

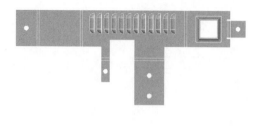

Figure 14-105 Flat pattern of the sheet metal part for Tutorial 2

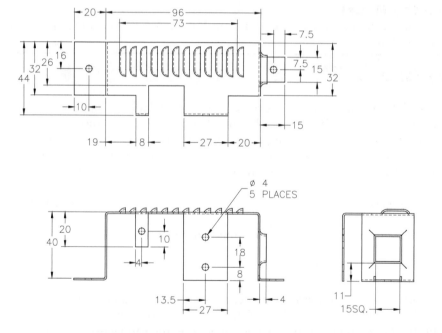

Figure 14-106 Dimensions for the sheet metal part

Starting a New Sheet Metal File

1. Start Solid Edge and then click on **Sheet Metal Part** in the **Create** area to start a new sheet metal file.

2. Choose **Tools > Material Table** from the menu bar to invoke the **Solid Edge Material Table** dialog box.

3. Choose the **Gage** tab and set the value of the material thickness, bend radius, relief depth, and relief width to 1mm.

Creating the Top Face

1. Choose the **Tab** button from the **Features** toolbar to invoke this tool; you will be prompted to click on a planar face or a reference plane.

2. Select the **Top (xy)** plane as the sketching plane and invoke the sketching environment.

3. Draw the sketch for the top face of the part, as shown in Figure 14-107.

4. Exit the sketching environment and specify the thickness of the sheet metal part in the upward direction. Exit the **Tab** tool to create the base of the sheet metal part, as shown in Figure 14-108.

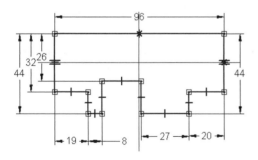
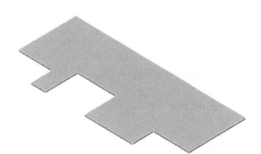

Figure 14-107 Sketch for the top face of the part   *Figure 14-108 Base of the sheet metal part*

Creating the Flanges

Next, you need to create various flanges on the top face of the sheet metal part. These flanges will be created using the **Flange** tool.

1. Choose the **Flange** button from the **Features** toolbar to invoke this tool; you will be prompted to click on a thickness face edge.

2. Select the top edge to create the flange and then specify the distance of the flange as

40 mm. Figure 14-109 shows the preview of the flange. In the preview, the value displayed in the drawing window is 40. The length of flange is equal to difference between the value entered in the **Distance** edit box and the thickness of the sheet metal. Choose the **Finish** button to create the flange.

3. Select the top right edge and specify the distance of the flange as **40**, as shown in Figure 14-110. Choose the **Finish** button to create the flange.

4. Select the outer bottom edge of the flange created last and then choose the **Centered** button from the ribbon bar to create a centered flange.

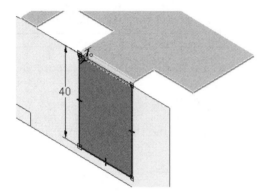

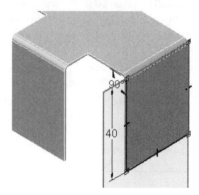

Figure 14-109 Preview of the first flange   *Figure 14-110 Preview of the second flange*

5. Specify the distance of the flange as 15 mm and then place the flange. In the preview of the flange, modify the width also to 15 mm, as shown in Figure 14-111. Choose the **Finish** button to create the flange.

6. Select the top edge of the top face, as shown in Figure 14-112 to create the fourth flange.

7. Specify the distance of the flange as **21** mm, as shown in Figure 14-112, and choose the **Finish** button to create the flange.

8. Select the upper left edge of the top face to create the fifth flange.

9. Specify the distance of the flange as **40** mm, as shown in Figure 14-113, and choose the **Finish** button to create the flange.

10. Create the sixth flange of distance 20 on the bottom edge of the previous flange, as shown in Figure 14-114.

Creating Louvers on the Top Face

Next, you need to create the louvers on the top face. You will first create one of the louvers using the **Louver** tool and then create its rectangular pattern.

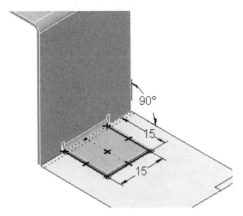

Figure 14-111 *Preview of the centered flange*

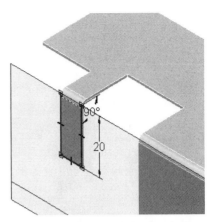

Figure 14-112 *Preview of the fourth flange*

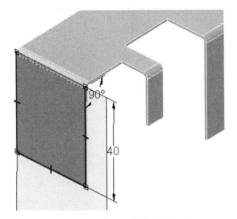

Figure 14-113 *Preview of the fifth flange*

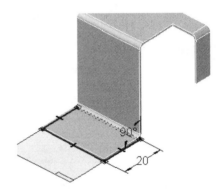

Figure 14-114 *Preview of the sixth flange*

1. Choose the **Louver** button from the **Features > Dimple** toolbar to invoke this tool; the **Plane or Sketch Step** will be activated and you will be prompted to click on a planar face.

2. Select the top face of the base feature to invoke the sketching environment. Draw the profile of the louver, which is a vertical line, as shown in Figure 14-115.

3. Exit the sketching environment; the **Depth Step** will be activated. Enter the depth as **4** mm in the **Distance** edit box and specify the depth on the left side of the sketch; the **Height** step will be activated.

4. Enter the height of the louver as **2.5** mm in the **Distance** edit box and specify the height in the upward direction; the preview of the louver will be displayed.

5. Choose the **Finish** button to create this louver, as shown in Figure 14-116.

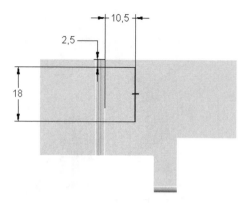

Figure 14-115 *Profile of the louver*

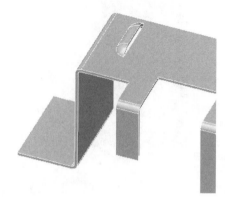

Figure 14-116 *Louver created on the top face*

6. Create a rectangular pattern of the louver with 12 instances along the X direction and 1 instance along the Y direction.

Creating Holes

1. Create five holes on the sheet metal part for dimensions, refer to Figure 14-106. The part after creating the holes is shown in Figure 14-117.

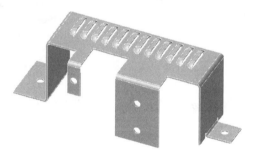

Figure 14-117 *Sheet metal part after creating the five holes*

Creating the Drawn Cutout on the Right Face of the Model

Next, you need to create the drawn cutout on the right face. The sketch for this cutout will be a square that you will draw in the sketching environment.

1. Choose the **Drawn Cutout** button from the **Features > Dimple** toolbar to invoke this tool; the **Plane or Sketch Step** will be activated and you will be prompted to click on a planar face.

2. Select the right face of the model; the sketching environment will be invoked. Draw the profile of the drawn cutout, as shown in Figure 14-118.

3. Exit the sketching environment; the **Extent Step** will be activated. Enter the extent of the cutout as **4** mm in the **Distance** edit box and specify the side on the right of the face.

4. Choose the **Finish** button to create the drawn cutout. Figure 14-119 shows the final sheet metal part.

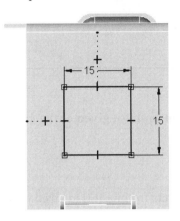

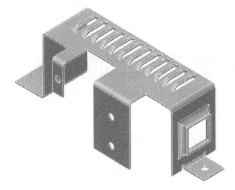

Figure 14-118 *Profile of the drawn cutout*   ***Figure 14-119*** *The final sheet metal part*

Generating the Flat Pattern

Next, you need to generate the flat pattern of the sheet metal part. The flat pattern will be generated in the **Flat Pattern Model** environment.

1. Choose **Applications > Flatten Model** from the menu bar; the **Flat Pattern Model** environment will be invoked and the **Flatten** tool will be activated by default. As a result, you will be prompted to click on a face to be oriented upward.

2. Select the top face of the sheet metal part; you will be prompted to click on an edge to define the X axis and origin.

3. Select the bottom left horizontal edge of the top face, close to the left endpoint of the edge; the flat pattern of the model will be created, as shown in Figure 14-120.

4. Restore the sheet metal modeling environment by choosing **Applications > Design Model** from the menu bar.

Saving the Model

1. Save the model with the name given below and then close the file.

    \Solid Edge\c14\c14tut2.psm

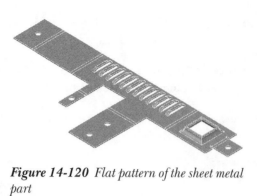

Figure 14-120 *Flat pattern of the sheet metal part*

Self-Evaluation Test

Answer the following questions and then compare them to those given at the end of this chapter:

1. The sheet metal files are saved as the *.psm* files. (T/F)

2. When you invoke a new sheet metal file, the sketching environment is invoked by default. (T/F)

3. You can use a spline to create the contour flange. (T/F)

4. You can draw a closed or an open sketch for the dimple feature. (T/F)

5. You can unbend a sheet metal part by using the _____ tool.

6. The unbent sheet metal parts can be bent again using the _____ tool.

7. In Solid Edge, the sheet metal parts are bent using a sketched _____.

8. Solid Edge allows you to close the corner between two flanges using the _____ tool.

9. To create the flange at the center of the selected edge, you need to choose the _____ button from the **Flange** ribbon bar.

10. To convert a solid model into a sheet metal component, you first need to _____ it.

Review Questions

Answer the following questions:

1. After creating a sheet metal part, you can modify its thickness using the **Gage** tab of the **Solid Edge Material Table** dialog box. (T/F)

2. The flat pattern is generated in a separate environment. (T/F)

3. You can set the material for the sheet metal part using the **Solid Edge Material Table** dialog box. (T/F)

4. There is no relation between the height and the width of the louver. (T/F)

5. The method of creating drawn cutouts is similar to that of creating dimples. (T/F)

6. Beads can be created using open or closed sketches. (T/F)

7. Which of the following can be the shape of louver?

    (a) Lanced   (b) Formed-end
    (c) Both   (d) None

8. Which one of the following is not a type of treatment for a 2-bend corner?

    (a) Open   (b) Close
    (c) Circle cutout   (d) Square cutout

9. Which of the following tools is used to create the base of the sheet metal component?

    (a) **Flange**   (b) **Contour Flange**
    (c) **Tab**   (d) **Louver**

10. Which of the following tools can be used to fillet all the corners of the base feature?

    (a) **Round**   (b) **Break Corner**
    (c) **Chamfer**   (d) **2-Bend Corner**

Exercises

Exercise 1

Create the sheet metal part shown in Figure 14-121. The flat pattern of the part is shown in Figure 14-122. Its dimensions are shown in Figure 14-123. The material thickness, bend radius, relief depth, and relief width is 0.5 mm. Assume the missing dimensions.

(Expected time: 30 min)

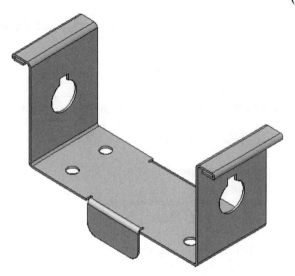

Figure 14-121 Sheet metal part for Exercise 1

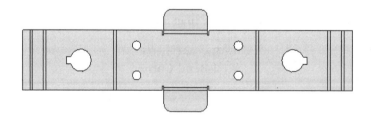

Figure 14-122 Flat pattern of the part

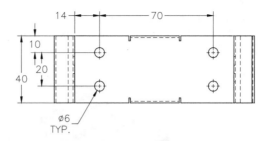

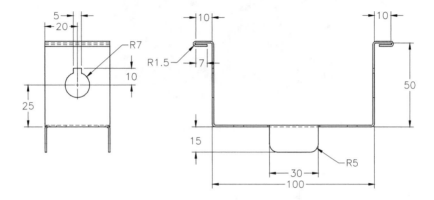

Figure 14-123 Dimensions for the sheet metal part

Exercise 2

Create the sheet metal part shown in Figure 14-124. Its dimensions are shown in Figure 14-125. The value of the material thickness, bend radius, relief depth, and relief width is 0.5mm. Assume the missing dimensions. **(Expected time: 30 min)**

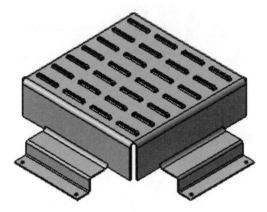

Figure 14-124 Sheet metal part for Exercise 2

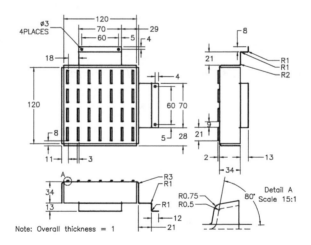

Figure 14-125 Dimensions for the Sheet metal part

Answers to Self-Evaluation Test
1. T, **2.** F, **3.** F, **4.** T, **5. Unbend**, **6. Rebend**, **7.** line, **8. Close 2-Bend Corner**, **9. Centered**, **10.** shell

Chapter 15

Student Projects

After completing this chapter, you will be able to:
* *Create components of the project assemblies in the Part environment of Solid Edge.*
* *Assemble the components of assemblies in the Assembly environment.*
* *Generate the drawing views of assemblies in the Draft environment.*

Project 1

In this project, you will create the components of the Motor Blower assembly shown in Figure 15-1. The exploded view of the assembly is shown in Figure 15-2. The details of the components of the Motor Blower assembly are shown in Figures 15-3 through 15-8. You will also generate the following drawing views of the assembly:

a. Top view
b. Front view
c. Left-side view
d. Isometric view

(Expected time: 5 hrs)

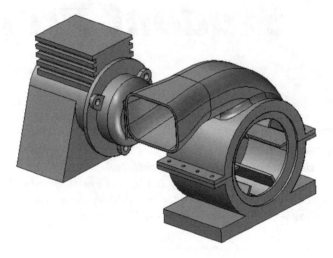

Figure 15-1 *Motor Blower assembly*

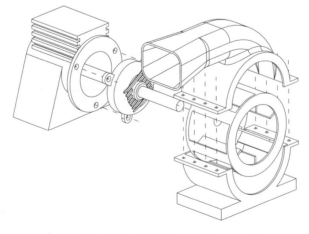

Figure 15-2 *Exploded view of the assembly*

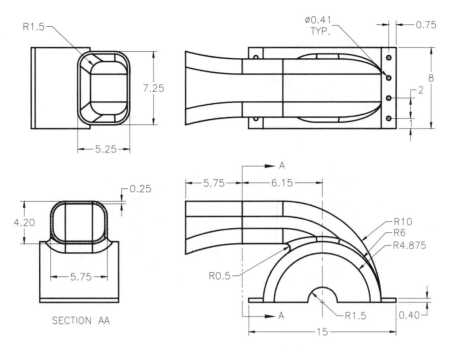

Figure 15-3 *Dimensions of the Upper Housing*

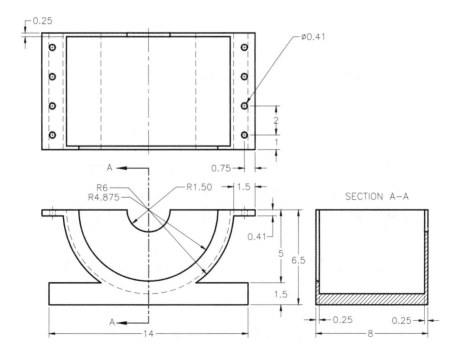

Figure 15-4 *Dimensions of the Lower Housing*

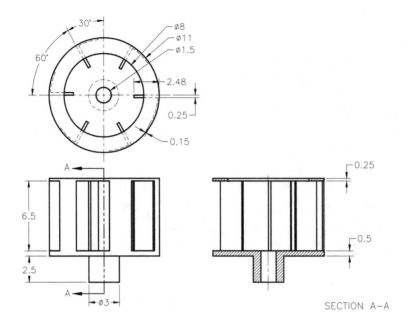

Figure 15-5 *Dimensions of the Blower*

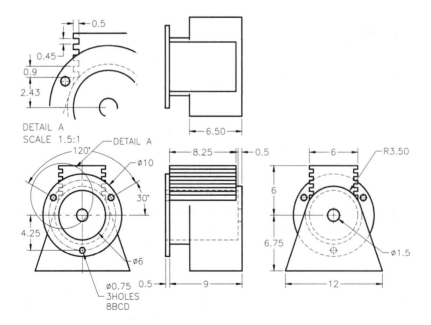

Figure 15-6 *Dimensions of the Motor*

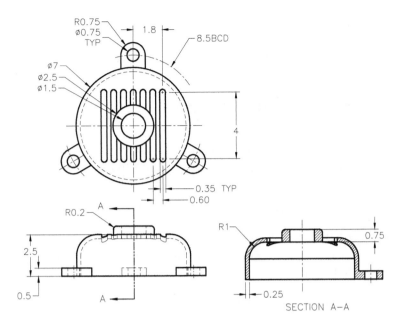

Figure 15-7 *Dimensions of the Cover*

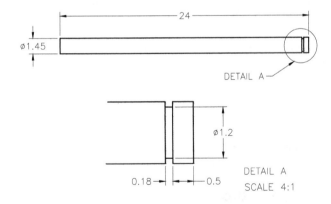

Figure 15-8 *Dimensions of the Shaft*

The following steps are required to complete this project:

a. Create the components of the Motor Blower assembly in separate part files.
b. Open a new assembly file and assemble the Lower Housing with the assembly reference planes.
c. Assemble the Upper Housing with the Lower Housing by applying the assembly relationships, refer to Figure 15-45.

d. Assemble the Blower with the Lower Housing, refer to Figure 15-48.

e. Assemble the Shaft with the Lower Housing, refer to Figure 15-50.

f. Assemble the Motor with the Shaft and then assemble the Cap with the Motor, refer to Figures 15-52 and 15-54.

g. Open a new drawing file in the **Draft** environment and generate the required drawing views, refer to Figure 15-56.

CREATING THE COMPONENTS

To create the assembly, you first need to create its components. The components will be created in the **Part** environment of Solid Edge. The Upper Housing was already created in Chapter 9. You can create it again or copy the part in the \Solid Edge\c15\Motor Blower folder.

Creating the Lower Housing

Starting a New File

The dimensions of the Lower Housing are in inches, so you need to select a template that has units in inches.

1. Choose the **New** button from the **Main** toolbar to display the **New** dialog box.

2. Choose the **More** tab from the dialog box and double-click on the **Normeng.Par**.

Creating the Base Feature

The file you have opened has units set to inches. Therefore, the model that you create will have the dimensions in inches.

1. Invoke the **Protrusion** tool and select the front plane to draw the profile of the base feature.

2. Draw the profile of the base feature, as shown in Figure 15-9, and exit the sketching environment.

3. Extrude the sketch symmetrically to both sides of the front plane up to the depth of 8. The isometric view of the base feature is shown in Figure 15-10.

Creating the Revolved Cutout

The second feature is a revolved cutout.

1. Choose the **Revolved Cutout** button.

2. Select the top face of the base feature and draw the sketch, as shown in Figure 15-11.

3. After drawing the sketch, exit the sketcher environment.

4. Enter the angle of revolution as **180** in the **Angle** edit box; the cutout is created, as shown in Figure 15-12.

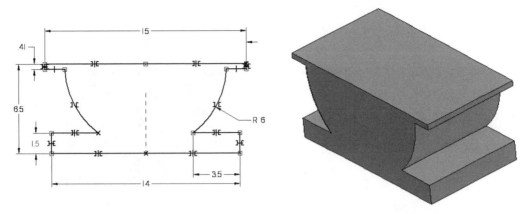

Figure 15-9 *Sketch of the base feature of the lower feature*   ***Figure 15-10*** *Base feature of the lower feature*

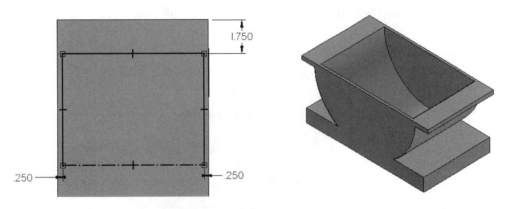

Figure 15-11 *Sketch of a revolved cutout*   ***Figure 15-12*** *Model after creating the revolved cutout*

Creating the Cutout

The cutout will be created on the front face of the base feature.

1. Choose the **Cutout** button and select the front face as the sketch plane.

2. Draw the sketch of the cutout feature, as shown in Figure 15-13.

3. After drawing the sketch, exit the sketcher environment.

4. Specify the direction of material removal inside the sketch.

5. Choose the **Through Next** button from the ribbon bar and specify the direction of the cut. The cutout is created, as shown in Figure 15-14.

6. Exit the **Cutout** tool.

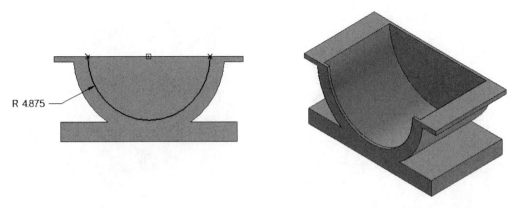

Figure 15-13 *Sketch of the cutout feature*   **Figure 15-14** *Model after creating the cutout*

7. Similarly, create another cutout on the back face of the base feature, as shown in Figure 15-15.

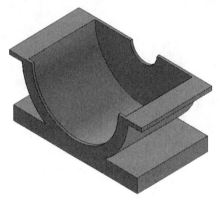

Figure 15-15 *Model after creating the second cutout*

Adding a Hole Feature

1. Choose the **Hole** button from the **Features** toolbar to display the **Hole** ribbon bar.

2. Choose the **Hole Options** button from the ribbon bar to display the **Hole Options** dialog box.

3. Enter **0.41** in the **Diameter** edit box in the **Settings** area.

4. Accept the remaining default options and choose **OK** from this dialog box; you are prompted to click on a planar face or reference plane.

5. Select the top face of the base feature to place the hole. The sketching environment is invoked and a circle, which is the profile of the hole feature, is attached to the cursor.

6. Place the profile of the hole on the top face of the base feature and add the required dimensions, as shown in Figure 15-16. Exit the sketching environment; the **Extent Step** is invoked.

7. Specify the side of the feature downward; the preview of the feature is displayed. Choose the **Finish** button from the ribbon bar to complete the feature and then exit the **Hole** tool by choosing the **Cancel** button. The model, after creating the hole, is shown in Figure 15-17.

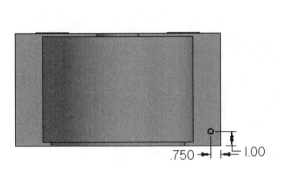

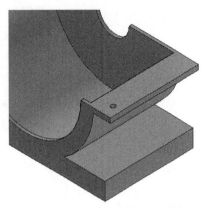

Figure 15-16 *Hole profile placed on the top face*   *Figure 15-17* *Resulting hole*

Creating a Pattern of the Hole

Next, you need to create a rectangular pattern of the hole feature. As mentioned earlier, to create a rectangular pattern, you need to draw its profile in the sketching environment. The sketching environment is invoked in the **Profile Step** of the **Pattern** tool.

1. Choose the **Pattern** button from the **Features** toolbar to display the **Pattern** ribbon bar.

2. Select **Hole 1** from the **EdgeBar**; it is highlighted. Right-click to accept the feature; the **Plane or Sketch Step** is invoked and you are prompted to click on a planar face or a reference plane.

3. Select the top face of the base feature to draw the profile of the rectangular pattern.

4. Choose the **Rectangular Pattern** button from the **Features and Relationships** toolbar. You are prompted to click for the start point of the rectangle.

5. Select the center of the circular hole as the start point of the rectangle; you are prompted to click for the second point of the rectangle.

6. Specify the opposite corner of the rectangle. Now, select the rectangle, if it is not already selected and enter the value **6** for the shorter side. Next, enter the value **13.5** for the longer side. Click to confirm the values.

7. Now enter **4** in the edit box for the number of instances on the shorter side.

8. Exit the sketching environment and choose the **Smart** button.

9. Choose the **Finish** button to complete the pattern. The isometric view of the final model, after creating the pattern, is shown in Figure 15-18.

Figure 15-18 Final model of the Lower Housing

Saving the Model
1. Save the model with the name given below and then close the file.
    \Solid Edge\c15\Motor Blower\lower housing.par

Creating the Blower
Starting a New File
1. Choose the **New** button from the **Main** toolbar to display the **New** dialog box.

2. Choose the **More** tab from the dialog box and double-click on **Normeng.Par**.

Creating the Base Feature
1. Invoke the **Revolved Protrusion** tool and select the front plane to draw the profile.

2. Draw the profile of the base feature, as shown in Figure 15-19, and then exit the sketching environment.

3. Choose the **Revolve 360** button from the ribbon bar to create the revolved feature, as shown in Figure 15-20.

Creating the Protrusion
1. Invoke the **Protrusion** tool and select the top face of the bottom plate to draw the profile of the base feature.

2. Draw the profile of the base feature, as shown in Figure 15-21, and then exit the sketching environment.

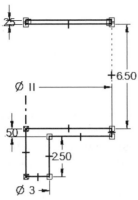

Figure 15-19 *Sketch of the base feature of the blower*

Figure 15-20 *Revolved feature*

3. Choose the **Through Next** button from the ribbon bar to extrude the sketch and specify the direction of extrusion. The protrusion feature is created, as shown in Figure 15-22.

Creating the Pattern

1. Choose the **Pattern** button from the **Features** toolbar to display the **Pattern** ribbon bar.

2. Select the previous feature from the **EdgeBar**; the selected feature is highlighted. Right-click to accept it; the **Plane or Sketch Step** is invoked and you are prompted to click on a planar face or a reference plane.

3. Select the top face of the bottom plate to draw the profile of the circular pattern.

4. Choose the **Circular Pattern** button from the **Features and Relationships** toolbar; you are prompted to click for the center of the circle.

5. Select the center of the circular protrusion feature; you are prompted to click for the start point of the arc.

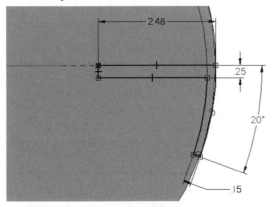

Figure 15-21 *Sketch with dimensions*

Figure 15-22 *Protrusion feature*

6. Move the cursor to the circumference of the base feature and click when the cursor snaps to the circumference. At this point, click for a point on the arc.

7. Enter **6** in the **Count** edit box. This is because there are six instances of the protrusion feature.

8. Exit the sketching environment; the **Pattern_1** dialog box is displayed and you are informed that errors have been detected and the pattern has not been created.

9. Choose **OK** from the dialog box and then choose the **Smart** button from the ribbon bar; the preview of the pattern is displayed. Choose the **Finish** button to complete the pattern.

    The isometric view of the model, after creating the pattern, is shown in Figure 15-23.

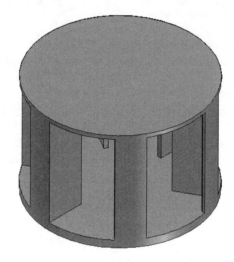

Figure 15-23 Model after creating the pattern

Adding a Hole

1. Choose the **Hole** button from the **Features** toolbar to display the **Hole** ribbon bar.

2. Choose the **Hole Options** button from the ribbon bar to display the **Hole Options** dialog box.

3. Enter **1.5** in the **Diameter** edit box in the **Settings** area.

4. Accept the remaining default options and choose **OK** from this dialog box. You are prompted to click on a planar face or a reference plane.

5. Select the face of the base feature, as shown in Figure 15-24, to place the hole. The sketching environment is invoked and a circle, which is the profile of the hole feature, is attached to the cursor.

6. Place the profile of the hole concentric to the profile of the circular base feature. Exit the sketching environment; the **Extent Step** is invoked.

7. Specify the side of the feature upward. Choose the **Through Next** button and specify the surface upto which the hole feature has to be create. The preview of the feature is displayed. Choose the **Finish** button from the ribbon bar to complete the feature and then exit the **Hole** tool by choosing the **Cancel** button. The model, after creating the hole, is shown in Figure 15-25.

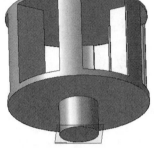

Figure 15-24 Face selected to place the hole

Figure 15-25 Model after adding the hole

Creating the Cutout
The cutout will be created on the top face of the base feature.

1. Choose the **Cutout** button and select the top face of the base feature as the sketch plane.

2. Draw a circle, as shown in Figure 15-26, and modify its diameter to 8.

3. After drawing the circle, exit the sketcher environment.

4. Enter the value **0.25** in the **Distance** edit box and specify the direction of the cut; the cutout is created, as shown in Figure 15-27.

5. Exit the **Cutout** tool.

Creating the Motor
Starting a New File
1. Choose the **New** button from the **Main** toolbar; the **New** dialog box is displayed.

2. Choose the **More** tab from the dialog box and double-click on **Normeng.Par**.

Creating the Base Feature
1. Invoke the **Protrusion** tool and select the front plane to draw the sketch of the base feature.

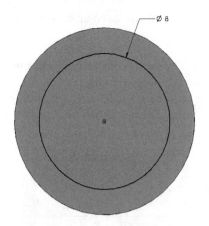

Figure 15-26   *Sketch of the cutout feature*   *Figure 15-27*   *Model after creating the cutout*

2. Draw the profile of the base feature, as shown in Figure 15-28, and then exit the sketching environment.

3. Extrude the sketch to a depth of 6.5; the base feature is created, as shown in Figure 15-29.

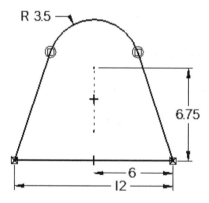

Figure 15-28   *Sketch with dimensions*   *Figure 15-29*   *Base feature*

Creating the Second Protrusion Feature

1. Invoke the **Protrusion** tool and select the back face of the base feature to draw the sketch.

2. Draw the profile of the base feature, as shown in Figure 15-30 and exit the sketching environment.

3. Extrude the sketch to a depth of 2.25; the protrusion feature is created, as shown in Figure 15-31.

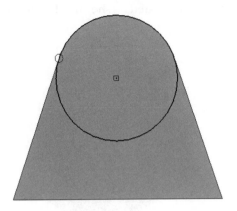

Figure 15-30 *Sketch with a constraint*

Figure 15-31 *Isometric view of the model after creating the second feature*

Creating the Third Protrusion Feature

1. Invoke the **Protrusion** tool and select the back face of the second feature to draw the sketch.

2. Draw a circle, as shown in Figure 15-32, and modify its diameter to 10. Now, exit the sketching environment.

3. Extrude the sketch to a distance of 0.5; the third feature is created, as shown in Figure 15-33.

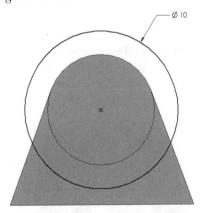

Figure 15-32 *Sketch of the third feature*

Figure 15-33 *Protrusion feature*

Creating the Fourth Protrusion Feature

1. Invoke the **Protrusion** tool and select the front face of the third feature to draw the sketch.

2. Draw the profile of the protrusion feature, as shown in Figure 15-34, and then exit the sketching environment.

3. Extrude the sketch to a distance of 8; the fourth feature is created, as shown in Figure 15-35.

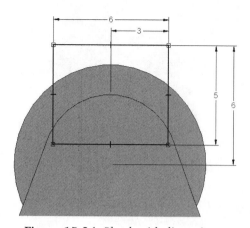

Figure 15-34 Sketch with dimensions

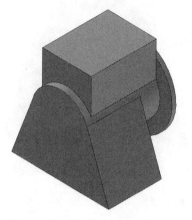

Figure 15-35 Protrusion feature

Creating the Cutout

The cutout will be created on the front face of the previous feature.

1. Choose the **Cutout** button and select the front face of the previous feature as the sketch plane.

2. Draw the sketch, as shown in Figure 15-36.

3. After drawing the sketch, exit the sketcher environment.

4. Choose the **From/To Extent** button from the ribbon bar and specify the front and back faces as the from and to faces, respectively. The cutout feature is created, as shown in Figure 15-37.

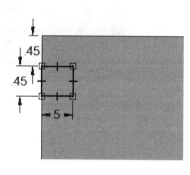

Figure 15-36 Sketch of the cutout

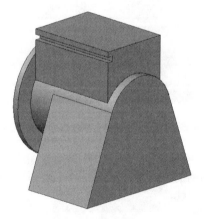

Figure 15-37 Cutout feature created

Creating a Pattern of the Cutout

Next, you need to create a rectangular pattern of the cutout feature.

1. Choose the **Pattern** button from the **Features** toolbar to display the **Pattern** ribbon bar.

2. Select **Cutout 1** from the **EdgeBar**; the selected feature is highlighted. Right-click to accept the feature; the **Plane or Sketch Step** is invoked and you are prompted to click on a planar face or a reference plane.

3. Select the front face of the fourth feature to draw the profile of the rectangular pattern.

4. Choose the **Rectangular Pattern** button, if it is not chosen, and enter **4** in the **Y** edit box. This is because there are four instances in the Y-direction.

5. Select the top-right corner of the rectangular slot as the start point of the rectangle, see Figure 15-38. You are prompted to click for the second point of the rectangle.

6. Specify the second point to draw the rectangle. Next, dimension the rectangle, as shown in Figure 15-38.

7. Exit the sketching environment; the **Pattern_1** dialog box is displayed and you are informed that errors have been detected and pattern has not been created.

8. Choose **OK** from the dialog box and then choose the **Smart** button from the ribbon bar; the preview of the pattern is displayed. Choose the **Finish** button to complete the pattern. The model, after creating the pattern, is shown in Figure 15-39.

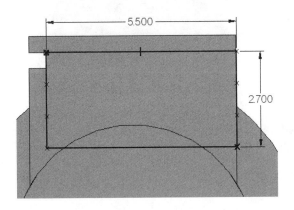

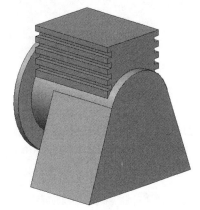

Figure 15-38 Sketch for the pattern   *Figure 15-39* Pattern created

Adding Holes

1. Add a hole of diameter 6 on the motor, as shown in Figure 15-40. The depth of this hole is 8.25.

2. Next, add a hole of diameter 1.5, as shown in Figure 15-41.

Figure 15-40 *First hole created*

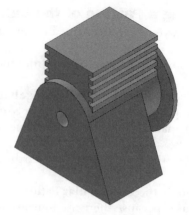

Figure 15-41 *Second hole created*

3. Add the third hole of diameter 0.75 on BCD (Bolt Circle Diameter) 8.5, as shown in Figure 15-42, and then create its circular pattern, as shown in Figure 15-43.

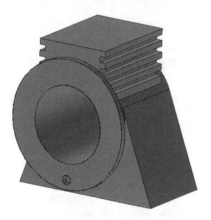

Figure 15-42 *Third hole created*

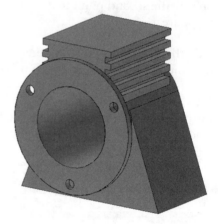

Figure 15-43 *Pattern created*

Creating the Remaining Components

Similarly, use the **Part** environment of Solid Edge to create other components of the Motor Blower assembly.

Creating the Assembly

All parts of the Motor Blower assembly are created. Next, you need to assemble them in the **Assembly** environment of Solid Edge. Remember that all parts are saved in the *\Solid Edge\c15\Motor Blower* folder.

Starting a New Assembly File

As Solid Edge is already running, you can start a new assembly file using the **New** dialog box.

1. Choose the **New** button from the **Main** toolbar; the **New** dialog box is displayed.

2. Choose the **More** tab from the dialog box and double-click on **Normeng.Asm**.

3. After entering the **Assembly** environment, choose **Tools>EdgeBar** option from the menu bar if it is not already selected.

Assembling the Base Component with the Reference Planes

As mentioned earlier, the first part that is placed in the assembly is called the base component. The base component is generally the component that does not have any motion relative to the other components in the assembly.

1. Choose the **Parts Library** button from the top of the **EdgeBar**.

2. Browse and open the folder *Motor Blower*.

3. Double-click on the Lower Housing from the **EdgeBar**; the base component is assembled with the reference planes.

    Note that the assembly window should not be in the maximized state. If it is, then bring the window to the restored state. This is because if it is maximized, the placement part window will fully overlap the target assembly window. Assembling the parts using the window in the maximized state is not recommended because you will not be able to see both parts at the same time.

    If the assembly window is set to **Restore**, then a subwindow appears at the top right corner of the main window. In this case, you can view both parts and apply the assembly relationships easily.

Assembling the Second Component

After assembling the base component, you need to assemble the second component, which is the Upper Housing.

1. From the **EdgeBar**, drag the Upper Housing into the assembly window.

 Note
The part that is being placed in the assembly is called the placement part. The part that is in the assembly, to which the placement part has to be constrained, is called the target part.

2. From the **Relationship** ribbon bar, choose the **Options** button to display the **Options** dialog box.

3. Select the **Use Reduced Steps when placing parts** check box in the dialog box, if it is not selected, and then exit the dialog box.

4. Select the face on the Upper Housing, as shown in Figure 15-44.

5. Select the face of the Lower Housing, as shown in Figure 15-44; the placement part is constrained to the target part.

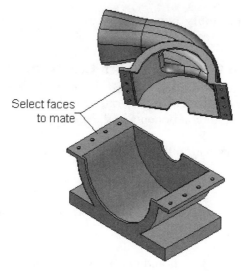

*Figure 15-44 Faces to be selected to apply the **Mate** relationship*

6. Choose the **Axial Align** button from the **Relationship Types** flyout. Now, you will align two axes of any two holes. To align the two axes of holes, you can also select their cylindrical faces.

7. Select the cylindrical surface of any two holes individually. Similarly, apply the **Axial Align** relationship to another set of holes. The Upper Housing assembled to the Lower Housing is shown in Figure 15-45.

Assembling the Third Component

Now, you need to assemble the third component, which is the Blower.

1. Drag the Blower into the assembly window from the **EdgeBar**; the placement part is displayed in a separate window.

2. Choose the **Insert** button from the **Relationship Types** flyout. Remember that the insert relationship uses two constraints, namely **Mate** and **Axial Align**.

3. Spin the Blower in its window and select the cylindrical face, as shown in Figure 15-46. After you select the element on the placement part, the subwindow is removed from the display, thus enabling you to select the corresponding element on the target part.

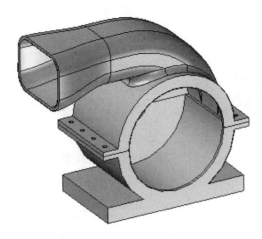

Figure 15-45 *Assembly of two components*

4. Select the cylindrical face of the Upper Housing, as shown in Figure 15-46. After selecting the cylindrical face, the subwindow is redisplayed.

   Now, you will select the faces to mate.

5. Select the face on the Blower, as shown in Figure 15-47.

6. Select the corresponding face on the Upper Housing, as shown in Figure 15-47.

   The Blower is assembled with the Upper Housing in the assembly, as shown in Figure 15-48.

Assembling the Fourth Component

Next, you need to assemble the fourth component, which is the Shaft.

1. Drag the Shaft into the assembly window from the **EdgeBar**,; the placement part is displayed in a separate window.

2. Choose the **Insert** button from the **Relationship Types** flyout.

3. Select the cylindrical face of the Shaft that is in the subwindow.

4. Next, select the cylindrical face of the target part, which is the Blower.

5. Select the faces of the Shaft and the Blower, as shown in Figure 15-49.

   The Shaft is assembled with the Blower, as shown in Figure 15-50. As is evident in this figure, you need to flip the Shaft.

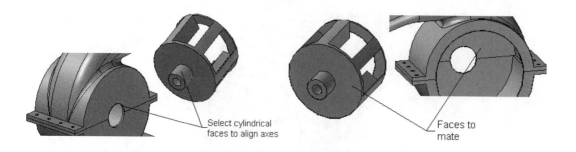

Select cylindrical
faces to align axes

Faces to
mate

Figure 15-46 *Cylindrical faces to selected*   *Figure 15-47* *Faces to mate*

Figure 15-48 *Assembly of the Blower with the other components*

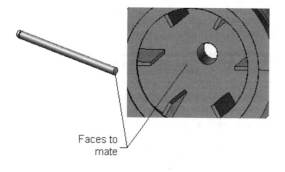

Faces to
mate

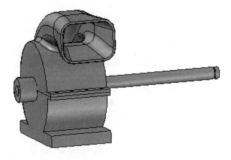

Figure 15-49 *Faces to mate*   *Figure 15-50* *Shaft partially assembled*

6. Choose the **Assembly PathFinder** button from the **EdgeBar**.

7. Select **shaft.par:1** from the top pane of the **EdgeBar**. Notice that in the bottom pane, the relationships applied to the component are displayed.

8. Select the first relationship, which is the **Mate** relationship. Right-click and choose the **Flip** option; the assembly is displayed, as shown in Figure 15-51.

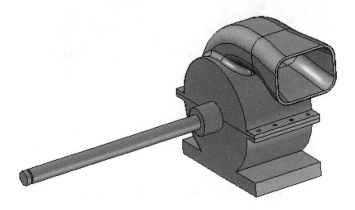

Figure 15-51 *Assembly after assembling the Shaft*

9. Choose **OK** from the ribbon bar.

Assembling the Fifth Component

After assembling the fourth component, you need to assemble the fifth component, which is the Motor.

1. From the **EdgeBar**, drag the Motor into the assembly window; the placement part is displayed in a separate window.

2. Choose the **Insert** button from the **Relationship Types** flyout.

3. Select the hole on the back face of the Motor.

4. Now, select the cylindrical face of the Shaft.

5. Select the inner front face of the Motor and then the end face of the Shaft; the Motor is assembled. Now, you need to flip the orientation of the Motor.

6. Follow the steps 6, 7, and 8 given in the previous section to flip the Motor.

7. Apply the **Planar Align** relationship to position the Motor. The Motor is assembled with the assembly, as shown in Figure 15-52.

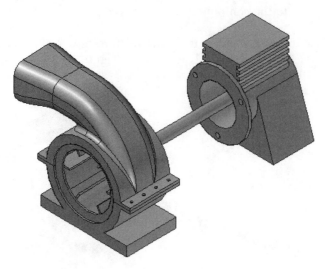

Figure 15-52 *Assembly with the Motor*

Assembling the Sixth Component

Next, you need to assemble the sixth component, which is the Cover.

1. From the **EdgeBar**, drag the Cover into the assembly window.

2. Choose the **Axial Align** button from the **Relationship Types** flyout.

3. Select the hole on the Cover, as shown in Figure 15-53, and then select the hole on the Motor that is shown in Figure 15-53. The Cover partially positions itself with the Motor.

4. Similarly, align the axes of the other two holes of the Cover with the axes of the two holes on the Motor.

5. Choose the **Mate** button from the **Relationship Types** flyout.

6. Select the bottom planar face of the Cover with the front face of the Motor; the assembly is created, as shown in Figure 15-54.

Saving the File

1. Choose the **Save** button from the **Main** toolbar; the **Save As** dialog box is displayed.

2. Enter the name of the assembly as Motor Blower and choose the **Save** button to exit the dialog box.

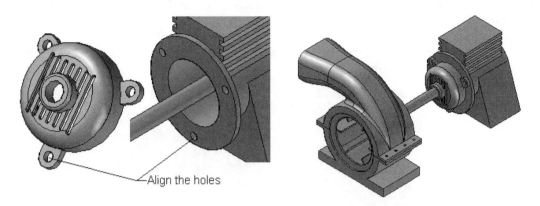

Figure 15-53 *Holes to align*   *Figure 15-54* *Completed assembly*

3.   Choose **File > Close** to close the file.

Generating the Drawing Views of the Assembly

After creating the Motor Blower assembly, you can generate its drawing views in the **Draft** environment using third angle projection method. Remember that all parts are saved in the *\Solid Edge\c15\Motor Blower* folder.

Starting a New Draft File

As Solid Edge is already running, you can start a new file in the **Draft** environment using the **New** dialog box.

1.   Choose the **New** button from the **Main** toolbar; the **New** dialog box is displayed.

2.   Choose the **More** tab from the dialog box and double-click on **Normeng.Dft**.

3.   If the **Edge Bar** is displayed, choose the **Tools>EdgeBar** option from menu bar to hide it because you will not use it. Turning off its display will increase the working area on the screen.

Generating the Drawing Views

After starting a new file in the **Draft** environment, you need to generate the drawing views. To generate the drawing views, follow the steps discussed next.

1.   Choose **Tools > Options** from the menu bar to invoke the **Options** dialog box. Choose the **Drawing Standards** tab and select the **Third** radio button from the **Projection Angle** area. Then, choose the **OK** button.

2.   Next, choose the **Drawing View Wizard** button from the **Drawing Views** toolbar; the **Select Model** dialog box is displayed.

3.   Select the Motor Blower assembly and choose the **Open** button; the **Drawing View Creation Wizard** dialog box is displayed. Choose the **Next** button.

4. The **Drawing View Orientation** page is displayed. Select **front** and choose the **Next** button.

5. Select the views from the **Drawing View Layout** area, as shown in Figure 15-55 and then choose the **Finish** button.

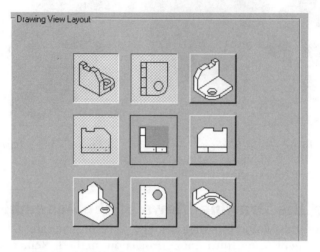

*Figure 15-55 The **Drawing View Layout** area*

6. Place the drawing views on the sheet. Notice that you need to increase the scale of the views. The scale of any one orthographic view, when modified, changes the scale of the other two orthographic views also.

7. Select any orthographic view and the ribbon bar is displayed. Enter **0.3** in the **Scale value** edit box; all orthographic views are scaled to the specified value.

8. Similarly, scale the isometric view.

9. Now, right-click on the isometric the view to invoke the shortcut menu. Choose the **Properties** option to invoke the **High Quality View Properties** dialog box.

10. Choose the **Display** tab and clear the **Hidden edge style** check box; the **Changing Drawing View Default Display Properties** message box is displayed.

11. Choose the **OK** button; the hidden edges will not be visible in the selected drawing view.

12. Similarly, turn off the display of the hidden edges in other views.

13. You can move the views on the sheet by dragging them. Arrange all views, as shown in Figure 15-56.

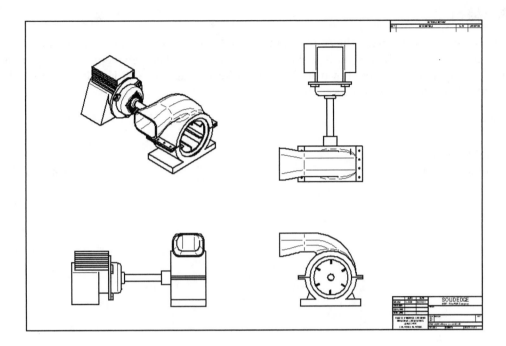

Figure 15-56 *Drawing views of the assembly*

Saving the File

After generating the drawing views, you need to save the file.

1. Choose **File > Save** from the menu bar; the **Save As** dialog box is displayed.

2. Save the file with the name *c15motorblower.dft*.

3. Choose **File > Close** to close the file.

Project 2

In this project, you will create the components of the Fixture assembly shown in Figure 15-57. The exploded view of the assembly is shown in Figure 15-58. The details of the components of the Fixture assembly are shown in Figures 15-59 through 15-62. Finally, generate the following drawing views of the assembly, refer to figure 15-63.

a.   Top view
b.   Front view
c.   Right-side view
d.   Isometric view   **(Expected time: 3 hrs)**

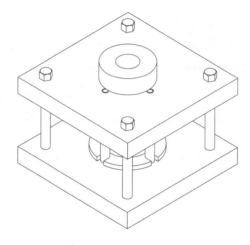

Figure 15-57 *Fixture assembly*

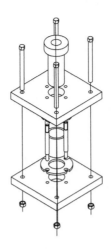

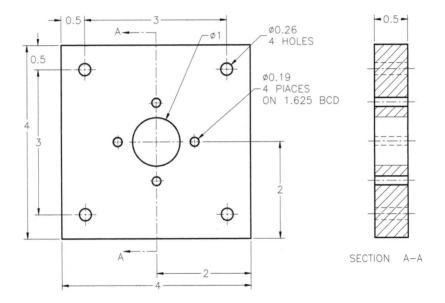

Figure 15-58 *Exploded view of the assembly displaying various components*

Figure 15-59 *Dimensions of the End Plate*

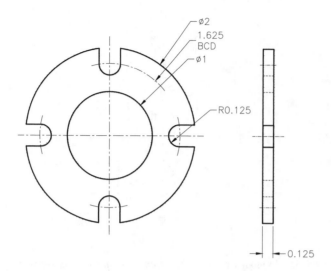

Figure 15-60 *Dimensions of the Disk*

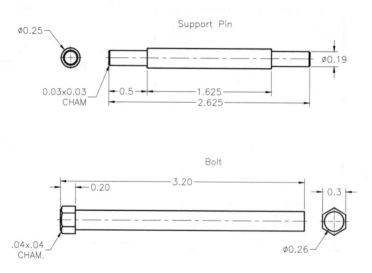

Figure 15-61 *Dimensions of the Support Pin and the Bolt*

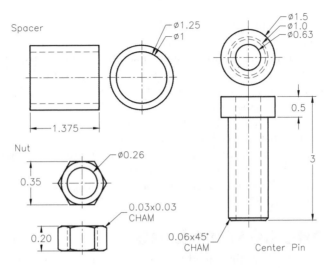

Figure 15-62 *Dimensions of the Spacer, Center Pin, and Nut*

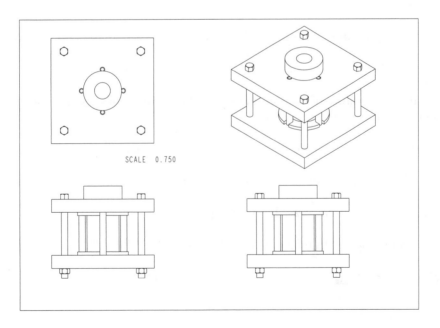

Figure 15-63 *Drawing views of the Fixture assembly*

The following steps are required to complete this tutorial:

a. Create the components in separate part files.
b. Open a new assembly file and assemble the End Plate with the assembly reference planes.
c. Assemble the Disk with End Plate by applying assembly relationships, refer to Figure 15-81.
d. Assemble the first instance of the Support Pin with the End Plate and then create a reference pattern of the Support Pin, refer to Figures 15-83 and 15-84.
e. Assemble the Spacer with the Disk, refer to Figure 15-85.
f. Assemble the second instance of the Disk with the Spacer.
g. Assemble the second instance of the End Plate with the Spacer.
h. Assemble the Nut and Bolt with the assembly and then create their pattern to assemble their remaining instances, refer to Figure 15-86.
i. Open a new drawing file in the **Draft** environment and generate the required drawing views, refer to Figure 15-87.

CREATING THE COMPONENTS

To create the assembly, you first need to create its components. They will be created in the **Part** environment of Solid Edge.

Creating the End Plate

The dimensions of the End Plate are in inches, so you will select a template that has units in inches.

1. Choose the **New** button from the **Main** toolbar; the **New** dialog box is displayed.

2. Choose the **More** tab from the dialog box and double-click on **Normeng.Par**.

3. Create the base feature of the End Plate. The base feature has a square profile. Specify the depth of the extrusion to be 0.5.

4. Create the set of holes using the **Hole** tool and the **Pattern** tool, as shown in Figure 15-64.

5. Create a hole at the center of the plate, as shown in Figure 15-65.

6. Create another set of holes, as shown in Figure 15-66.

7. Save the component with the name *End Plate* at the location *Solid Edge\c15\Fixture*.

Creating the Disk

1. Create the base feature of the Disc on the top plane. The sketch of the base feature is shown in Figure 15-67.

2. Extrude the sketch to a distance of 0.125; the base feature is created, as shown in Figure 15-68.

3. Create a hole at the center of the Disk, as shown in Figure 15-69.

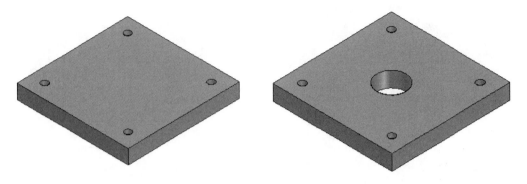

Figure 15-64 Holes on the base feature   *Figure 15-65* Hole at the center

4. Save the model.

Creating the Center Pin

1. Create the base feature of the Center Pin, which is a revolved feature. The sketch is shown in Figure 15-70.

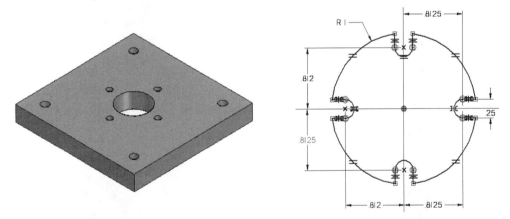

Figure 15-66 Holes created on the base feature   *Figure 15-67* Sketch of the base feature of the disc

2. Revolve the sketch through 360-degrees; the base feature is created, as shown in Figure 15-71.

3. Create a hole on the top face of the Center Pin, as shown in Figure 15-72.

4. Create a chamfer at the bottom edge of the Center Pin, as shown in Figure 15-73.

5. Save the model.

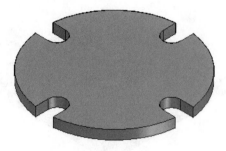

Figure 15-68 *Base feature of the Disk*

Figure 15-69 *Final model of the Disk*

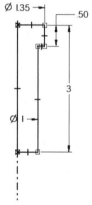

Figure 15-70 *Sketch of the base feature of the central pin with dimensions*

Figure 15-71 *Base feature of the Center Pin*

Figure 15-72 *Hole on the base feature of the center pin*

Figure 15-73 *Chamfer on the base feature of the center pin*

Creating the Nut

1. Draw the sketch of the base feature of the Nut on the top plane, as shown in Figure 15-74.

2. Extrude the sketch to a distance of 0.20; the base feature is symmetrically created, as shown in Figure 15-75.

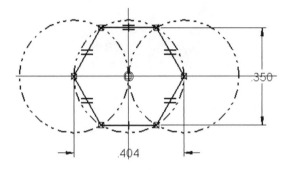

Figure 15-74 Sketch with dimensions   *Figure 15-75 Base feature of the Nut*

3. The second feature is a revolved cut, whose sketch is shown in Figure 15-76. This sketch is drawn on the reference plane that passes through the two farthest corners of the hexagon.

4. Revolve the sketch through 360-degrees; the second feature is created, as shown in Figure 15-77.

5. Next, create a mirror copy of the revolved cut that you created in the previous step, see Figure 15-78.

6. Next, create a hole of diameter 0.25 on the top face of the base feature; the Nut is created, as shown in Figure 15-79.

7. Similarly, use the **Part** environment to create the remaining components of this assembly.

Creating the Assembly

Once all parts of the Fixture assembly are created; you need to assemble them in the **Assembly** environment of Solid Edge. Remember that all parts are saved in the *Solid Edge\c15\Fixture* folder.

Starting Solid Edge Session in the Assembly Environment

As Solid Edge is already running, you can start a new file in the **Assembly** environment using the **New** dialog box.

1. Choose the **New** button from the **Main** toolbar; the **New** dialog box is displayed.

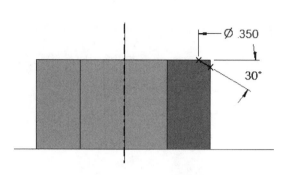

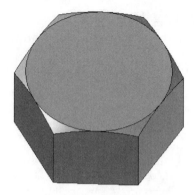

Figure 15-76 Sketch of the revolved cut

Figure 15-77 Revolved cut on the base feature of the nut

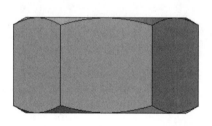

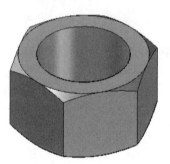

Figure 15-78 Mirror copy of the revolved cut

Figure 15-79 Final model of the Nut

2. Choose the **More** tab from the dialog box and double-click on **Normeng.Asm**.

Assembling the Base Component with the Reference Planes

1. Choose the **Parts Library** button from the top of the **EdgeBar**.

2. Browse and open the *Fixture* folder.

3. Double-click on the End Plate from the **EdgeBar**; the base component is assembled with the reference planes.

Assembling the Second Component

After assembling the base component, you need to assemble the second component, which is the Disk.

1. From the **EdgeBar**, drag the Disk into the assembly window.

2. Choose the **Mate** relationship and select the bottom face of the Disk.

3. Select the top face of the End Plate.

4. Choose the **Axial Align** button from the **Relationship Types** flyout.

5. Align the axes of the hole on the End Plate and the hole on the Disk, refer to Figure 15-80. Also, align the central axes of both the components.

   The two components are assembled, as shown in Figure 15-81.

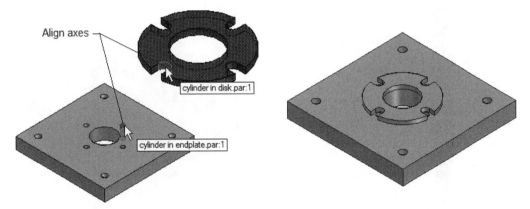

Figure 15-80 *Cylindrical surfaces to be selected for aligning the axes*   *Figure 15-81* *Disk assembled with the End Plate*

Assembling the Third Component

Next, you need to assemble the third component, which is the Support Pin.

1. Drag the Support Pin into the assembly window from the **EdgeBar**.

2. Choose the **Insert** button from the **Relationship Types** flyout.

3. Select the face on the Support Pin, as shown in Figure 15-82, and then select the top face of the End Plate.

4. Next, align the axis of the cylindrical surface on the Support Pin with the axis of any one of the holes on the End Plate. The two components are assembled, as shown in Figure 15-83.

Creating the Pattern

You will create the pattern of the Support Pin to assemble its remaining instances.

1. Choose the **Pattern Parts** button from the **Assembly Commands** toolbar; the **Pattern**

Parts ribbon bar is displayed and you are prompted to select the part that will be included in the pattern.

2. Select the Support Pin from the assembly and choose the **Accept** button from the ribbon bar. Next, you are prompted to select the part or sketch that contains the pattern. This is because Solid Edge will reference the part to be patterned with the existing pattern.

3. Select the End Plate from the assembly; you are prompted to select a pattern.

4. Select the existing pattern by selecting any one of the holes. Now, you are prompted to click on a reference feature in the pattern. The reference feature will be the hole that was the parent hole while patterning it on the End Plate.

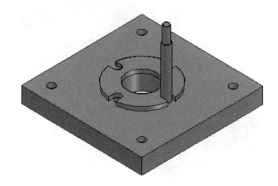

Figure 15-82 *Face to be selected to add the* *Insert* *relationship*

Figure 15-83 *Support Pin assembled with the End Plate*

5. To select the parent hole feature, move the cursor on the holes one by one. The hole that gets highlighted will be the parent hole. Select the hole.

6. Choose the **Finish** button from the ribbon bar; the pattern is created, as shown in Figure 15-84.

Assembling the Fourth Component

After assembling the third component and creating its pattern, you need to assemble the fourth component, which is the Spacer.

1. Drag the Spacer into the assembly window from the **EdgeBar**,.

2. Choose the **Insert** relationship.

3. Select the bottom face of the Spacer and then, select the top face of the Disk.

4. Align the axis of the Spacer with the axis of the hole on the Disk.

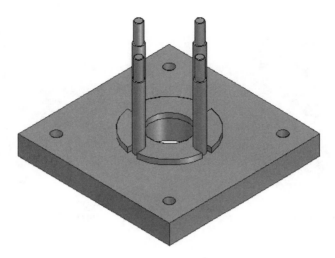

Figure 15-84 *Support Pins assembled in the assembly*

5.   The Spacer is assembled, as shown in Figure 15-85.

6.   Similarly, using the assembly relationships in the **Assembly** environment, assemble the Disk, End Plate, Center Pin, Bolts, and Nuts in the assembly. The final assembly is shown in Figure 15-86.

Generating the Drawing Views

After creating the Fixture assembly, you can generate its drawing views in the **Draft** environment. Remember that all parts are saved in the *\Solid Edge\c15\Fixture* folder.

Starting a New File in the Draft Environment

You need to start a new file in which the required drawing views will be created.

1.   Choose the **New** button from the **Main** toolbar; the **New** dialog box is displayed.

2.   Select the draft file and choose the **OK** button to exit the dialog box and start a new file. Now, you have entered the **Draft** environment. Select **D Wide (34in x 22in)** sheet from the **Sheet Setup** dialog box.

Generating the Base Drawing Views

As mentioned earlier, the drawing views are generated from their parent part. To generate the drawing views, follow the steps discussed next.

1.   Choose the **Drawing View Wizard** button from the **Drawing Views** toolbar; the **Select Model** dialog box is displayed.

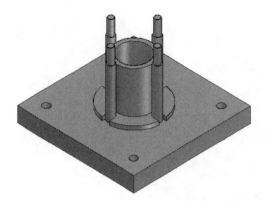

Figure 15-85 *Spacer assembled in the assembly*   ***Figure 15-86*** *Fixture assembly*

2. Select the Fixture assembly and choose the **Open** button; the **Drawing View Creation Wizard** dialog box is displayed. Choose the **Next** button

3. From the **Drawing View Orientation** area, select **front** and choose the **Next** button.

4. Next, select the top, isometric, and right views in the dialog box and then, choose the **Finish** button.

5. Turn off the display of the hidden edges by using the **High Quality View Properties** dialog box as discussed in the previous project.

6. Place the drawing views on the sheet. Notice that you need to scale down the views. The scale of any one orthographic view, when modified, changes the scale of the other orthographic views also.

7. Modify the scale value to **2** in the **Scale Value** edit box of the ribbon bar.

8. You can move the views on the sheet by dragging them. Arrange the views, as shown in Figure 15-87.

Saving the File

1. Choose **File > Save** from the menu bar.

2. Save the file with the name *c15fixture.dft*.

3. Choose **File > Close** to close the file.

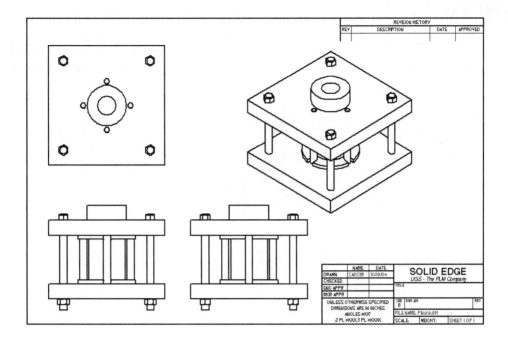

Figure 15-87 *Drawing views of the assembly*

Exercise 1

Create all components of the Butterfly Valve shown in Figure 15-88 and then assemble them. The dimensions of the components are given in Figures 15-89 through 15-93. Assume the missing dimensions for the components.   **(Expected time: 3 hrs)**

Figure 15-88 Butterfly Valve assembly

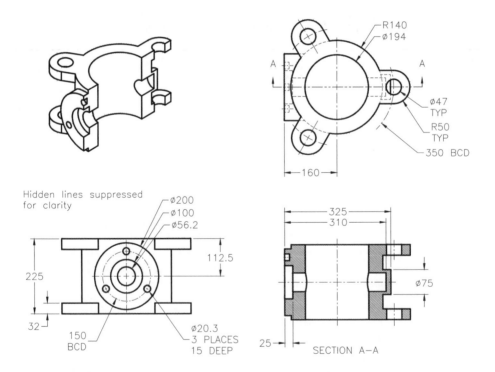

Figure 15-89 Dimensions of the Body

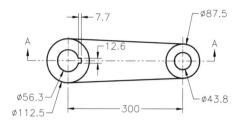

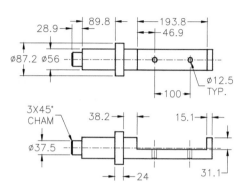

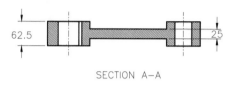

SECTION A–A

Figure 15-90 *Dimensions of the Arm*

Figure 15-91 *Dimensions of the Shaft*

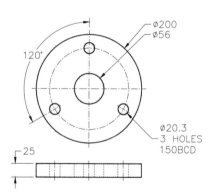

Figure 15-92 *Dimensions of the Retainer*

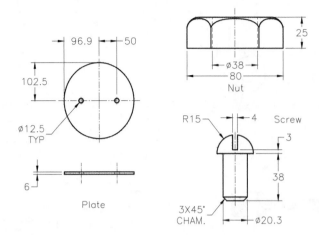

Figure 15-93 *Dimensions of the Plate, Nut, and Screw*

Index

Other Publications by CADCIM Technologies

The following is the list of some of the publications by Prof. Sham Tickoo and the CAD Engineers of CADCIM Technologies. Please visit www.cadcim.com for the complete listing.

Computer Programming Textbooks
- Learning C++ Programming Concepts
  CADCIM/Tickoo Publication, USA
- Learning VB.NET Programming Concepts
  CADCIM/Tickoo Publication, USA

Computer Animation Textbook
- 3ds Max 2008: A Comprehensive Guide
  CADCIM/Tickoo Publication, USA

Solid Edge Textbooks
- Solid Edge V19 for Designers
  CADCIM Technologies, USA
- Solid Edge V18 for Designers
  CADCIM Technologies, USA
- Solid Edge for Designers, Version 16
  CADCIM Technologies, USA
- Solid Edge for Designers, Version 15
  CADCIM Technologies, USA

NX Textbooks
- NX 5 for Designers
  CADCIM Technologies, USA
- NX 4 for Designers
  CADCIM Technologies, USA
- NX 3 for Designers
  CADCIM Technologies, USA

SolidWorks Textbooks
- SolidWorks 2008 for Designers
  CADCIM Technologies, USA
- SolidWorks 2007 for Designers
  CADCIM Technologies, USA

- SolidWorks 2006 for Designers
  Piter Publishing Press, Russia
- SolidWorks for Designers, Release 2005
  CADCIM Technologies, USA
- SolidWorks for Designers, Release 2005
  Piter Publishing Press, Russia
- SolidWorks for Designers, Release 2004
  CADCIM Technologies, USA

CATIA Textbooks
- CATIA V5R17 for Designers
  CADCIM Technologies, USA
- CATIA V5R16 for Designers
  CADCIM Technologies, USA
- CATIA V5R15 for Designers
  CADCIM Technologies, USA
- CATIA for Designers, V5R14
  CADCIM Technologies, USA

Autodesk Inventor Textbooks
- Autodesk Inventor 2008 for Designers
  CADCIM Technologies, USA
- Autodesk Inventor 11 for Designers
  CADCIM Technologies, USA
- Autodesk Inventor for Designers, Release 10
  CADCIM Technologies, USA
- Autodesk Inventor for Designers, Release 9
  CADCIM Technologies, USA

EdgeCAM Textbooks
- EdgeCAM 11.0 for Manufacturers
  CADCIM Technologies, USA
- EdgeCAM 10.0 for Manufacturers
  CADCIM Technologies, USA

Pro/ENGINEER Textbooks
- Pro/ENGINEER Wildfire 3.0 for Designers
  CADCIM Technologies, USA
- Pro/ENGINEER Wildfire for Designers Release 2.0
  CADCIM Technologies, USA
- Pro/ENGINEER Wildfire for Designers
  CADCIM Technologies, USA

Autodesk Revit Building Textbooks

- Autodesk Revit Building 2008 for Architects & Designers
  CADCIM Technologies, USA
- Autodesk Revit Building 9 for Designers & Architects
  CADCIM Technologies, USA
- Autodesk Revit Building 8 for Designers & Architects
  CADCIM Technologies, USA
- Autodesk Revit for Building Designers & Architects, Release 7.0
  CADCIM Technologies, USA

AutoCAD LT Textbook

- AutoCAD LT 2008 for Designers
  CADCIM Technologies, USA
- AutoCAD LT 2007 for Designers
  CADCIM Technologies, USA
- AutoCAD LT 2006 for Designers
  CADCIM Technologies, USA

Mechanical Desktop Textbook

- Mechanical Desktop Instructor, Release 5

AutoCAD Textbooks (US Edition)

- AutoCAD 2008: A Problem-Solving Approach
  Autodesk Press
- AutoCAD 2007: A Problem-Solving Approach
  Autodesk Press
- Customizing AutoCAD 2007
  Autodesk Press
- AutoCAD 2006: A Problem-Solving Approach
  Autodesk Press
- Customizing AutoCAD 2006
  Autodesk Press

AutoCAD Textbooks (Russian Edition)

- AutoCAD 2006
  Piter Publishing Press, Russia
- AutoCAD 2005
  Piter Publishing Press, Russia

AutoCAD Textbooks (Italian Edition)

- AutoCAD 2000 Fondamenti
- AutoCAD 2000 Tecniche Avanzate

AutoCAD Textbook (Chinese Edition)

- AutoCAD 2000

3D Studio MAX and VIZ Textbooks

- Learning 3ds max5: A Tutorial Approach
  (Complete manuscript available for free download on *www.cadcim.com*)
- Learning 3ds Max: A Tutorial Approach, Release 4
  Goodheart-Wilcox Publishers (USA)
- Learning 3D Studio VIZ: A Tutorial Approach
  Goodheart-Wilcox Publishers (USA)
- Learning 3D Studio R4: A Tutorial Approach
  Goodheart-Wilcox Publishers (USA)

Paper Craft Book

- Constructing 3-Dimensional Models: A Paper-Craft Workbook
  CADCIM Technologies

Coming Soon: New Textbooks from CADCIM Technologies

- CATIA V5R18 for Designers
- ANSYS for Design Analysts
- AutoCAD Civil 3D 2008 for Engineers
- AutoCAD Map 3D 2008 for Geospatial Professionals
- Mastercam for Manufacturers
- Autodesk Inventor 2009 for Designers
- Pro/ENGINEER Wildfire 4.0 for Designers
- AutoCAD Electrical 2008 for Electrical Control Designers
- Autodesk AliasStudio for Industrial Designers
- Learning Java Programming Concepts
- Flash CS3
- Learning VB.NET 2008 Programming Concepts

Online Training Program Offered by CADCIM Technologies

CADCIM Technologies provides effective and affordable virtual online training on various software packages including computer programming languages, Computer Aided Design and Manufacturing (CAD/CAM), animation, architecture, and GIS. The training will be delivered 'live' via Internet at any time, any place, and at any pace to individuals, students of colleges, universities, and CAD/CAM training centers. For more information, please visit the following link:

http://www.cadcim.com

Rendered Image of the Radial Engine Assembly

Rendered Image of the Shaper's Tool Head Assembly

Rendered Image of the Pipe Vice Assembly

Rendered Image of the Motor Blower Assembly